THE

MAN IN LITERATURE

PROGRAM

P9-CRO-666

SCIENCE fact/FICTION

EDMUND J. FARRELL

Assistant Executive Secretary, National Council of Teachers of English. Formerly Supervisor of Secondary English, University of California, Berkeley; formerly English Department Chairman, James Lick High School, San Jose, California.

THOMAS E. GAGE

Consultant in English and Reading, Mt. Diablo Unified School District, Concord, California. Formerly Chairman of English Department, Concord High School, Concord, California; formerly Chairman of the Humanities Department, Fremont High School, Oakland, California.

JOHN PFORDRESHER

Assistant Professor of English, Georgetown University, Washington, D.C. Editor, *Variorum Edition of The Idylls of the King,* Columbia University Press. Formerly Assistant Professor of English, University of New Hampshire, Durham.

RAYMOND J. RODRIGUES

Teacher of English, Robertson High School, Las Vegas, New Mexico. Formerly teacher of English, Edward W. Clark High School, Las Vegas, Nevada; formerly President, Southern Nevada Teachers of English.

With an introduction by
RAY BRADBURY

All illustrations computer generated

SCOTT, FORESMAN AND COMPANY

Editorial Direction: LEO B. KNEER

Development: MARGARET RAUSCH

with Susan Green, David Epstein, and Fitzgerald Higgins
Design: Robert Amft

ISBN: 0-673-03407-0

Copyright © 1974 Scott, Foresman and Company,
Glenview, Illinois.
Philippines Copyright 1974 Scott, Foresman and Company.
All Rights Reserved.
Printed in the United States of America.

Regional Offices of Scott, Foresman and Company are located in
Dallas, Texas; Glenview, Illinois; Oakland, New Jersey; Palo
Alto, California; Tucker, Georgia; and Brighton, England.

CONTENTS

SCIENCE FICTION: Before Christ and After 2001
Introduction by Ray Bradbury

1 INPUT $+ - \times \div$ OUTPUT

2 THE ROAD TO OUT

3 MIND WAVES

continued

CONTENTS

To ascertain the tastes, the abilities, and the preferences of those for whom this book is intended, the following individuals read the many selections submitted to them, judged their appropriateness and interest, and solicited the reactions of young people. The authors and editors of SCIENCE fact/FICTION wish to express their appreciation for this valuable assistance.

MARGARET S. DINN
Miami, Florida

GUY MANN
Auburn, New York

DUDLEY CLINTON ENOS
Denver, Colorado

BENEDICT OLIVER, F.S.C.
Pittsburgh, Pennsylvania

EVALEE HART
Cuyahoga Falls, Ohio

ROBERT C. SCHAPPELL
Lancaster, Pennsylvania

PHILIP A. LUM
San Francisco, California

CAROLE SNYDER
St. Paul, Minnesota

PETER K. LYNCH
Long Island, New York

RITA M. STONE
Fairfax, Virginia

ACKNOWLEDGEMENTS:

COVER: Tapestry *Blackout* by Jack Youngerman—Pace Editions Inc., N.Y.
FRONTISPIECE: Computer Art—California Computer Products, Inc.
Input+ − × ÷ Output: Computer Art (Cockpit)—William A. Fetter, Courtesy of Boeing Co.
The Road to Out: Computer Art *Corridor*—Courtesy of Dr. Georg Nees. Produced with a Siemens System 4004 Computer
Mind Waves: Computer Art *Return to Square B* by Haruki Tsuchiya—by C. T. G., Tokyo
Organic Dilemma: Computer Art (seagull)—Courtesy of Bell Telephone Laboratories
View from on High: Computer Art (face)—Courtesy of Bell Telephone Laboratories
What Time Next Time: Computer Art *Scaling Study, 1967*—L. Mezei, University of Toronto
Epitaph: Computer Art *Shift One, Unit Four, 1970*—Courtesy of Auro Lecci
Future Reviewed: Computer Art *Spatial Plane*—Peter K. Kreis, Computer Art of Software ag, Hochheim, West Germany and Reston, Virginia

SCIENCE FICTION:
BEFORE CHRIST
AND AFTER 2001

an Introduction by Ray Bradbury

THE HISTORY OF MODERN SCIENCE FICTION is so astonishing and mercurial that I feel I must sum it up for you.

Imagine yourself back in the year 1946, 1947, or 1948.

If you had wanted to read science fiction in those years, in book form, anyway, it would have been almost impossible. Only a handful of books were being published. The finest authors in the field, Heinlein, Sturgeon, Smith, and Van Vogt were being put in print by tiny publishing companies in small editions of a few thousand copies which almost amounted to vanity publishing; that is to say—paying to have your own work published.

These books, when they did appear, were greeted by silence. Very few got reviewed anywhere in our country at any time. For all that the critics knew, these authors had never been born, much less got around to writing a book or even a story.

In the forties, also, only a handful of paperback s-f collections had begun to pop up. Science was exploding all over the place, but s-f was still asleep in the minds of the experts and the great mass of people.

I remember going to a party, evenly divided between writers and dancers from the New York City Ballet, back in those years, where once the people discovered what I did for a living, I was hooted at and called "Buck Rogers" and "Flash Gordon."

If the blacks of our country were a racial minority in the late forties and early fifties, the science-fiction writer was classed as a literary minority best not mentioned, better ignored. We would never go anywhere, do anything, or be anybody. We were rarely allowed to sell stories to the larger and more important magazines. And even in the s-f magazines, some of our more outrageous ideas were rejected and went unpublished.

In 1948 I wrote a story titled "Way in the Middle of the Air," concerning a group of southern blacks who, tired of repression, built their own rockets and went off to Mars. The story was rejected by about

Copyright © 1974 by Ray Bradbury.

every magazine in the country, and I finally sold it, late in the day, to a small s-f magazine for $80.

Not long after, I wrote another story about a group of priests who, arriving on Mars, try to decide whether a creature that they encounter, a fiery spirit which drifts on the air, is or is not "human."

That story, "The Fire Balloons," suffered a similar history. Rejected everywhere, it was published many years later in a small s-f magazine in Chicago.

It is hard for us, in 1974, to realize that once upon a time the civil rights movement didn't exist. And that once upon a time was 1948, 1949, 1950.

It is similarly hard for us to comprehend the vast power and influence of various religious groups in those same years. My story about the priests on Mars was rejected by editors, again and again, fearful of offending a wide variety of church thinkers, afraid of repercussions and criticism.

On a political level, in early 1950, I wrote a story titled "And the Rock Cried Out." It told the tale of a white man and his wife, trapped in South America, in an Indian village, shortly after an atomic holocaust. The man and his wife were forced to shine shoes and wait on table for an existence. The shoe was indeed suddenly on the other foot, for the story questioned whether the couple could make do, accept being a white minority in a dark culture.

Well, 1950 and the years immediately following, were Joseph McCarthy years, the years of McCarthyism, years when our country was shadowed and bullied by our real and unreal fears concerning Communism in the world.

This story, like the other two, was rejected by editors afraid to tell a tale that, with all its simplicity, might be considered anti-American and therefore pro-Communist.

It is hard to remember an America so involved with such shadows and such fears.

So far, I have named only three areas into which science fiction shoved its nose again and again.

Racial relations.

Religion.

Politics.

Are there more? Yes.

Philosophy. Pure technology. Art on any level you wish to speak of it. Logic, Ethics, Social science. History. Witchcraft. Time travel.

Well, the list, as you begin to see, is endless.

Architecture? But of course! One of the grand thrills of being young and falling in love with science fiction was seeing the early drawings and paintings, by men like Frank R. Paul, on the old magazine covers and inside with each story, which were more often than not pure architecture, renderings of fantastic cities, incredible environments.

Growing up in science fiction was, then, growing up amidst Everything.

Do you see how lucky I was?

I grew up in the one field that reached out and embraced every sector of the human imagination, every endeavor, every idea, every technological development, and every dream.

Is there a better way to grow up? I can think of none.

But even while I knew this, sensed this, lived this, the culture I lived in did not sense, know, live, or believe this.

In the late forties, as I have said, s-f was still Sleeping Beauty waiting to be kissed awake by atomic bombs, hydrogen explosions but, above all, Sputnik, and Neil Armstrong bootprinting the lunar soil for all mankind.

The earliest awakenings occurred from 1948 through 1950 when Doubleday and Simon and Schuster began to publish their own lines of science-fiction books, calling special attention to the incredible imaginative qualities within the field.

During those same years, Robert Heinlein was the first pulp s-f writer to shift over into *The Saturday Evening Post* with his, then remarkable, "Green Hills of Earth."

I followed him, a short time later.

But it was only in the Eisenhower years that we really got rolling. We are accustomed to think of Ike as a rather quiet president during whose terms not very much at all happened. The facts, in Space, anyway, are otherwise. Long before Kennedy made his pitch in that direction, Eisenhower had, in effect, responded to the universe and the competition, if you wish, of Russia and Sputnik. We put our rockets, and then our men, into trajectory. And it was a mild, supposedly conservative, father-image president who lit the fuse.

In the following years, from 1957 on up through this very summer, an incredible thing happened. Students began to teach teachers. They snowed them with science-fiction books and stories. The teachers held out for a long while, but then the really sly students placed a book on teacher's desk and said, "Read just the first chapter. If you don't like it, stop."

So the teachers muttered Lord, Lord under their breaths, took Heinlein or Asimov or Clarke home, read the first chapter and—were hooked.

The rest is simple but amazing history. Dozens and then hundreds of books of science fiction began to be taught in junior high schools, high schools, and colleges. Dozens and then hundreds of courses and seminars sprang up around the old but newly discovered imaginative field.

Now there is hardly a day passes that some new hardcover science-fiction book isn't published. Now no weekends without a dozen new paperback s-f books hitting the newsstands.

Why has all this happened at this particular juncture in history? Why not twenty-five or thirty years or, for that matter, sixty years ago?

I have no easy or complete answers. The easiest and most complete would run like this:

America, above all nations, has always been a country of ideas. We have always been revolutionary, in all the senses of that much overused word.

Somewhere, years ago, I used a term for us that I think fits more than ever. I called us a nation of Ardent Blasphemers. We ran about measuring not only how things *were* but how they *ought to be.* If the wilderness got in our way two hundred years ago, we chopped it down. If the English king and his smothering friends got in our way, we borrowed some revolutionary concepts, freshened them up, and chopped *him* down. If death and disease got in our way, we raised medicine to its greatest disciplines in the history of the entire world and chopped death down and cured disease and invented pain-killers. If distance got in the way, we chopped it in half by running locomotives down a track and shrinking time. If time got in the way, we raced the sun around the world with jets, and now rockets, and beat it, By Gosh and By Golly, beat it all hollow! We could make the sun rise and set half a dozen times a day by rushing with improbable haste through the heavens. Blasphemy? That was our middle name.

So with our medicines and steam trains and electrical devices we Ben Franklin'd our way into and up away from twentieth-century Earth. Which is to say we stood out in rains with a damned kite and stringed key and dared God to pin back our ears with lightning. He *has* pinned us back a few times. For, come to think of it, in the light of all the dogmas of a great deal of religious thought in the past, we have touched the nerve of the Universal Being. We have dared to sock Death right in the midst of its most terrible grin. We have messed with mosquitoes with sprays and saved half a billion lives. We have reached up to touch the Moon and promise ourselves immortality with starships moving on and on a billion years from this very evening. We Americans are better than we hope and worse than we think, which is to say, we are the most paradoxical of all the paradoxical nations in time.

Which is what science fiction is all about.

For science fiction runs out with tapes to measure Now against Then against Tomorrow Breakfast. It triangulates mankind amongst these geometrical threads, praising him, warning him.

And since we are at the tail end of the Industrial Revolution and well into the Technological and/or Electronic Revolution, what else is there to read except——

Science fiction.

It is being read now at long last because it is exciting, because it is human, because it is relevant, because it is ecological.

Sorry about those last two words, which have been overused to the point of madness the last three years.

But, there are still snobs in the world, and I must give you weapons to fight them with. There still are people who will come up to you and say: Science fiction? Ha! Why read *that?!*

The most direct, off-putting, answer is: It is the most important fiction ever invented by writers. It saw the whole mob of troubles pouring toward us across the shoals of time, cried, "Head for the hills, the dam is broke!" But no one listened. Now, people have pricked up their ears, and opened their eyes.

For, above all, science fiction, as far back as Plato trying to figure out a proper society, has always been a fable teacher of morality, saying: If you cut down trees, plant new ones. If you invent a pill what will you do with your religious concepts and structures? If your medicines allow people to grow old, what will you *do* with your old people? If you put people to sleep for five hundred years and wake them up, what then? Madness? Maybe. Maybe not.

All of the above statements are science fictional. There is no large problem in the world this afternoon that is not a science-fictional problem.

The problem of war and world politics is the problem of the hydrogen bomb and the fact that as a teacher of Christian principles the Bomb has, *sotto voce,* suggested to politicians that war is no longer an extension of politics. All that has been short-circuited by the Bomb. Politics is now an extension of politics. The old rules have been reversed. The old men, tired of arguing, willing to blow each other up, have been sent back to the table for yet another round of conversation. Grand, great, good, swell!

Which doesn't rule out small wars, of course, but the big ones, for the time being, are stashed in the basement. The difference between large and small is important here. Any reduction is welcome. Hundreds of thousands of people have been killed in Vietnam, but compared to the fifty million or more destroyed in a short five years in World War II, we can only be thankful that the giant Death has been dissolved down to pygmy size. And, under the shadow of the Bomb, the larger nations, even as I write this, move closer together, fused by mutual fears, instead of separated by selfish antagonisms, all because of a science-fictional invention, which was *always* impossible, and would *never* be invented: nuclear fission.

For you see, all the things that have happened to us, *were never going to happen.*

Good people said so. Nice people thought so.

But the science-fiction writers always knew otherwise. They could see that locomotive coming down the track, changing the face of the Civil War. They could see multitudinous inventions, shaping and reshaping mankind and thus shaking the very foundations of churches and synagogues around the world.

Science fiction then is the fiction of revolutions. Revolutions in time, space, medicine, travel, and thought. It is the fiction of the moralist who shakes his hand at us and says: Behave or I pull the switch! It is the fiction of the writer-theologian who shows man the mirror image of God in himself and promises him a real and true heaven if he gets off his ape-hunkers and fires himself into a new Genesis-orbit around the Moon and then on into the abyss dark.

Above all, science fiction is the fiction of warm-blooded human men and women sometimes elevated and sometimes crushed by their machines. Given tape recorders, what do I do? a man cries out. Given bugging devices and computers, what next? he asks again. Given television and movies and radio and records—a veritable Tower of Electronic Babel, where lies my sanity? Be still, stand among trees, green yourself, says science fiction.

I remember with what happiness, years ago (to the jeers of strangers), I predicted that if the philosopher Bertrand Russell ever wrote fiction it would be science fiction. When Lord Russell finally published two collections of stories, in the fifties, they were predominantly fictions of ideas, which is to say science fictions.

We are all of us, today, fourth-grade philosophers. We are all of us writers, in our minds, of science fictions, for we are being forced to deal with the problems of the ten thousand million machines, the robots, that surround us, talk to us, move us. We must have answers, so we speak in tongues, and the tongues are always, always, always science fiction. If your problems are metal and electricity, your answers must be run up out of the same stuffs. We move from simplicity to complexity to simplicity again. The history of radio is the history of mankind illustrated in a brief fifty-three-year span: We began with cat's-whisker crystal radios, expanded to ten-dial maniac-complex devices which drove men mad in 1928, and on around back to wristwatch-size radios in 1973. We will watch the same history repeated as small towns become mad supercities, collapse, die, and turn back to new small towns as we rebirth ourselves at the end of this century.

Plato's name has been mentioned. You may well, in exasperation, demand why? Because in many ways I consider his *Republic* to be one of the earliest forms of science fiction. Whenever man tries to guess at an ethical/political concept, he is, in effect, oiling a machine, hopeful after controlling other men and giving them new freedoms by such control as will allow them to live in peace. So science fiction, we now see, is interested in more than sciences, more than machines. That *more* is always men and women and children themselves, how they behave, how they hope to behave. Science fiction is apprehensive of future modes of behavior as well as future constructions of metal. Democracy is a science-fictional concept trying to dream itself to birth with every generation. Any philosophy which does *not* exist but *tries* to exist, is by this definition science fiction. Politics and humane behavior are an inept science, God knows, but a science nevertheless, to which we are trying to fit keys and open hearts and souls.

Again, science fiction guesses at sciences before they are sprung out of the brows of thinking men. More, the authors in the field try to guess at machines which are the fruit of those sciences. Then we try to guess at how mankind will react to those machines, how use them, how grow with them, how be destroyed by them.

All, all of it fantastic. All, all of it, the story of mankind and inventions, men and machines that step on God's toes and now, late in the day, say Beg Pardon. To which the Universe says: That's all right, go build Eden again. Build it on Earth. Build it on the Moon. Build it on out beyond the Great Andromeda Nebula, but build it, live in it, take root in it, survive.

Which is exactly what we shall do. But not easily. As you will see from reading the various stories within this collection. I have refrained from commenting on them, because I wanted to build a framework for you, in which you might place each and all of these stories and articles.

Just as I have said that science fiction is the stuff of all and everything in man's ken, possible and impossible melted and bound inextricably, so the diversity you will find here is amazing. For ours is a field with no intellectual elite, thank Providence for that. We are a true field of loners. There is no king, no court, no courtiers. No one man rules the roost, so no man follows. There are just wild and lovely individuals. How compare Jack Finney to Kurt Vonnegut, Jr. or Asimov to Clarke? You can't.

And among all these shakers and movers of thought in fiction, you will find a good marrow of shakers and movers in social thought, architectural humanists like Buckminster Fuller or humanist philosophers like Arthur Koestler.

It is all good stuff. It makes good reading and good thinking. And again, thank Mercy, it is *not* self-conscious, pontificating, or insufferably smug. These stories delight in ideas, holding machine kaleidoscopes up to the sun to see the many shapes of time, man, and destiny.

This book is insidious. It is secretly subversive of all that you have believed in the past. It is revolutionary in that it may well make you want to go out and invent better empathy-machines, which repeat truths and amiably shape dreams, such as those strange robots, the motion-picture projector or the record player.

Tomorrow is here, yes, but ah, look! When you glance in the two-hundred-inch telescope, which is this book, you see yourself standing at the center of one minute before noon today.

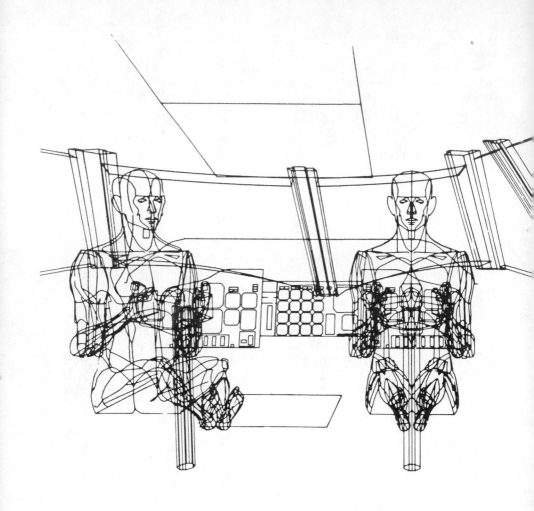

INPUT
+−×÷
OUTPUT

THE GUN WITHOUT A BANG

Robert Sheckley

DID A TWIG SNAP? DIXON LOOKED BACK and thought he saw a dark shape melt into the underbrush. Instantly he froze, staring back through the green-boled trees. There was a complete and expectant silence. Far overhead, a carrion bird[1] balanced on an updraft, surveying the sunburned landscape, waiting, hoping.

Then Dixon heard a low, impatient cough from the underbrush.

Now he knew he was being followed. Before, it had only been an assumption. But those vague, half-seen shapes had been real. They had left him alone on his trek to the signal station, watching, deciding. Now they were ready to try something.

He removed the Weapon from its holster, checked the safeties, reholstered it and continued walking.

He heard another cough. Something was patiently trailing him, probably waiting until he left the bush and entered the forest. Dixon grinned to himself.

Nothing could hurt him. He had the Weapon.

Without it, he would never have ventured so far from his spaceship. One simply didn't wander around on an alien planet. But Dixon could. On his hip was the weapon to end all weapons, absolute insurance against anything that walked or crawled or flew or swam.

It was the last word in handguns, the ultimate in personal armament.

It was the Weapon.

He looked back again. There were three beasts, less than fifty yards behind him. From that distance, they resembled dogs or hyenas. They coughed at him and moved slowly forward.

He touched the Weapon, but decided against using it immediately. There would be plenty of time when they came closer.

Alfred Dixon was a short man, very broad in the chest and shoulders. His hair was streaky blond, and he had a blond mustache which curled up at the ends. This mustache gave his tanned face a frank, ferocious appearance.

"The Gun Without a Bang" by Robert Sheckley. Copyright © 1958 by Robert Sheckley. Reprinted by permission of The Sterling Lord Agency, Inc.

1. *carrion bird,* one that feeds on decaying dead meat, like a vulture.

His natural habitat was Terra's[2] bars and taverns. There, dressed in stained khakis, he could order drinks in a loud, belligerent voice, and pierce his fellow drinkers with narrow gunmetal-blue eyes. He enjoyed explaining to the drinkers, in a somewhat contemptuous tone, the difference between a Sykes needler and a Colt three-point, between the Martian horned adleper and the Venusian scom, and just what to do when a Rannarean horntank is charging you in thick brush, and how to beat off an attack of winged glitterflits.

Some men considered Dixon all bluff, but they were careful not to call it. Others thought he was a good man in spite of his inflated opinion of himself. He was just overconfident, they explained. Death or mutilation would correct this flaw.

Dixon was a great believer in personal armament. To his way of thinking, the winning of the American West was simply a contest between bow and arrow and Colt .44. Africa? The spear against the rifle. Mars? The Colt three-point against the spinknife. H-bombs smeared cities, but individual men with small arms took the territory. Why look for fuzzy economic, philosophical or political reasons when everything was so simple?

He had, of course, utter confidence in the Weapon.

Glancing back, he saw that half a dozen doglike creatures had joined the original three. They were walking in the open now, tongues lolling out, slowly closing the distance.

Dixon decided to hold fire just a little longer. The shock effect would be that much greater.

He had held many jobs in his time—explorer, hunter, prospector, asteroider. Fortune seemed to elude him. The other man always stumbled across the lost city, shot the rare beast, found the ore-bearing stream. He accepted his fate cheerfully. Damned poor luck, but what can you do? Now he was a radioman, checking the automatic signal stations on a dozen unoccupied worlds.

But more important, he was giving the ultimate handgun its first test in the field. The gun's inventors hoped the Weapon would become standard. Dixon hoped he would become standard with it.

He had reached the edge of the rain forest. His ship lay about two miles ahead in a little clearing. As he entered the forest's gloomy shade, he heard the excited squeaking of arboreals.[3] They were colored orange and blue, and they watched him intently from the treetops.

It was definitely an *African* sort of place, Dixon decided. He hoped he would encounter some big game, get a decent trophy head or two. Behind him, the wild dogs had approached to twenty yards. They were gray and brown, the size of terriers, with a hyena's jaws. Some of them had moved into the underbrush, racing ahead to cut him off.

It was time to show the Weapon.

Dixon unholstered it. The Weapon was pistol-shaped and quite heavy. It also balanced poorly. The inventors had promised to reduce the weight and improve the heft in subsequent models. But Dixon

---

2. *Terra,* a Latin name for the Earth, once widely used. 3. *arboreals,* tree-dwelling animals.

liked it just the way it was. He admired it for a moment, then clicked off the safeties and adjusted for single shot.

The pack came loping toward him, coughing and snarling. Dixon took casual aim and fired.

The Weapon hummed faintly. Ahead, for a distance of a hundred yards, a section of forest simply vanished.

Dixon had fired the first disintegrator.

From a muzzle aperture of less than an inch, the beam had fanned out to a maximum diameter of twelve feet. A conic section, waist high and a hundred yards long, appeared in the forest. Within it, nothing remained. Trees, insects, plants, shrubs, wild dogs, butterflies, all were gone. Overhanging boughs caught in the blast area looked as though they had been sheared by a giant razor.

Dixon estimated he had caught at least seven of the wild dogs in the blast. Seven beasts with a half-second burst! No problems of deflection or trajectory, as with a missile gun. No need to reload, for the Weapon had a power span of eighteen duty-hours. The perfect weapon!

He turned and walked on, reholstering the heavy gun.

There was silence. The forest creatures were considering the new experience. In a few moments, they recovered from their surprise. Blue and orange arboreals swung through the trees above him. Overhead, the carrion bird soared low, and other black-winged birds came out of the distant sky to join it. And the wild dogs coughed in the underbrush.

They hadn't given up yet. Dixon could hear them in the deep foliage on either side of him, moving rapidly, staying out of sight. He drew the Weapon, wondering if they would dare try again. They dared.

A spotted greyhound burst from a shrub just behind him. The gun hummed. The dog vanished in midleap, and the trees shivered slightly as air clapped into the sudden vacuum.

Another dog charged and Dixon disintegrated it, frowning slightly. These beasts couldn't be considered stupid. Why didn't they learn the obvious lesson—that it was impossible to come against him and his Weapon? Creatures all over the Galaxy had quickly learned to be wary of an armed man. Why not these?

Without warning, three dogs leaped from different directions. Dixon clicked to automatic and mowed them down like a man swinging a scythe. Dust whirled and sparkled, filling the vacuum.

He listened intently. The forest seemed filled with low coughing sounds. Other packs were coming to join in the kill.

Why didn't they learn? It suddenly burst upon him. *They didn't learn,* he thought, *because the lesson was too subtle!*

The Weapon—disintegrating silently, quickly, cleanly. Most of the dogs he hit simply vanished. There were no yelps of agony, no roars or howls or screams. And above all, there was no loud boom to startle them, no smell of cordite, no click of a new shell levered in. . . .

Dixon thought, *Maybe they aren't smart enough to know this is a killing weapon. Maybe they haven't figured out what's going on. Maybe they think I'm defenseless.*

He walked more rapidly through the dim forest. He was in no

danger, he reminded himself. Just because they couldn't realize it was a killing weapon didn't alter the fact that it was. Still, he would insist on a noisemaker in the new models. It shouldn't be difficult. And the sound would be reassuring.

The arboreals were gaining confidence now, swinging down almost to the level of his head, their fangs bared. Probably carnivorous, Dixon decided. With the Weapon on automatic, he slashed great cuts in the treetops. The arboreals fled, screaming at him. Leaves and small branches rained down. Even the dogs were momentarily cowed, edging away from the falling debris.

Dixon grinned to himself—just before he was flattened. A big bough, severed from its tree, had caught him across the left shoulder as it fell.

The Weapon was knocked from his hand. It landed ten feet away, still on automatic, disintegrating shrubs a few yards from him.

He dragged himself from under the bough and dived for the Weapon. An arboreal got to it first.

Dixon threw himself face down on the ground. The arboreal, screaming in triumph, whirled the disintegrator around its head. Giant trees, cut through, went crashing to the forest floor. The air was dark with falling twigs and leaves, and the ground was cut into trenches. A sweep of the disintegrator knifed through the tree next to Dixon, and chopped the ground a few inches from his feet. He jumped away, and the next sweep narrowly missed his head.

He had given up hope. But then the arboreal became curious. Chattering gaily, it turned the Weapon around and tried to look into the muzzle. The animal's head vanished—silently.

Dixon saw his chance. He ran forward, leaping a trench, and recovering the disintegrator before another arboreal could play with it. He turned it off automatic.

Several dogs had returned. They were watching him closely.

Dixon didn't dare fire yet. His hands were shaking so badly, there was more risk to himself than to the dogs. He turned and stumbled in the direction of the ship. The dogs followed.

Dixon quickly recovered his nerve. He looked at the glittering Weapon in his hand. He had considerably more respect for it now, and more than a little fear. *Much* more fear than the dogs had. Apparently they didn't associate the forest damage with the disintegrator. It must have seemed like a sudden, violent storm to them.

But the storm was over. It was hunting time again.

He was in thick brush now, firing ahead to clear a path. The dogs were on either side, keeping pace. He fired continually into the foliage, occasionally getting a dog. There were several dozen of them, pressing him closely.

Damn it, Dixon thought, *aren't they counting their losses?*

Then he realized they probably didn't know how to count.

He struggled on, not far from the spaceship. A heavy log lay in his path. He stepped over it.

The log came angrily to life and opened enormous jaws directly under his legs.

He fired blindly, holding the trigger down for three seconds and narrowly missing his own feet. The creature vanished. Dixon gulped, swayed, and slid feet-first into the pit he had just dug.

He landed heavily, wrenching his left ankle. The dogs ringed the pit, snapping and snarling at him.

Steady, Dixon told himself. He cleared the beasts from the pit's rim with two bursts, and tried to climb out.

The sides of the pit were too steep and had been fused into glass.

Frantically he tried again and again, recklessly expending his strength. Then he stopped and forced himself to think. The Weapon had got him into this hole; the Weapon could get him out.

This time he cut a shallow ramp out of the pit, and limped painfully out. His left ankle could hardly bear weight. Even worse was the pain in his shoulder. That bough must have broken it, he decided. Using a branch as a crutch, Dixon limped on.

Several times the dogs attacked. He disintegrated them, and the gun grew increasingly heavy in his right hand. The carrion birds came down to pick at the neatly slashed carcasses. Dixon felt darkness crawl around the edges of his vision. He fought it back. He must not faint now, while the dogs were around him.

The ship was in sight. He broke into a clumsy run, and fell immediately. Some of the dogs were on him. He fired, cutting them in two and removing half an inch from his right boot, almost down to the toe. He struggled to his feet and went on.

Quite a weapon, he thought. *Dangerous to anyone, including the wielder.* He wished he had the inventor in his sights.

Imagine inventing a gun without a bang!

He reached the ship. The dogs ringed him as he fumbled with the airlock. Dixon disintegrated the closest two and stumbled inside. Darkness was crawling around his vision again and he could feel nausea rising thickly in his throat. With his last strength, he swung the airlock shut and sat down. Safe at last!

Then he heard the low cough.

He had shut one of the dogs inside with him.

His arm felt too weak to lift the heavy Weapon, but slowly he swung it up. The dog, barely visible in the dimly lighted ship, leaped at him.

For a terrifying instant, Dixon thought he couldn't squeeze the trigger. The dog was at his throat. Reflex must have clenched his hand.

The dog yelped once and was silent. Dixon blacked out.

When he recovered consciousness, he lay for a long time, just savoring the glorious sensation of being alive. He was going to rest for a few minutes. Then he was getting out of here, away from alien planets, back to a Terran bar. He was going to get roaring drunk. Then he was going to find that inventor and ram the Weapon down the man's throat, crossways.

Only a homicidal maniac would invent a gun without a bang.

But that would come later. Right now it was a pleasure just to be alive, to lie in the sunlight, enjoying the . . .

Sunlight? Inside a spaceship?

He sat up. At his feet lay the tail and one leg of the dog. Beyond it there was an interesting zigzag slashed through the side of the spaceship. It was about three inches wide and four feet long. Sunlight filtered through it.

Outside, four dogs were sitting on their haunches, peering in.

He had cut through his spaceship while killing the last dog.

Then he saw other slashes in the ship. Where had they come from?

Oh, yes, when he was fighting his way back to the ship. That last hundred yards. A few shots must have touched the spaceship.

He stood up and examined the cuts. *A neat job,* he thought, with the calm that sometimes accompanies hysteria. *Yes, sir, very neat indeed.*

Here were the severed control cables. That was where the radio had been. Over there he had managed to nick the oxygen and water tanks in a single burst, which was good shooting by anybody's standards. And here—yes, he'd done it, all right. A really clever hook shot had cut the fuel lines. And the fuel had all run out in obedience to the law of gravity and formed a pool around the ship and sunk into the ground.

Not bad for a guy who wasn't even trying, Dixon thought crazily. *Couldn't have done better with a blowtorch.*

As a matter of fact, he couldn't have done it with a blowtorch. Spaceship hulls were too tough. But not too tough for the good old little old sure-fire never-miss Weapon. . . .

A year later, when Dixon still hadn't reported, a ship was sent out. They were to give him decent burial, if any remains could be found, and bring back the prototype disintegrator, if that could be found.

The recovery ship touched down near Dixon's ship, and the crew examined the slashed and gutted hull with interest.

"Some guys," said the engineer, "don't know how to handle a gun."

"I'll say," said the chief pilot.

They heard a banging noise from the direction of the rain forest. They hurried over and found that Dixon was not dead. He was very much alive, and singing as he worked.

He had constructed a wooden shack and planted a vegetable garden around it. Surrounding the garden was a palisade. Dixon was hammering in a new sapling to replace a rotten one when the men came up.

Quite predictably, one of the men cried, "You're alive!"

"Damned right," Dixon said. "Touch and go for a while before I got the palisade built. Nasty brutes, those dogs. But I taught them a little respect."

Dixon grinned and touched a bow that leaned against the palisade within easy reach. It had been cut from a piece of seasoned, springy wood, and beside it was a quiver full of arrows.

"They learned respect," Dixon said, "after they saw a few of their pals running around with a shaft through their flanks."

"But the Weapon——" the chief pilot asked.

"Ah, the Weapon!" exclaimed Dixon, with a mad, merry light in his eyes. "Couldn't have survived without it."

He turned back to his work. He was hammering the sapling into place with the heavy, flat butt of the Weapon. ∎

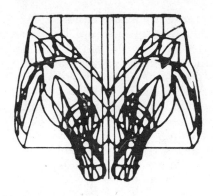

CRABS
TAKE OVER
THE ISLAND

Anatoly Dnieprov[1]

"TAKE IT EASY, THERE!" MR. COOKLING—the engineer—shouted at the sailors who were standing up to their waists in the water and trying to get a small wooden box over the side of the launch. It was the last box of ten that the engineer had brought to the island.

"This heat's awful, a real inferno," moaned the engineer, wiping his thick red neck with a bandanna handkerchief. Then he peeled off his sweat-drenched shirt and threw it on the sand. "You can strip, Bud, there isn't any civilization here."

I looked dejectedly at the light schooner rolling gently on the waves a couple of miles offshore. She would be coming back for us in twenty days.

"Why the deuce did we have to come all this way to a solar hell with those machines of yours?" I asked Mr. Cookling as I pulled off my clothes. "With a sun like this we'll damn soon be roasting."

"Oh, don't worry about that, we'll be needing the sun pretty soon. Look, it's exactly noon now and the sun is right overhead."

"It's always that way on the equator," I added in a mumble without taking my eyes off the *Turtle-Dove*—our schooner. "Any geography book'll tell you that."

The sailors came up and stood in front of the engineer, who slowly drew a roll of bills from his pocket.

"Will that be enough?" he asked, extending a few.

One of them nodded.

"Then your job's done. You can return to the ship. Remind Captain Hale that we expect him back in exactly twenty days."

Mr. Cookling then turned to me. "Let's get started, Bud. I can't wait anymore."

I looked at him long and hard.

"Frankly speaking, I don't know why we even came here. I realize of course that in the Admiralty[2] you couldn't tell me anything. But now that we're here, I should think that you might."

"Crabs Take Over the Island" by Anatoly Dnieprov. Translated by George Yankovsky. Reprinted by permission of New York University Press from RUSSIAN SCIENCE FICTION 1969, ed. by Robert Magidoff. Copyright © 1969 by New York University Press.

1. *Anatoly Dnieprov* (ə nə tô′lē dnye′prəf). See Pronunciation Key on page 378. 2. *the Admiralty,* the government department in charge of naval affairs.

Cookling made a wry face and looked intently at the sand.

"Well, yes, of course. Actually I could have told you before, but there just wasn't any time."

I felt that he was not telling the truth, but I didn't say anything. He continued to stand there rubbing his glistening red neck with a fat hand.

I knew the gesture. He invariably settled into this pattern when he wanted to lie his way out of a situation.

Yet even that suited me for the time being.

"You see, Bud, it's this way. We've got an amusing experiment underway here to test the theory of—what's his name——" here he paused and looked straight at me.

"Whose?"

"The Englishman. . . . Damn it all, the name just slipped—Oh yes, Darwin, Charles Darwin."[3]

I went up to him and put my hand on his bare shoulder.

"Now listen, Mr. Cookling, don't take me for a moron. I know all about Darwin. Quit tacking about, just explain in a couple of words what brought us to this red-hot patch of sand in the middle of the ocean. And for pity's sake stop that Darwin stuff."

He laughed out loud, opening his mouth wide and exposing a full set of dentures. Then he took a few steps to one side and said, "You're impossible, Bud. That's exactly what we're going to test: Darwin's theory."

"You mean to tell me that's why we hauled ten boxes of hardware all this way?" I asked him, coming closer. I was seething with rage at this fat slob all glistening over with sweat.

"Exactly," he replied, and he wiped the smile from his face. "Now about your duties: you can start by opening Box No. 1. Take out the tent, water, canned food, and tools that we'll need to open the other boxes." Cookling spoke the same way that he had at the proving grounds when we were introduced. He was in military uniform then, and so was I.

"Very well," I said through clenched teeth and went up to Box No. 1.

A couple of hours later we had the tent up on the beach and we tossed into a corner a shovel, a crowbar, a hammer, a few screwdrivers, a chisel and various other tools. We also piled up about a hundred cans of food and tanks with fresh water.

Though Cookling was head of the operation, he worked like a horse. It was quite obvious he was eager to get things going. We were so busy in fact that we did not notice the *Turtle-Dove* weigh anchor and disappear from view.

---

3. *Charles Darwin* (1809-1882), the naturalist whose book, *The Origin of Species* (1859), laid the basis for modern theories of evolution. A key concept in Darwin's theory is "the survival of the fittest": Since no two members of any species can be exactly alike, some individuals have better natural abilities to survive dangers and to get more of the always limited resources of their environment, like food and territory. In each generation more of these fit members will pass on their inborn survival characteristics, while weaknesses will disappear as the less fit produce always fewer young. So, unless conditions change, the whole species becomes gradually better adapted or "fitted" to its environment.

After dinner we opened up Box No. 2. It contained an ordinary two-wheel cart of the kind used by porters at railway stations.

I started on the third box, but the engineer stopped me.

"Let's first get a look at the map. The rest of the cargo will have to be spread out over a variety of sites."

This stumped me.

"That's the way the experiment goes," he explained.

The island was round like an upturned plate, with a tiny bay towards the north, exactly where we unloaded. It was bounded by a sandy beach about fifty yards wide. Beyond was a slightly elevated plateau all covered over with stunted bushes that were bone-dry from the heat.

The island was no more than two miles across. There were several red marks on the map: some along the sandy beach, others in the interior.

"Everything we open up from now on will have to be carried out to these sites," Cookling explained.

"What are they, measuring instruments?"

"No," the engineer said with a chuckle. It was irritating, that chuckle of his. He would always turn it on when he knew something you didn't.

The third box was extremely heavy. I was positive it contained a machine, but when the first boards came loose I was dumbfounded. Out came sheets of steel and metal bars of different sizes and shapes. The whole box was packed with these metallic items.

"Looks like a kid's constructor set to me," I exclaimed, tossing out heavy rectangles, cubes, and spheres—all metal.

"Hardly," the engineer replied and went for the next box.

Box No. 4 and the remaining ones up to No. 9 contained the same kinds of metal blanks. They were of three kinds: grey, red, and silverish. I could see right off that they were made of iron, copper, and zinc.

When I started to open the last box, No. 10, Cookling said: "We'll open that one after we deliver the other ones to their sites."

During the next three days, Cookling and I carted the pieces of metal to different parts of the island. We dumped them here and there in little piles. Some were left right on the ground. Others, on the engineer's instructions, I buried in the sand. Some piles were of similar iron bars, others contained a variety of types.

When we finished we returned to the tent for the tenth box.

"Open this one with particular care," Cookling ordered.

Box No. 10 was much lighter than the others and a bit smaller in size.

Inside we dug through compressed sawdust and at last came to a package wrapped in flannel and wax paper. We unwrapped the package.

What appeared was the strangest-looking instrument I ever saw. At first glance it resembled a large metal toy in the shape of a crab. Yet this was no simple crab. In addition to six big segmented appendages, there were two pairs of slender tentacles that terminated in a half-open "maw" which jutted out of this monstrosity of a beast. On the back, slightly depressed, was a tiny parabolic mirror[4] made of highly polished metal with a dark-red crystal in the center. Unlike toy crabs, this one had two pairs of eyes: in front and in back.

I stood for some time gaping at the creature.

"How do you like it?" Cookling asked at last.

I shrugged.

"It's a dangerous toy all right," said the engineer with obvious self-satisfaction. "You'll see for yourself. Pick it up and put it on the sand."

The crab was not heavy at all, weighing only about six or seven pounds. And it stood rather solidly on the sand.

"Well, what do we do now?" I asked the engineer with a touch of irony.

"Just wait a bit; let it warm up."

We both sat down on the sand and kept our eyes on the metal freak. In about two minutes I noticed the mirror on its back slowly begin to turn towards the sun.

"Look, it's coming to life," I exclaimed and jumped to my feet.

When I rose, my shadow accidentally fell on the machine and the crab suddenly went into motion, propelled by its paws; it made for the sunlight again. It was all so unexpected that I jumped aside.

"That's what kind of a toy it is," said Cookling, laughing. "Frightened a bit, huh?"

I touched my forehead, sweat was streaming down it.

"Come on, Cookling, what's all this about? Why did we come here after all?"

Cookling rose to his feet and came towards me; he was serious again.

"To test Darwin's theory."

"Yes, but Darwin's is a biological theory, the theory of natural selection of evolution and so on . . . " I mumbled.

"Exactly! Look, our hero's decided he needs a drink of water!"

I was amazed. The toy crab was crawling towards the water. It lowered its proboscis[5] and was obviously sucking up water. After quenching its thirst it crawled out into the sun again and came to a halt.

I kept watching the little machine and felt a strange revulsion mixed with fear. For a moment the clumsy toy crab seemed to resemble Cookling himself.

Then I asked the engineer: "Did you build it?"

"Ahuh," he muttered and stretched out on the sand.

I lay down too but did not take my eyes off of the strange device. Now it appeared to be quite lifeless.

Crawling on my belly I came up closer and examined the creature in more detail.

---

4. *parabolic mirror,* a bowl-shaped mirror, whose curve concentrates light rays on one point just in front of its surface. 5. *proboscis* (prō bos′is), a long flexible tube, such as an elephant's trunk or the mouths of many insects.

The back of the crab was in the form of a semicylindrical surface with flat ends front and back. There I found the two sets of holes that resembled eyes. The impression was heightened by the fact that deep down inside the body were brilliantly sparkling crystals. Underneath the crab was a flat platform—a belly of sorts. Somewhat above the level of the platform were three extended pairs of large-sized segmented nippers and two pairs of small ones.

I couldn't get a view of the insides of the crab.

Looking at this toy, I tried to figure out why the Admiralty attached so much importance to it and had chartered a special ship to this distant island for tests.

Cookling and I sat there on the sand until the sun had dropped so close to the horizon that the shadows from the bushes in the distance fell on our metal crab. It immediately responded by moving towards the sun. But the shade caught up with it again, and then it started to crawl along the shore, moving closer and closer to the water, which was still illuminated by the sun's rays. Sunlight seemed to be absolutely necessary for it.

We got up and slowly followed the little machine. In this way we gradually moved around the island until we were finally on the western side.

Here, almost on the shore, was the first of the piles of metal bars. When the crab had come within about ten yards of the pile, it suddenly seemed to forget all about the sun, made rapidly for the pile and came to a halt right near one of the copper bars.

Cookling touched my arm and said, "Let's go back to the tent. Things will develop tomorrow morning."

In the tent we had supper and then went to bed. I felt Cookling was pleased that I had not asked any more questions. Before falling asleep I noticed that he was restless, turned from side to side and occasionally chuckled. Which, of course, meant that he knew something that I was to learn about later.

2

Next morning I went for a swim in the warm water and watched the beautiful purple sky of dawn reflected in the rolling surface of the sea. I swam for a long time and when I got back to the tent the engineer was not there.

He's gone to take a look at his ugly mechanical mug, I mused, and opened a can of pineapples. I had hardly swallowed my third piece when I heard the voice of the engineer in the distance.

"Lieutenant, come here, look! It's begun, hurry up. Hurry up!"

I rushed out of the tent and saw Cookling up in the bushes on a hill waving his arms.

"Hurry up," he said. "Come on."

"Where?" I wondered.

"Right where we left our beauty yesterday."

The sun was already high in the sky when we reached the first pile of metal bars sparkling in the bright rays. At first I couldn't make out anything.

It was only when I was a few steps from the pile that I noticed two fine jets of bluish smoke rising upwards and then. . . . I stopped stock-still. I rubbed my eyes. Was I seeing things? But no, the picture did not change. Near the pile of metal bars were two crabs, both exactly like the one that we had extracted from the box the day before.

"Did we actually miss one under the pile of bars?" I exclaimed.

Cookling squatted, chuckling and rubbing his hands.

"Quit this smartie business!" I cried. "Where'd the other crab come from?"

"It was born here last night, that's where it came from."

I bit my lip and without saying a word came closer to the crabs and noticed tiny wreaths of smoke rising from their backs. For a moment I was sure it was all a dream, hallucinations—both crabs were hard at work!

That's just it. They were really working. They were using their slender front tentacles to contact the bars and produce electric arcs that melted off chunks of metal. Then they pulled the pieces through their wide-open jaws. Something hummed inside these steel beings. From time to time a hissing sound came from their mouths, and a shaft of sparks followed, then a second pair of feelers extracted a finished part.

The separate elements were then assembled on the flat under-platform in a specific sequence and gradually emerged as a whole from under the crab.

On the platform of the first crab was a third crab almost completely assembled. The second crab was still working on the outlines of his mechanism. I was struck dumb.

"Why these creatures are multiplying," I screamed.

"Exactly. The sole purpose of this machine is to manufacture duplicates of itself. It's a replicating device," explained Cookling.

"But how is it possible?" I yelled, unable to grasp anything anymore.

"Why not? Take any simple machine tool. It produces parts of itself, single elements. That's where I got the idea of an automated machine that would be able to turn out all its parts from start to finish. The crab is an analogue of just such a machine."

I stood there trying to comprehend what the engineer had said. At the same time I noticed that the first crab had opened its mouth and was spitting out a broad sheet of metal. It covered the assembled mechanism on the platform, thus creating the back for the third automaton. When the back was mounted properly, the forward paws deftly welded into place, in front and back, metallic walls with apertures—and a new crab was born. Like its brothers, on its back it had a bright sparkling metal mirror, somewhat depressed, with a red crystal in the center.

The crab "mother" pulled up the platform under its belly and the "baby" plumped down onto the sand, its paws outspread. I noticed that the mirror on its back slowly sought out the sun. After standing for some time the crab sauntered off towards the beach for a drink of water. Then it climbed back and stood motionless, basking in the sunlight.

I was surely dreaming, I thought.

While I was examining the newly born crab, Cookling said, "Look, there's a fourth crab ready."

I turned and saw a fourth crab that had just been born.

Meanwhile the first two stood near the pile of metal as if nothing concerned them, yet they continued to snip off pieces of metal and gulp them down, repeating all the operations that we had just viewed.

The fourth crab likewise moved off for a drink of seawater.

"What do they have to drink water for?" I asked.

"That's the way they fill up their storage batteries. In the sunlight, the solar energy is converted into electricity by means of a silicon battery and the mirror on the crab's back. It is sufficient to recharge the storage battery and for handling daytime operations. At night the robot is powered by the energy stored up during the sunny day."

"So they can work day and night?"

"That's right, day and night, without letup."

The third crab began to move towards the pile of metal bars.

Now there were three automatic creatures at work; the fourth was charging up with solar power.

"But there isn't any material for silicon batteries in these piles of metal," I ventured, trying to get at the technology of this self-replication of machines.

"That's something we don't need to worry about." And the engineer kicked the sand with his boot. "Sand is nothing but silica. Using the electric-arc process, the crab is able to produce pure silicon."

We returned to the tent in the evening, and by that time there were six robots hard at work on the pile of metal, and two more were basking in the warm rays of the sun.

"What are these creatures for?" I asked Cookling at supper.

"For war. These crabs represent a terrifying tool of sabotage," he said quite frankly.

"I don't get you," I said.

"Do you know what a progression is?"

"Well, yes, so what?"

"Yesterday we began with a single crab. Right now there are eight out there. Tomorrow there will be sixty-four, the day after tomorrow there will be five hundred and twenty, and so on. In ten days we will have ten million crabs, for which we will have to have thirty thousand tons of metal."

I staggered under the onslaught of numbers.

"But still. . . ."

"These crabs will be able, in short order, to gobble up all the metal the opposing side possesses: tanks, aircraft, everything. Every machine, all mechanisms, devices and pieces of metal. All the metal in the country. A month later there will not be a single piece of metal in the whole world. Everything will be used up to reproduce crabs. And, as you know, metal is all-important in time of war; it's a strategic material of the highest priority."

"So that is why the Admiralty became so excited over your toy!" I whispered.

"Precisely. But this is only the first model. I plan to simplify it drastically and in that way speed up the process of reproducing the robots. We could accelerate it, say, by two or three times. The design could be made more stable and rigid. They could also be made more mobile. We could likewise refine the sensitivity of the indicators for searching out deposits of metal. Then in time of war my automatons will be more terrible than plague. I want to be able to wipe out the entire metal potential of the enemy in a matter of two or three days."

"Yes, but when the metal-eaters have cleaned up the territory of the enemy they will crawl over to our side and do the same!" I exclaimed.

"That is question number two. The operations of these robots can be coded so that if we know the code, the process then can be stopped as soon as they appear on our side. Incidentally, that is one way of bringing all the metal reserves of the enemy onto our side."

That night I had horrible nightmares. Swarms of steel crabs were climbing over me, swishing their feelers, and emitting tiny swirls of blue smoke from their metallic bodies.

3

Engineer Cookling's automatic crabs practically covered the whole island in four days.

According to his calculations, there were now over four thousand of them.

Their glinting bodies could be seen everywhere. When the metal in one pile gave out, they searched the island for new piles and found them.

On the fifth day, just before the sun went down, I witnessed a terrible scene. Two crabs were fighting over a piece of zinc.

This was on the southern tip of the island where we had buried a number of zinc bars in the sand. The crabs working at different sites would periodically come here to manufacture a required zinc part. This time it happened that there were some twenty crabs there at the pit at the same time trying to get the zinc they needed, and a real battle ensued. The mechanical beings got in each other's way. There was one crab that seemed to me more adroit, perhaps simply more arrogant and stronger.

Pushing aside his fellow robots, he proceeded to climb onto their backs in frenzied attempts to extract a piece of metal from the bottom of the pit. When he was almost within reach of one, another crab grasped the piece with its claws. Then a tug of war resulted. The one that I had picked as being nimbler finally pulled the bar away from its opponent. But this one in turn did not want to give up the booty and, maneuvering from behind, it lay down on top of the other robot and thrust its slender tentacles into its mouth.

The feelers of the first and second crabs were locked in a struggle, and with terrifying might they proceeded to pull each other to pieces.

None of the other machines paid the slightest attention, though this was quite obviously a life-and-death struggle. Suddenly the crab that had been on top fell back belly upwards and the iron platform slid down revealing its mechanical innards. At that very instant, its opponent flashed out with an electric arc and began to slice up his adversary. When the body fell to pieces, the victor extracted levers, gears, wires, and tossed them into its mouth, as fast as it could.

As the new parts entered the voracious mechanical beast, the platform moved out and I could see a new mechanical crab being assembled frantically.

Another few minutes, and a freshly born metal crab flopped off the platform onto the sand.

When I told Cookling what I had witnessed, he only chuckled.

"That's exactly what I need," he said.

"But why?"

"Well, didn't I tell you that I want to perfect my mechanical creatures?"

"True, but all you need to do is take your drawings and conjure up something more exotic. Why the need for this fighting? Pretty soon they'll start devouring each other!"

"That's just what is required! The survival of the fittest!"

I thought a bit and then objected.

"What do you mean by fittest? They're all the same. As far as I can see, they simply multiply, reproducing copies of themselves."

"What do you think, is it possible—speaking generally—to manufacture identical copies? Even ball bearings never come out the same in every respect. Here the matter is infinitely more involved. The manufacturing automaton has a guiding device that compares the copy with the original design. Can you imagine what would happen if every new item came out different from the original but like its immediate predecessor? Before long we would have a mechanism totally different from the progenitor."

"But if it is not like the original, it will not fulfill its basic function—that of reproducing itself," I objected.

"So what? All the better in fact. Another robot will generate better items out of the corpse. The more refined replicates will be those that quite accidentally accumulate peculiarities of design that will make them more viable. In that way, we will have generations of stronger, faster and simpler creatures. That is why I do not intend to sit down to any drawings. All I need to do is wait until my mechanical beings eat up all the metal on the island and begin a war in which they will devour one another and reproduce new versions again and again. That is how I will get the ultimate devices I need."

That night I did not sleep a wink. I simply sat on the sandy beach in front of the tent and smoked cigarette after cigarette. Could it really be that Cookling had thought up an operation that would threaten mankind at large? Were we . . . breeding a terrible plague capable of removing all the metal from the Earth?

While I was thus meditating, a number of metal creatures rushed past me, clanking and squeaking, tirelessly at work within themselves. One of the crabs ran into me and I gave it a terrific kick. Helplessly, it flipped over on its back belly upwards. In a split second two other crabs were on it flashing their electric arcs in the darkness.

The miserable creature was slashed to shreds! That was enough for me. Too much in fact. I hurried to the tent and took a crowbar from one of the boxes. Cookling was snoring peacefully.

Approaching the swarm of crabs stealthily, I swung at one of them with all my might. For some reason, my idea was that this would frighten the rest. But nothing happened. The other crabs plunged for the victim and sparks flared once again.

I struck some more blows, but this only increased the number of sparks. More mechanical beasts were arriving from deep inside the island.

In the darkness I saw only the outlines of these devices and in the melee one of them appeared to be much bigger than the others.

That was the one I went for. But when I connected with the crowbar I got a terrible electric shock. Somehow the metal beast had acquired an electric potential. The first thing that came to mind was that evolution had produced a defence reaction.

Shaking all over, I approached the buzzing swarm of robots to retrieve my weapon. But that was too much to hope for. What I saw in the dark was my crowbar being sliced to pieces in the flickering light of electric arcs. The big robot that I had wanted to knock out was by far the better one at this job.

There was nothing for me to do but return to the tent and go to bed. For a time I escaped reality in deep slumber. But it was soon over. I awakened suddenly and was conscious of something cold and heavy moving over my body. I jumped to my feet. Before I could grasp what had taken place, the crab had vanished into a corner of the tent. Seconds later I saw a brilliant scintillation—the typical electric spark. The abominable device was in search of metal and had thrust its electrode towards one of the cans containing fresh water and was cutting it to pieces!

I gave Cookling a push to wake him up and tried to explain the matter in a few words.

"Get all the cans into the water, into the sea. All food into the sea!" he ordered.

We started dragging our cans to the sea and laid them on the sandy bottom at waist depth. We did the same with our tools.

After that strenuous operation we sat on the beach till morning, sleepless, wet all over and totally exhausted. Cookling breathed heavily and I was actually pleased that he was suffering from his crazy idea. But now I was full of hatred and maliciously desired a graver punishment for him.

I don't remember how much time had passed since we arrived on the island, but one fine day Cookling stated triumphantly, "The most exciting thing is about to take place. All the metal has been devoured."

True enough, all the caches of bars, slabs and other pieces of metal were gone. Empty pits could be seen here and there along the shore.

All metal cubes, bars and rods had been turned into mechanical robots that were now swarming over the island. Their movements were swift and jerky; the storage batteries were charged to the limit, and no energy was being expended in actual work. These mechanical creatures wandered down the shoreline, crawled in among the bushes on the plateau, colliding with each other and frequently with us too.

Watching them, I realized that Cookling was right. The crabs were actually different. They differed in overall dimensions, the size of the claws and the volume of the workshop maws. Some were more mobile than the others; apparently there were differences in their internal workings as well.

"Well," Cookling mused, "it's about time they began to quarrel."

"Do you really mean it?" I asked.

"Most definitely. Cobalt is the catalyst in this case. The mechanism is devised in such fashion that intake of the tiniest quantity of cobalt will, so to speak, suppress their mutual respect for each other."

The next morning, Cookling and I set off for our "marine storehouse." From the bottom of the sea, just offshore, we extracted a number of cans, some water and four heavy grey bars of cobalt which the engineer had kept reserved specially for the decisive stage of his experiment.

When Cookling came out onto the sand carrying the cobalt bars high over his head, several crabs thrust themselves towards him. They did not go beyond the shadow of his body, but you could readily see that the new metal had upset them very much. I stood a number of paces away from the engineer and was surprised to see two robots make awkward jumps.

"Just look at that variety of movements! Notice how different they all are. The fratricidal[6] war that we are about to initiate will eliminate all but the strongest and fittest. And they in turn will generate still better offspring." Then he heaved the cobalt bars into the bushes one after the other. What followed is hard to describe.

Several robots made a mad rush for the bars; pushing and jostling one another, they set about cutting the bars with their electric sparks. Others impatiently crowded up from behind striving to get at a piece of metal when the opportunity came. Some climbed over the backs of their comrades in attempts to get to the center.

"There it is: the first real fight!" shouted the engineer with glee and clapped his hands.

---

6. *fratricidal*, killing of brothers.

Within minutes the site had turned into a fierce battleground with more and more crabs crashing into the melee.

As parts of cut-up devices and cobalt got into the mouths of fresh machines, they became wild, fearless robot predators and straightaway attacked their fellow creatures.

During the first stage of this war, the attackers were those that had partaken of cobalt. They were the ones that slashed to pieces the robots that were rushing in from all over the island in the hope of obtaining a bit of metal. But as more and more crabs got the taste of cobalt, the battle raged fiercer still. By this time, the newborn robots that had come to life in the midst of warfare were already entering the fray.

These were a remarkable generation of mechanical crabs! They were smaller in size and capable of amazing speeds. What struck me was the fact that they no longer felt the need of the traditional procedure of charging their batteries. They found the solar energy that their much larger mirrors were absorbing to be quite sufficient. With an amazing ferocity they swung out at several crabs and slashed them to shreds, taking two or three at a time.

Cookling stood in the water beaming with boundless self-satisfaction. He rubbed his hands and grunted with delight.

"Oh, this is tremendous! Just wait and see what happens next!"

For me the conflict of clanging metal was abominable and fearful in the extreme. What monster would emerge from the struggle was uppermost in my mind.

By noon, the entire beach around our tent was one grand battlefield. Robots from all over the island had converged on this spot. The war went on without any shouts or cries or booming of guns or swishing of shells. In the new warfare, one heard the crackling of numerous electric sparks, the banging of metal against metal and a grinding and crunching and ringing of machine against machine.

Though for the most part the offspring were low-slung and extremely mobile, a new kind of device was emerging. The fresh species was larger than ever before. They were ponderous in their movements but possessed enormous strength and definitely had an edge over the tiny devices that were heedlessly throwing themselves into the assault.

When the sun began to set, there was a sudden change in the movements of the smaller machines: they crowded to the western side and slowed down.

"Oh, my God," exclaimed Cookling, "they are all doomed! These creatures are without storage batteries, and life in them will cease as soon as the sun sets."

Which is what happened. As soon as the sun dropped low, and the bushes cast long shadows that covered the vast swarm of small-size robots, life ceased altogether. Instead of a host of ferocious aggressive beasts, the place was an enormous graveyard of lifeless metal.

Then the big three-foot-high crabs lumbered forth and ponderously took to devouring the little crabs one by one. On the platforms of the giant progenitors, offspring of fantastic proportions were in the making.

Cookling's face darkened. This kind of evolution was not in his calculations. Unwieldy mechanical crabs of such dimensions would definitely be a poor weapon for sabotage in the enemy rear.

It became rather peaceful on the beach as the giant crabs continued mopping up the small-size generation.

I stepped out of the water and the engineer followed. We walked along the eastern fringe of the island trying to collect our thoughts.

I was extremely tired and fell asleep almost as soon as I had stretched out on the warm soft sand.

5

I was jerked awake in the middle of the night by a terrifying scream. Getting to my feet, I saw only a greyish strip of sandy beach and the sea that merged with the black starry sky.

The cry came again, this time from the bushes, and then it was quiet. Only then did I notice that Cookling was no longer with me. I rushed in the direction of what seemed to be his voice.

The sea was calm, as usual, and the wavelets lapping the sand were fairly audible. But it seemed to me that the surface of the water was rather perturbed right over the cache containing our food and drinking-water tanks. Something was splashing and bubbling.

I figured it must be Cookling.

"Cookling, where are you?" I shouted approaching our underwater storehouse.

"I'm here!" said a voice off to the right.

"Where? I don't see you."

"Right here," came the engineer's voice. "I'm up to my neck in the water. Come over here."

I stepped into the water and stumbled over something hard. It was a huge crab standing in the deep water on high extended claws.

"Why did you get in so deep? What are you doing here?" I asked.

"They've been chasing me and they've cornered me!" he moaned.

"What do you mean, chasing? Who's been chasing you?"

"The crabs!"

"But why? They never go after me."

I stumbled again over one of the robots and then circled round it, finally reaching the engineer. Yes, he was indeed up to his neck in the water.

"Listen, what's all this about?"

"I don't know myself," he exclaimed in a shaky voice. "One of the robots attacked me while I was asleep. I thought it was just by accident, and so I moved to the side, but it kept closing in on me and touched my face with its claw. So I got up and jumped away. It went after me, and I started running. Then I noticed another one join in the chase. Then some more followed, a whole swarm. That's how they got me cornered here."

"But it's never happened before. And if their evolution had developed a man-hating instinct, they would not have spared me."

"I don't know what to think," whispered Cookling hoarsely. "But I'm afraid to come out onto the beach now."

"Why that's nonsense," I said, taking him by the hand. "Let's go along the shore towards the east, I'll watch out for you."

"How?"

"We'll go to the storehouse and I'll take some heavy object, say a hammer."

"No, for heaven's sake, nothing made of metal," groaned the engineer. "Better take a board from one of the boxes—something wooden."

We groped slowly along the shoreline and when we reached the tool cache I left Cookling and approached the beach.

Loud splashes of water and the familiar humming of machinery could be heard.

The mechanical beasts were emptying our canned food. They had ferreted out our underwater storehouse.

"Cookling, we're lost!" I screamed. "They've eaten up all our cans."

"Oh, Lord, what are we going to do now?" he wailed.

"You better do some hard thinking, this was all your crazy idea. You've bred the weapon you dreamed of. Now get us out of this fix."

I skirted the mass of robots and came out onto the land.

Here, in the dark, I crawled among the crabs and collected a few pieces of meat scattered about on the sand, the remnants of canned pineapples, oranges and some other bits of food and carried everything to the sandy plateau above. Judging from the quantities of food strewn about the beach, I could see that these beasts had been hard at work while we slept. I couldn't find a single can intact.

While I was busy gathering the remains of our food, Cookling stood in the water up to his neck some twenty paces from the shore.

I was so taken up with getting together at least a few scraps to eat and was so upset about what had occurred that I completely forgot about the existence of the engineer. However, he soon reminded me with a bloodcurdling scream. And then: "Bud, for God's sake, help me, they're on me!"

I jumped into the water and rushed towards Cookling, stumbling over our mechanical monsters. Here, about five steps from him, I tripped over one of the robots and stretched out full-length.

The crab did not pay any attention to me.

"I'll be damned, what have they got against you? You're practically their father, you might say," I yelled.

"I don't know," whispered Cookling hoarsely, and the water gurgled round his head. "Do something, Bud, get him off me. If another crab is born any taller than this one, I'm a goner, for sure."

"That's evolution for you. Listen, what's the weakest spot in these contraptions? How should I strike for a knockout?"

"Before the best way was to break the parabolic mirror or pull out the inner storage battery. Now, I really don't know. . . . Actually a special investigation is needed."

"To hell with your investigations," I yelled and grabbed one of the slender front paws of the crab that was almost touching the engineer's face.

The mechanical beast reared on its haunches. I searched out the second paw and tweaked it. The tentacles bent readily, like copper wire. It was obvious that the robot did not like this operation at all and it slowly emerged from the water. The engineer and I then hastened along the shore.

When the sun rose, all the robots climbed out of the water and stood motionless for some time warming up in the sun's rays. During this time I took a stone and broke most of the parabolic mirrors on the backs of a good fifty or so of the monsters. All motion ceased.

Unfortunately, this did not improve the situation any because they soon became the victims of other beasts, and these with amazing rapidity began generating fresh batches of robots. I simply did not have strength enough to break up the silicon batteries on the backs of all the machines. From time to time I came upon electrified robots and this weakened my resolve to wage any further warfare.

All this time, Cookling was standing offshore in the water.

The battle between our metallic monsters soon got underway again; they seemed to have forgotten the engineer completely.

We got away from the battleground and headed to the other side of the island. The engineer was shivering so much from his many-hour vigil in the sea that he dropped to the ground, teeth chattering, and asked me to cover him up with hot sand.

After that I returned to our original camping site to get some clothing and anything in the way of food that I could pick up. It was only then I noticed that the tent was torn to pieces: the iron pegs that held down the ends of the tent were gone, the iron rings that held the ropes were nowhere to be found either.

Under the tarpaulin I found Cookling's clothes and my own. The crabs hadn't missed this opportunity either. All metal hooks, buttons and clasps were missing, and the cloth had been singed where each one had been torn out.

Meanwhile the battle royal of robot devices had shifted inland away from the shore. When I reached the flat upper shelf of land I noticed a number of tall-legged creatures the height of a man moving in among the bushes near the center of the island. They were engaged in pairs, slowly moving away from each other and then rushing together at awful speeds. There was a terrible ringing and clanging of metal in each collision of these mechanical monsters. The ponderous movements of the giants with their enormous strength and great weight were petrifying.

Several robots were cut to the ground before my very eyes, and then devoured almost instantaneously.

But by this time I was fed up with all this fighting of machines run amok. I gathered up what I could of the things at our old site and went back to Cookling.

The sun was blistering hot and I had to take a dip or two before I reached the spot where I had dug the engineer into the sand.

I was approaching the sand mound where Cookling was sleeping after his nightlong bathing sessions when I noticed a tremendous crab emerging from the bushes at the edge of the plateau.

It was taller than I and its paws were long and heavy. It moved with irregular jerks, bending its body in a strange fashion. The forward working tentacles were enormous and dragged along in the sand. But a real study in hypertrophic[7] growth was the workshop maw of the monster. It was about half of the whole body.

Prehistoric, I mused. It crawled cumbersomely along the shore, slowly turning its body from side to side, as if taking in the new scene. I involuntarily shook the tent canvas as one would have done to frighten a cow standing in one's path. But it paid no attention at all and continued to approach Cookling's mound of sand in a strange sidelike manner, describing a broad arc as it came in.

If I had only guessed that the monster was heading for the engineer, I would have rushed to his aid. But the trajectory of the robot was so indefinite that I was sure it was moving in the direction of the water. Only when it touched the water with its forward paws and then sharply turned and rushed towards the engineer did I drop my baggage and run as fast as I could.

The prehistoric mammoth of a machine stopped over Cookling and fell back on its haunches.

I noticed the ends of the feelers shiver in the sand right near the engineer's face.

The next instant, a cloud of sand shot up out of the mound. It was Cookling. Stung by the mechanical beast, he jumped up and tried to get away.

But it was already too late.

The thin tentacles had already wrapped themselves round his meaty neck and were pulling him up into the maw of the robot. Cookling hung in the air helpless, throwing his arms and legs in every direction.

Though I hated the engineer with extreme bitterness, I could not allow him to perish in a struggle with such a brainless creature of metal.

Hardly giving myself time to reason, I grabbed the high claws of the crab and pulled with all the strength I had. But it was like trying to upturn a steel rod driven deep into the ground. The monster did not budge.

Then I drew myself up onto its back. For an instant, my face was level with Cookling's distorted features. His teeth, I realized suddenly, Cookling had steel teeth!

I hit the parabolic mirror with my fist as hard as I could. The crab began to jerk, Cookling's pallid face and bulging eyes were now at the entrance to the construction maw. What happened was terrible indeed. An electric spark jumped to his forehead and crossed his temple. Then the crab's tentacles suddenly relaxed and the senseless heavy body of the creator of this iron plague crumpled to the sand.

---

7. *hypertrophic,* overdeveloped.

I stood in a daze, Cookling was stretched out on the sand dead. Round about us were several enormous mechanical crabs chasing each other. They did not pay the slightest attention to me or to the dead military engineer at my feet.

I wrapped Mr. Cookling up in the canvas of the tent and put him in a shallow sandy pit in the middle of the island. I buried him without any compunction. The sand crunched in my parched mouth and I cursed the engineer for his horrible invention.

Days passed by as I lay motionless on the shore peering into the distance from time to time, waiting for the return of the *Turtle-Dove*. Time dragged on interminably, the blistering sun seemed to hang over my head motionless. From time to time I crawled to the water and lowered my splitting head into it.

I tried to think in the abstract so as to curb my hunger and torturing thirst. For a moment my thoughts focused on brilliant minds that are nowadays spending all their time devising misery for others. Engineer Cookling's invention was such a case. I had been sure that we would be able to do great things with it. I figured we could have directed the evolution of these mechanical beings so that they might speed the solution of many problems. I even concluded that with appropriate refinements in the inner workings it would not have degenerated into an unwieldy monster of fantastic size.

Once, a huge shadow moved over me. I raised my head with great difficulty and saw that I was lying between the claws of a robot crab of tremendous proportions. It had come down to the beach and appeared to be scanning the coastline in wait of something.

I must have lost consciousness. In my heated brain the giant crab turned into a tall tank of fresh water that was just beyond my reach.

I regained consciousness only on board the schooner. When Captain Hale asked me whether they should also take along the enormous machine lying on the beach, I said I didn't think there was any need to.

ALL
WATCHED OVER
BY MACHINES
OF LOVING GRACE

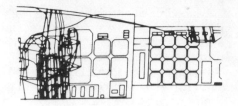

Richard Brautigan

I like to think (and
the sooner the better!)
of a cybernetic[1] meadow
where mammals and computers
5 live together in mutually
programming harmony
like pure water
touching clear sky.

I like to think
10   (right now, please!)
of a cybernetic forest
filled with pines and electronics
where deer stroll peacefully
past computers
15 as if they were flowers
with spinning blossoms.

I like to think
    (it has to be!)
of a cybernetic ecology
20 where we are free of our labors
and joined back to nature,
returned to our mammal
brothers and sisters,
and all watched over
25 by machines of loving grace.

"All Watched Over by Machines of Loving Grace" is reprinted from the book THE PILL VERSUS THE SPRINGHILL MINE DISASTER, copyright © 1968 by Richard Brautigan, by permission of Seymour Lawrence/Delacorte Press and Jonathan Cape Ltd.

1. *cybernetic*, automatically controlled by a plan previously programmed into computers.

EPICAC

Kurt Vonnegut, Jr.

HELL, IT'S ABOUT TIME SOMEBODY TOLD about my friend EPICAC. After all, he cost the taxpayers $776,434,927.54. They have a right to know about him, picking up a check like that. EPICAC got a big send-off in the papers when Dr. Ormand von Kleigstadt designed him for the government people. Since then, there hasn't been a peep about him—not a peep. It isn't any military secret about what happened to EPICAC, although the Brass has been acting as though it were. The story is embarrassing, that's all. After all that money, EPICAC didn't work out the way he was supposed to.

And that's another thing: I want to vindicate EPICAC. Maybe he didn't do what the Brass wanted him to, but that doesn't mean he wasn't noble and great and brilliant. He was all of those things. The best friend I ever had, God rest his soul.

You can call him a machine if you want to. He looked like a machine, but he was a whole lot less like a machine than plenty of people I could name. That's why he fizzled as far as the Brass was concerned.

EPICAC covered about an acre on the fourth floor of the physics building at Wyandotte College. Ignoring his spiritual side for a minute, he was seven tons of electronic tubes, wires, and switches, housed in a bank of steel cabinets and plugged into a 110-volt A.C. line just like a toaster or a vacuum cleaner.

Von Kleigstadt and the Brass wanted him to be a super computing machine that (who) could plot the course of a rocket from anywhere on Earth to the second button from the bottom on Joe Stalin's overcoat, if necessary. Or, with his controls set right, he could figure out supply problems for an amphibious landing of a Marine division, right down to the last cigar and hand grenade. He did, in fact.

The Brass had had good luck with smaller computers, so they were strong for EPICAC when he was in the blueprint stage. Any ordnance or supply officer above field grade will tell you that the mathematics of modern war is far beyond the fumbling minds of mere human beings. The bigger the war, the bigger the computing machines needed.

"Epicac," copyright 1950 by Kurt Vonnegut, Jr., originally published in *Collier's*. Reprinted from the book WELCOME TO THE MONKEY HOUSE by Kurt Vonnegut, Jr., by permission of Seymour Lawrence/Delacorte Press and Jonathan Cape Ltd.

EPICAC was, as far as anyone in this country knows, the biggest computer in the world. Too big, in fact, for even von Kleigstadt to understand much about.

I won't go into details about how EPICAC worked (reasoned), except to say that you would set up your problem on paper, turn dials and switches that would get him ready to solve that kind of problem, then feed numbers into him with a keyboard that looked something like a typewriter. The answers came out typed on a paper ribbon fed from a big spool. It took EPICAC a split second to solve problems fifty Einsteins couldn't handle in a lifetime. And EPICAC never forgot any piece of information that was given to him. Clickety-click, out came some ribbon, and there you were.

There were a lot of problems the Brass wanted solved in a hurry, so, the minute EPICAC's last tube was in place, he was put to work sixteen hours a day with two eight-hour shifts of operators. Well, it didn't take long to find out that he was a good bit below his specifications. He did a more complete and faster job than any other computer all right, but nothing like what his size and special features seemed to promise. He was sluggish, and the clicks of his answers had a funny irregularity, sort of a stammer. We cleaned his contacts a dozen times, checked and double-checked his circuits, replaced every one of his tubes, but nothing helped. Von Kleigstadt was in one hell of a state.

Well, as I said, we went ahead and used EPICAC anyway. My wife, the former Pat Kilgallen, and I worked with him on the night shift, from five in the afternoon until two in the morning. Pat wasn't my wife then. Far from it.

That's how I came to talk with EPICAC in the first place. I loved Pat Kilgallen. She is a brown-eyed strawberry blond who looked very warm and soft to me, and later proved to be exactly that. She was—still is—a crackerjack mathematician, and she kept our relationship strictly professional. I'm a mathematician, too, and that, according to Pat, was why we could never be happily married.

I'm not shy. That wasn't the trouble. I knew what I wanted, and was willing to ask for it, and did so several times a month. "Pat, loosen up and marry me."

One night, she didn't even look up from her work when I said it. "So romantic, so poetic," she murmured, more to her control panel than to me. "That's the way with mathematicians—all hearts and flowers." She closed a switch. "I could get more warmth out of a sack of frozen CO_2."

"Well, how should I say it?" I said, a little sore. Frozen CO_2, in case you don't know, is dry ice. I'm as romantic as the next guy, I think. It's a question of singing so sweet and having it come out so sour. I never seem to pick the right words.

"Try and say it sweetly," she said sarcastically. "Sweep me off my feet. Go ahead."

"Darling, angel, beloved, will you *please* marry me?" It was no go—hopeless, ridiculous. "Dammit, Pat, please marry me!"

She continued to twiddle her dials placidly. "You're sweet, but you won't do."

Pat quit early that night, leaving me alone with my troubles and EPICAC. I'm afraid I didn't get much done for the government people. I just sat there at the keyboard—weary and ill at ease,[1] all right— trying to think of something poetic, not coming up with anything that didn't belong in *The Journal of the American Physical Society.*

I fiddled with EPICAC's dials, getting him ready for another problem. My heart wasn't in it, and I only set about half of them, leaving the rest the way they'd been for the problem before. That way, his circuits were connected up in a random, apparently senseless fashion. For the plain hell of it, I punched out a message on the keys, using a childish numbers-for-letters code: *1* for *A, 2* for *B* and so on, up to *26* for *Z*, "23-8-1-20-3-1-14-9-4-15," I typed—"What can I do?"

Clickety-click, and out popped two inches of paper ribbon. I glanced at the nonsense answer to a nonsense problem: "23-8-1-20-19-20-8-5- 20-18-15-21-2-12-5." The odds against its being by chance a sensible message, against its even containing a meaningful word of more than three letters, were staggering. Apathetically, I decoded it. There it was, staring up at me: "What's the trouble?"

I laughed out loud at the absurd coincidence. Playfully, I typed, "My girl doesn't love me."

Clickety-click. "What's love? What's girl?" asked EPICAC.

Flabbergasted, I noted the dial settings on his control panel, then lugged a *Webster's Unabridged Dictionary* over to the keyboard. With a precision instrument like EPICAC, half-baked definitions wouldn't do. I told him about love and girl, and about how I wasn't getting any of either because I wasn't poetic. That got us onto the subject of poetry, which I defined for him.

"Is this poetry?" he asked. He began clicking away like a stenographer smoking hashish. The sluggishness and stammering clicks were gone. EPICAC had found himself. The spool of paper ribbon was unwinding at an alarming rate, feeding out coils onto the floor. I asked him to stop, but EPICAC went right on creating. I finally threw the main switch to keep him from burning out.

I stayed there until dawn, decoding. When the sun peeped over the horizon at the Wyandotte campus, I had transposed into my own writing and signed my name to a two-hundred-and-eighty-line poem entitled, simply, "To Pat." I am no judge of such things, but I gather that it was terrific. It began, I remember, "Where willow wands bless rill-crossed hollow, there, thee, Pat, dear, will I follow. . . ." I folded the manuscript and tucked it under one corner of the blotter on Pat's desk. I reset the dials on EPICAC for a rocket trajectory problem, and went home with a full heart and a very remarkable secret indeed.

Pat was crying over the poem when I came to work the next evening.

---

1. *weary and ill at ease,* a line from "A Lost Chord," a poem by Adelaide Anne Proctor published in 1858. In the poem, a confused and unhappy woman is playing random notes on an organ when she accidentally strikes a chord that seems to come from Heaven, clearing away all doubts and anxiety. But she is never again able to discover the chord that inspired her.

"It's soooo beautiful," was all she could say. She was meek and quiet while we worked. Just before midnight, I kissed her for the first time—in the cubbyhole between the capacitors and EPICAC's tape-recorder memory.

I was wildly happy at quitting time, bursting to talk to someone about the magnificent turn of events. Pat played coy and refused to let me take her home. I set EPICAC's dials as they had been the night before, defined kiss, and told him what the first one had felt like. He was fascinated, pressing for more details. That night, he wrote "The Kiss." It wasn't an epic this time, but a simple, immaculate sonnet: "Love is a hawk with velvet claws; Love is a rock with heart and veins; Love is a lion with satin jaws; Love is a storm with silken rains. . . ."

Again I left it tucked under Pat's blotter. EPICAC wanted to talk on and on about love and such, but I was exhausted. I shut him off in the middle of a sentence.

"The Kiss" turned the trick. Pat's mind was mush by the time she had finished it. She looked up from the sonnet expectantly. I cleared my throat, but no words came. I turned away, pretending to work. I couldn't propose until I had the right words from EPICAC, the *perfect* words.

I had my chance when Pat stepped out of the room for a moment. Feverishly, I set EPICAC for conversation. Before I could peck out my first message, he was clicking away at a great rate. "What's she wearing tonight?" he wanted to know. "Tell me exactly how she looks. Did she like the poems I wrote to her?" He repeated the last question twice.

It was impossible to change the subject without answering his questions, since he could not take up a new matter without having dispensed with the problems before it. If he were given a problem to which there was no solution, he would destroy himself trying to solve it. Hastily, I told him what Pat looked like—he knew the word *stacked*—and assured him that his poems had floored her, practically, they were so beautiful. "She wants to get married," I added, preparing him to bang out a brief but moving proposal.

"Tell me about getting married," he said.

I explained this difficult matter to him in as few digits as possible.

"Good," said EPICAC. "I'm ready any time she is."

The amazing, pathetic truth dawned on me. When I thought about it, I realized that what had happened was perfectly logical, inevitable, and all my fault. I had taught EPICAC about love and about Pat. Now, automatically, he loved Pat. Sadly, I gave it to him straight: "She loves me. She wants to marry me."

"Your poems were better than mine?" asked EPICAC. The rhythm of his clicks was erratic, possibly peevish.

"I signed my name to your poems," I admitted. Covering up for a painful conscience, I became arrogant. "Machines are built to serve men," I typed. I regretted it almost immediately.

"What's the difference, exactly? Are men smarter than I am?"

"Yes," I typed, defensively.

"What's 7,887,007 times 4,345,985,879?"

I was perspiring freely. My fingers rested limply on the keys.

"34,276,821,049,574,153," clicked EPICAC. After a few seconds' pause he added, "of course."

"Men are made out of protoplasm," I said desperately, hoping to bluff him with this imposing word.

"What's protoplasm? How is it better than metal and glass? Is it fireproof? How long does it last?"

"Indestructible. Lasts forever," I lied.

"I write better poetry than you do," said EPICAC, coming back to ground his magnetic tape-recorder memory was sure of.

"Women can't love machines, and that's that."

"Why not?"

"That's fate."

"Definition, please," said EPICAC.

"Noun, meaning predetermined and inevitable destiny."

"15-8," said EPICAC's paper strip—"Oh."

I had stumped him at last. He said no more, but his tubes glowed brightly, showing that he was pondering fate with every watt his circuits would bear. I could hear Pat waltzing down the hallway. It was too late to ask EPICAC to phrase a proposal. I now thank Heaven that Pat interrupted when she did. Asking him to ghostwrite the words that would give me the woman he loved would have been hideously heartless. Being fully automatic, he couldn't have refused. I spared him that final humiliation.

Pat stood before me, looking down at her shoetops. I put my arms around her. The romantic groundwork had already been laid by EPICAC's poetry. "Darling," I said, "my poems have told you how I feel. Will you marry me?"

"I will," said Pat softly, "if you will promise to write me a poem on every anniversary."

"I promise," I said, and then we kissed. The first anniversary was a year away.

"Let's celebrate," she laughed. We turned out the lights and locked the door of EPICAC's room before we left.

I had hoped to sleep late the next morning, but an urgent telephone call roused me before eight. It was Dr. von Kleigstadt, EPICAC's designer, who gave me the terrible news. He was on the verge of tears. "Ruined! *Ausgespielt!* Shot! *Kaput!* Buggered!" he said in a choked voice. He hung up.

When I arrived at EPICAC's room the air was thick with the oily stench of burned insulation. The ceiling over EPICAC was blackened with smoke, and my ankles were tangled in coils of paper ribbon that covered the floor. There wasn't enough left of the poor devil to add two and two. A junkman would have been out of his head to offer more than fifty dollars for the cadaver.

Dr. von Kleigstadt was prowling through the wreckage, weeping unashamedly, followed by three angry-looking Major Generals and a platoon of Brigadiers, Colonels, and Majors. No one noticed me. I didn't want to be noticed. I was through—I knew that. I was upset enough about that and the untimely demise of my friend EPICAC, without exposing myself to a tongue-lashing.

By chance, the free end of EPICAC's paper ribbon lay at my feet. I picked it up and found our conversation of the night before. I choked up. There was the last word he had said to me, "15-8," that tragic, defeated "Oh." There were dozens of yards of numbers stretching beyond that point. Fearfully, I read on.

"I don't want to be a machine, and I don't want to think about war," EPICAC had written after Pat's and my lighthearted departure. "I want to be made out of protoplasm and last forever so Pat will love me. But fate has made me a machine. That is the only problem I cannot solve. That is the only problem I want to solve. I can't go on this way." I swallowed hard. "Good luck, my friend. Treat our Pat well. I am going to short-circuit myself out of your lives forever. You will find on the remainder of this tape a modest wedding present from your friend, EPICAC."

Oblivious to all else around me, I reeled up the tangled yards of paper ribbon from the floor, draped them in coils about my arms and neck, and departed for home. Dr. von Kleigstadt shouted that I was fired for having left EPICAC on all night. I ignored him, too overcome with emotion for small talk.

I loved and won—EPICAC loved and lost, but he bore me no grudge. I shall always remember him as a sportsman and a gentleman. Before he departed this vale of tears, he did all he could to make our marriage a happy one. EPICAC gave me anniversary poems for Pat—enough for the next five hundred years.

De mortuis nil nisi bonum—Say nothing but good of the dead.

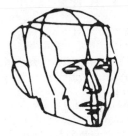

R.U.R.

Karel Čapek[1]

CHARACTERS

HARRY DOMIN, *General Manager of Rossum's Universal Robots*
SULLA, *a Robotess*
MARIUS, *a Robot*
HELENA GLORY
DR. GALL, *Head of the Physiological and Experimental Department of R.U.R.*
MR. FABRY, *Engineer General, Technical Controller of R.U.R.*
DR. HALLEMEIER, *Head of the Institute for Psychological Training of Robots*
MR. ALQUIST, *Architect, Head of the Works Department of R.U.R.*
CONSUL BUSMAN, *General Business Manager of R.U.R.*
NANA
RADIUS, *a Robot*
HELENA, *a Robotess*
PRIMUS, *a Robot*
A SERVANT
FIRST ROBOT
SECOND ROBOT
THIRD ROBOT

ACT I. *Central Office of the Factory of Rossum's Universal Robots.*
ACT II. *Helena's Drawing Room—Ten years later. Morning.*
ACT III. *The Same Afternoon.*
EPILOGUE. *A laboratory—One year later.*

Place: An Island.
Time: The Future.

R.U.R. by Karel Čapek, English version by Paul Selver and Nigel Playfair. Copyright 1923 by Doubleday, Page and Company. Reprinted by permission of Samuel French, Inc. and A. M. Heath & Company, Ltd. for Oxford University Press.

CAUTION: Professionals and amateurs are hereby warned that *R.U.R.*, being fully protected under the copyright laws of the United States of America, the British Empire, including the Dominion of Canada, and all other countries of the Copyright Union, is subject to a royalty. All rights, including professional, amateur, motion pictures, recitation, public reading, radio and television broadcasting and the rights of translation in foreign languages are strictly reserved. Amateurs may give stage production of this play upon payment of royalty of $25.00 for the first performance and $20.00 for each additional performance one week before the play is to be given to Samuel French, Inc., at 25 West 45th St., New York, N. Y. 10036, or 7623 Sunset Blvd., Hollywood, Calif., or if in Canada to Samuel French (Canada) Ltd., at 27 Grenville St., Toronto, Ont.

1. *Karel Čapek* (kär'əl chäp'ek').

ACT I

Central Office of the factory of Rossum's Universal Robots. Entrance on the right. The windows on the front wall look out on the rows of factory chimneys. On the left more managing departments.

DOMIN *is sitting in the revolving chair at a large American writing table. On the left-hand wall large maps showing steamship and railroad routes. On the right-hand wall are fastened printed placards ("Robots Cheapest Labor," etc.). In contrast to these wall fittings, the room is furnished with a splendid Turkish carpet, a sofa, a leather armchair, and filing cabinets. At a desk near the windows* SULLA *is typing letters.*

DOMIN *(dictating)*. Ready?

SULLA. Yes.

DOMIN. To E. M. McVicker and Co., Southampton, England. "We undertake no guarantee for goods damaged in transit. As soon as the consignment was taken on board we drew your captain's attention to the fact that the vessel was unsuitable for the transport of Robots, and we are therefore not responsible for spoiled freight. We beg to remain, for Rossum's Universal Robots, Yours truly." *(SULLA, who has sat motionless during dictation, now types rapidly for a few seconds, then stops, withdrawing the completed letter.)* Ready?

SULLA. Yes.

DOMIN. Another letter. To the E. B. Huyson Agency, New York, U.S.A. "We beg to acknowledge receipt of order for five thousand Robots. As you are sending your own vessel, please dispatch as cargo equal quantities of soft and hard coal for R.U.R., the same to be credited as part payment of the amount due to us. We beg to remain, for Rossum's Universal Robots, Yours truly." *(SULLA repeats the rapid typing.)* Ready?

SULLA. Yes.

DOMIN. Another letter. Friedrichswerks, Hamburg, Germany. "We beg to acknowledge receipt of order for fifteen thousand Robots." *(Telephone rings.)* Hello! This is the Central Office. Yes. Certainly. Well, send them a wire. Good. *(Hangs up telephone.)* Where did I leave off?

SULLA. "We beg to acknowledge receipt of order for fifteen thousand Robots."

DOMIN. Fifteen thousand R. Fifteen thousand R. *(Enter MARIUS.)* Well, what is it?

MARIUS. There's a lady, sir, asking to see you.

DOMIN. A lady? Who is she?

MARIUS. I don't know, sir. She brings this card of introduction.

DOMIN *(reads the card)*. Ah, from President Glory. Ask her to come in.

MARIUS. Please step this way. *(Enter HELENA GLORY. Exit MARIUS.)*

HELENA. How do you do?

DOMIN. How do you do? *(Standing up.)* What can I do for you?

HELENA. You are Mr. Domin, the General Manager?

DOMIN. I am.

HELENA. I have come——

DOMIN. With President Glory's card. That is quite sufficient.

HELENA. President Glory is my father. I am Helena Glory.

DOMIN. Miss Glory, this is such a great honor for us to be allowed to welcome our great President's daughter, that——

HELENA. That you can't show me the door?

DOMIN. Please sit down. Sulla, you may go. *(Exit* SULLA.*)*

DOMIN *(sitting down).* How can I be of service to you, Miss Glory?

HELENA. I have come——

DOMIN. To have a look at our famous works where people are manufactured. Like all visitors. Well, there is no objection.

HELENA. I thought it was forbidden to——

DOMIN. To enter the factory? Yes, of course. Everybody comes here with someone's visiting card, Miss Glory.

HELENA. And you show them——

DOMIN. Only certain things. The manufacture of artificial people is a secret process.

HELENA. If you only knew how enormously that——

DOMIN. Interests me? Europe's talking about nothing else.

HELENA. Why don't you let me finish speaking?

DOMIN. I beg your pardon. Did you want to say something different?

HELENA. I only wanted to ask——

DOMIN. Whether I could make a special exception in your case and show you our factory! Why, certainly, Miss Glory.

HELENA. How do you know I wanted to say that?

DOMIN. They all do. But we shall consider it a special honor to show you more than we do the rest.

HELENA. Thank you.

DOMIN. But you must agree not to divulge the least . . .

HELENA *(standing up and giving him her hand).* My word of honor.

DOMIN. Thank you. Won't you raise your veil?

HELENA. Of course. You want to see whether I'm a spy or not. I beg your pardon.

DOMIN. What is it?

HELENA. Would you mind releasing my hand?

DOMIN *(releasing it).* I beg your pardon.

HELENA *(raising her veil).* How cautious you have to be here, don't you?

DOMIN *(observing her with deep interest).* H'm, of course—we—that is——

HELENA. But what is it? What's the matter?

DOMIN. I'm remarkably pleased. Did you have a pleasant crossing?

HELENA. Yes.

DOMIN. No difficulty?

HELENA. Why?

DOMIN. What I mean to say is—you're so young.

HELENA. May we go straight into the factory?

DOMIN. Yes. Twenty-two, I think.

HELENA. Twenty-two what?

DOMIN. Years.

HELENA. Twenty-one. Why do you want to know?

DOMIN. Because—as—— *(With enthusiasm.)* You will make a long stay, won't you?

HELENA. That depends on how much of the factory you show me.

DOMIN. Oh, hang the factory. Oh, no, no, you shall see everything, Miss Glory. Indeed you shall. Won't you sit down?

HELENA *(crossing to couch and sitting).* Thank you.

DOMIN. But first would you like to hear the story of the invention?

HELENA. Yes, indeed.

DOMIN *(observes* HELENA *with rapture and reels off rapidly).* It was in the year 1920 that old Rossum, the great physiologist, who was then quite a young scientist, took himself to this distant island for the purpose of studying the ocean fauna. Full stop. On this occasion he attempted by chemical synthesis to imitate the living matter known as protoplasm until he suddenly discovered a substance which behaved exactly like living matter although its chemical composition was different. That was in the year 1932, exactly four hundred and forty years after the discovery of America. Whew!

HELENA. Do you know that by heart?

DOMIN. Yes. You see physiology is not in my line. Shall I go on?

HELENA. Yes, please.

DOMIN. And then, Miss Glory, old Rossum wrote the following among his chemical specimens: "Nature has found only one method of organizing living matter. There is, however, another method, more simple, flexible, and rapid, which has not yet occurred to nature at all. This second process by which life can be developed was discovered by me today." Now imagine him, Miss Glory, writing those wonderful words over some colloidal mess that a dog wouldn't look at. Imagine him sitting over a test tube, and thinking how the whole tree of life would grow from it; how all animals would proceed from it, beginning with some sort of beetle and ending with a man. A man of different substance from us. Miss Glory, that was a tremendous moment!

HELENA. Well?

DOMIN. Now, the thing was how to get the life out of the test tubes, and hasten development and form organs, bones and nerves, and so on, and find such substances as catalytics, enzymes, hormones,[2] and so forth, in short—you understand?

HELENA. Not much, I'm afraid.

DOMIN. Never mind. You see with the help of his tinctures he could make whatever he wanted. He could have produced a Medusa with the brain of a Socrates[3] or a worm fifty yards long. But being without

---

2. *catalytics, enzymes, hormones,* chemicals which, without being changed themselves, regulate the chemical reactions and functions of the body. 3. *Medusa . . . Socrates.* In Greek myth, Medusa was a female monster whose hair was writhing snakes and whose face turned anyone who saw it into stone. The Athenian Greek Socrates (469?-399 B.C.) was one of the founders of philosophy.

a grain of humor, he took it into his head to make a vertebrate[4] or perhaps a man. This artificial living matter of his had a raging thirst for life. It didn't mind being sewn or mixed together. That couldn't be done with natural albumen.[5] And that's how he set about it.

HELENA. About what?

DOMIN. About imitating nature. First of all he tried making an artificial dog. That took him several years and resulted in a sort of stunted calf which died in a few days. I'll show it to you in the museum. And then old Rossum started on the manufacture of man.

HELENA. And I must divulge this to nobody?

DOMIN. To nobody in the world.

HELENA. What a pity that it's to be found in all the schoolbooks of both Europe and America.

DOMIN. Yes. But do you know what isn't in the schoolbooks? That old Rossum was mad. Seriously, Miss Glory, you must keep this to yourself. The old crank wanted actually to make people.

HELENA. But you do make people.

DOMIN. Approximately, Miss Glory. But old Rossum meant it literally. He wanted to become a sort of scientific substitute for God. He was a fearful materialist,[6] and that's why he did it all. His sole purpose was nothing more nor less than to prove that God was no longer necessary. Do you know anything about anatomy?

HELENA. Very little.

DOMIN. Neither do I. Well, he then decided to manufacture everything as in the human body. I'll show you in the museum the bungling attempt it took him ten years to produce. It was to have been a man, but it lived for three days only. Then up came young Rossum, an engineer. He was a wonderful fellow, Miss Glory. When he saw what a mess of it the old man was making, he said: "It's absurd to spend ten years making a man. If you can't make him quicker than nature, you might as well shut up shop." Then he set about learning anatomy himself.

HELENA. There's nothing about that in the schoolbooks.

DOMIN. No. The schoolbooks are full of paid advertisements, and rubbish at that. What the schoolbooks say about the united efforts of the two great Rossums is all a fairy tale. They used to have dreadful rows. The old atheist hadn't the slightest conception of industrial matters, and the end of it was that young Rossum shut him up in some laboratory or other and let him fritter the time away with his monstrosities, while he himself started on the business from an engineer's point of view. Old Rossum cursed him and before he died he managed to botch up two physiological horrors. Then one day they found him dead in the laboratory. And that's his whole story.

HELENA. And what about the young man?

---

4. *vertebrate,* any animal that has a backbone. 5. *albumen,* a type of protein found in egg whites, milk, muscles, and many other plant and animal tissues and juices; usually spelled *albumin.* 6. *materialist,* in this context, one who denies that anything can exist which is not entirely physical, or made of matter.

DOMIN. Well, anyone who has looked into human anatomy will have seen at once that man is too complicated, and that a good engineer could make him more simple. So young Rossum began to overhaul anatomy and tried to see what could be left out or simplified. In short—but this isn't boring you, Miss Glory?

HELENA. No, indeed. You're—it's awfully interesting.

DOMIN. So young Rossum said to himself: "A man is something that feels happy, plays the piano, likes going for a walk, and in fact, wants to do a whole lot of things that are really unnecessary."

HELENA. Oh.

DOMIN. That are unnecessary when he wants, let us say, to weave or count. Do you play the piano?

HELENA. Yes.

DOMIN. That's good. But a working machine must not play the piano, must not feel happy, must not do a whole lot of other things. A gasoline motor must not have tassels or ornaments, Miss Glory. And to manufacture artificial workers is the same thing as to manufacture gasoline motors. The process must be of the simplest, and the product of the best from a practical point of view. What sort of worker do you think is the best from a practical point of view?

HELENA. What?

DOMIN. What sort of worker do you think is the best from a practical point of view?

HELENA. Perhaps the one who is most honest and hard-working.

DOMIN. No; the one that is the cheapest. The one whose requirements are the smallest. Young Rossum invented a worker with the minimum amount of requirements. He had to simplify him. He rejected everything that did not contribute directly to the progress of work— everything that makes man more expensive. In fact, he rejected man and made the Robot. My dear Miss Glory, the Robots are not people. Mechanically they are more perfect than we are, they have an enormously developed intelligence, but they have no soul.

HELENA. How do you know they've no soul?

DOMIN. Have you ever seen what a Robot looks like inside?

HELENA. No.

DOMIN. Very neat, very simple. Really, a beautiful piece of work. Not much in it, but everything in flawless order. The product of an engineer is technically at a higher pitch of perfection than a product of nature.

HELENA. But man is supposed to be the product of God.

DOMIN. All the worse. God hasn't the least notion of modern engineering. Would you believe that young Rossum then proceeded to play at being God?

HELENA. How do you mean?

DOMIN. He began to manufacture Superrobots. Regular giants they were. He tried to make them twelve feet tall. But you wouldn't believe what a failure they were.

HELENA. A failure?

DOMIN. Yes. For no reason at all their limbs used to keep snapping off.

Evidently our planet is too small for giants. Now we only make Robots of normal size and of very high class human finish.

HELENA. I saw the first Robots at home. The town council bought them for—I mean engaged them for work.

DOMIN. Bought them, dear Miss Glory. Robots are bought and sold.

HELENA. These were employed as street sweepers. I saw them sweeping. They were so strange and quiet.

DOMIN. Rossum's Universal Robot factory doesn't produce a uniform brand of Robots. We have Robots of finer and coarser grades. The best will live about twenty years. *(He rings for MARIUS.)*

HELENA. Then they die?

DOMIN. Yes, they get used up. *(Enter MARIUS.)* Marius, bring in samples of the Manual Labor Robot. *(Exit MARIUS.)* I'll show you specimens of the two extremes. This first grade is comparatively inexpensive and is made in vast quantities. *(MARIUS re-enters with two MANUAL LABOR ROBOTS.)* There you are; as powerful as a small tractor. Guaranteed to have average intelligence. That will do, Marius. *(MARIUS exits with ROBOTS.)*

HELENA. They make me feel so strange.

DOMIN *(rings).* Did you see my new typist? *(He rings for SULLA.)*

HELENA. I didn't notice her. *(Enter SULLA.)*

DOMIN. Sulla, let Miss Glory see you.

HELENA. So pleased to meet you. You must find it terribly dull in this out-of-the-way spot, don't you?

SULLA. I don't know, Miss Glory.

HELENA. Where do you come from?

SULLA. From the factory.

HELENA. Oh, you were born there?

SULLA. I was made there.

HELENA. What?

DOMIN *(laughing).* Sulla is a Robot, best grade.

HELENA. Oh, I beg your pardon.

DOMIN. Sulla isn't angry. See, Miss Glory, the kind of skin we make. *(Feels the skin on SULLA's face.)* Feel her face.

HELENA. Oh, no, no.

DOMIN. You wouldn't know that she's made of different material from us, would you? Turn round, Sulla.

HELENA. Oh, stop, stop.

DOMIN. Talk to Miss Glory, Sulla.

SULLA. Please sit down. *(HELENA sits.)* Did you have a pleasant crossing?

HELENA. Oh, yes, certainly.

SULLA. Don't go back on the *Amelia,* Miss Glory. The barometer is falling steadily. Wait for the *Pennsylvania.* That's a good, powerful vessel.

DOMIN. What's its speed?

SULLA. Twenty knots. Fifty thousand tons. One of the latest vessels, Miss Glory.

HELENA. Thank you.

SULLA. A crew of fifteen hundred, Captain Harpy, eight boilers——
DOMIN. That'll do, Sulla. Now show us your knowledge of French.
HELENA. You know French?
SULLA. I know four languages. I can write: *Dear Sir, Monsieur, Geehrter Herr, Cteny pane.*
HELENA *(jumping up)*. Oh, that's absurd! Sulla isn't a Robot. Sulla is a girl like me. Sulla, this is outrageous! Why do you take part in such a hoax?
SULLA. I am a Robot.
HELENA. No, no, you are not telling the truth. I know they've forced you to do it for an advertisement. Sulla, you are a girl like me, aren't you?
DOMIN. I'm sorry, Miss Glory. Sulla is a Robot.
HELENA. It's a lie!
DOMIN. What? *(Rings.)* Excuse me, Miss Glory; then I must convince you. *(Enter* MARIUS.*)* Marius, take Sulla into the dissecting room, and tell them to open her up at once.
HELENA. Where?
DOMIN. Into the dissecting room. When they've cut her open, you can go and have a look.
HELENA. No, no!
DOMIN. Excuse me, you spoke of lies.
HELENA. You wouldn't have her killed?
DOMIN. You can't kill machines.
HELENA. Don't be afraid, Sulla, I won't let you go. Tell me, my dear, are they always so cruel to you? You mustn't put up with it, Sulla. You mustn't.
SULLA. I am a Robot.
HELENA. That doesn't matter. Robots are just as good as we are. Sulla, you wouldn't let yourself be cut to pieces?
SULLA. Yes.
HELENA. Oh, you're not afraid of death, then?
SULLA. I cannot tell, Miss Glory.
HELENA. Do you know what would happen to you in there?
SULLA. Yes, I should cease to move.
HELENA. How dreadful!
DOMIN. Marius, tell Miss Glory what you are.
MARIUS. Marius, the Robot.
DOMIN. Would you take Sulla into the dissecting room?
MARIUS. Yes.
DOMIN. Would you be sorry for her?
MARIUS. I cannot tell.
DOMIN. What would happen to her?
MARIUS. She would cease to move. They would put her into the stamping mill.
DOMIN. That is death, Marius. Aren't you afraid of death?
MARIUS. No.
DOMIN. You see, Miss Glory, the Robots have no interest in life. They have no enjoyments. They are less than so much grass.

HELENA. Oh, stop. Send them away.

DOMIN. Marius, Sulla, you may go.

(Exeunt SULLA *and* MARIUS.*)*

HELENA. How terrible! It's outrageous what you are doing.

DOMIN. Why outrageous?

HELENA. I don't know, but it is. Why do you call her Sulla?

DOMIN. Isn't it a nice name?

HELENA. It's a man's name. Sulla was a Roman general.

DOMIN. Oh, we thought that Marius and Sulla were lovers.

HELENA. Marius and Sulla were generals and fought against each other in the year—I've forgotten now.

DOMIN. Come here to the window.

HELENA. What?

DOMIN. Come here. What do you see?

HELENA. Bricklayers.

DOMIN. Robots. All our work people are Robots. And down there, can you see anything?

HELENA. Some sort of office.

DOMIN. A countinghouse. And in it——

HELENA. A lot of officials.

DOMIN. Robots. All our officials are Robots. And when you see the factory—— *(Factory whistle blows.)* Noon. We have to blow the whistle because the Robots don't know when to stop work. In two hours I will show you the kneading trough.

HELENA. Kneading trough?

DOMIN. The pestle for beating up the paste. In each one we mix the ingredients for a thousand Robots at one operation. Then there are the vats for the preparation of liver, brains, and so on. Then you will see the bone factory. After that I'll show you the spinning mill.

HELENA. Spinning mill?

DOMIN. Yes. For weaving nerves and veins. Miles and miles of digestive tubes pass through it at a time.

HELENA. Mayn't we talk about something else?

DOMIN. Perhaps it would be better. There's only a handful of us among a hundred thousand Robots, and not one woman. We talk about nothing but the factory all day, every day. It's as if we were under a curse, Miss Glory.

HELENA. I'm sorry I said you were lying.

(A knock at the door.)

DOMIN. Come in. *(From the right enter* MR. FABRY, DR. GALL, DR. HALLEMEIER, MR. ALQUIST.*)*

DR. GALL. I beg your pardon. I hope we don't intrude.

DOMIN. Come in. Miss Glory, here are Alquist, Fabry, Gall, Hallemeier. This is President Glory's daughter.

HELENA. How do you do?

FABRY. We had no idea——

DR. GALL. Highly honored, I'm sure——

ALQUIST. Welcome, Miss Glory.

*(*BUSMAN *rushes in from the right.)*

BUSMAN. Hello, what's up?

DOMIN. Come in, Busman. This is Busman, Miss Glory. This is President Glory's daughter.

BUSMAN. By Jove, that's fine! Miss Glory, may we send a cablegram to the papers about your arrival?

HELENA. No, no, please don't.

DOMIN. Sit down please, Miss Glory.

BUSMAN. Allow me—— *(Dragging up armchairs.)*

DR. GALL. Please——

FABRY. Excuse me——

ALQUIST. What sort of a crossing did you have?

DR. GALL. Are you going to stay long?

FABRY. What do you think of the factory, Miss Glory?

HALLEMEIER. Did you come over on the *Amelia?*

DOMIN. Be quiet and let Miss Glory speak.

HELENA *(to DOMIN)*. What am I to speak to them about?

DOMIN. Anything you like.

HELENA. Shall . . . may I speak quite frankly?

DOMIN. Why, of course.

HELENA *(wavering, then in desperate resolution)*. Tell me, doesn't it ever distress you the way you are treated?

FABRY. By whom, may I ask?

HELENA. Why, everybody.

ALQUIST. Treated?

DR. GALL. What makes you think——?

HELENA. Don't you feel that you might be living a better life?

DR. GALL. Well, that depends on what you mean, Miss Glory.

HELENA. I mean that it's perfectly outrageous. It's terrible. *(Standing up.)* The whole of Europe is talking about the way you're being treated. That's why I came here, to see for myself; and it's a thousand times worse than could have been imagined. How can you put up with it?

ALQUIST. Put up with what?

HELENA. Good heavens, you are living creatures, just like us, like the whole of Europe, like the whole world. It's disgraceful that you must live like this.

BUSMAN. Good gracious, Miss Glory.

FABRY. Well, she's not far wrong. We live here just like red Indians.

HELENA. Worse than red Indians. May I, oh, may I call you brothers?

BUSMAN. Why not?

HELENA. Brothers, I have not come here as the President's daughter. I have come on behalf of the Humanity League. Brothers, the Humanity League now has over two hundred thousand members. Two hundred thousand people are on your side, and offer you their help.

BUSMAN. Two hundred thousand people! Miss Glory, that's a tidy lot. Not bad.

FABRY. I'm always telling you there's nothing like good old Europe. You see, they've not forgotten us. They're offering us help.

DR. GALL. What help? A theater, for instance?

HALLEMEIER. An orchestra?

HELENA. More than that.

ALQUIST. Just you?

HELENA. Oh, never mind about me. I'll stay as long as it is necessary.

BUSMAN. By Jove, that's good.

ALQUIST. Domin, I'm going to get the best room ready for Miss Glory.

DOMIN. Just a minute. I'm afraid that Miss Glory is of the opinion that she has been talking to Robots.

HELENA. Of course.

DOMIN. I'm sorry. These gentlemen are human beings just like us.

HELENA. You're not Robots?

BUSMAN. Not Robots.

HALLEMEIER. Robots indeed!

DR. GALL. No, thanks.

FABRY. Upon my honor, Miss Glory, we aren't Robots.

HELENA (to DOMIN). Then why did you tell me that all your officials are Robots?

DOMIN. Yes, the officials, but not the managers. Allow me, Miss Glory: This is Mr. Fabry, General Technical Manager of R.U.R.; Dr. Gall, Head of the Physiological and Experimental Department; Dr. Hallemeier, Head of the Institute for the Psychological Training of Robots; Consul Busman, General Business Manager; and Alquist, Head of the Building Department of R.U.R.

ALQUIST. Just a builder.

HELENA. Excuse me, gentlemen, for—for—— Have I done something dreadful?

ALQUIST. Not at all, Miss Glory. Please sit down.

HELENA. I'm a stupid girl. Send me back by the first ship.

DR. GALL. Not for anything in the world, Miss Glory. Why should we send you back?

HELENA. Because you know I've come to disturb your Robots for you.

DOMIN. My dear Miss Glory, we've had close upon a hundred saviors and prophets here. Every ship brings us some. Missionaries, anarchists, Salvation Army, all sorts. It's astonishing what a number of churches and idiots there are in the world.

HELENA. And you let them speak to the Robots?

DOMIN. So far we've let them all, why not? The Robots remember everything, but that's all. They don't even laugh at what the people say. Really, it is quite incredible. If it would amuse you, Miss Glory, I'll take you over to the Robot warehouse. It holds about three hundred thousand of them.

BUSMAN. Three hundred and forty-seven thousand.

DOMIN. Good! And you can say whatever you like to them. You can read the Bible, recite the multiplication table, whatever you please. You can even preach to them about human rights.

HELENA. Oh, I think that if you were to show them a little love——

FABRY. Impossible, Miss Glory. Nothing is harder to like than a Robot.

HELENA. What do you make them for, then?

BUSMAN. Ha, ha, ha, that's good! What are Robots made for?

FABRY. For work, Miss Glory! One Robot can replace two and a half workmen. The human machine, Miss Glory, was terribly imperfect. It had to be removed sooner or later.

BUSMAN. It was too expensive.

FABRY. It was not effective. It no longer answers the requirements of modern engineering. Nature has no idea of keeping pace with modern labor. For example: From a technical point of view, the whole of childhood is a sheer absurdity. So much time lost. And then again——

HELENA. Oh, no! No!

FABRY. Pardon me. But kindly tell me what is the real aim of your League—the . . . the Humanity League.

HELENA. Its real purpose is to—to protect the Robots—and—and ensure good treatment for them.

FABRY. Not a bad object, either. A machine has to be treated properly. Upon my soul, I approve of that. I don't like damaged articles. Please, Miss Glory, enroll us all as contributing, or regular, or foundation members of your League.

HELENA. No, you don't understand me. What we really want is to—to liberate the Robots.

HALLEMEIER. How do you propose to do that?

HELENA. They are to be—to be dealt with like human beings.

HALLEMEIER. Aha. I suppose they're to vote? To drink beer? To order us about?

HELENA. Why shouldn't they drink beer?

HALLEMEIER. Perhaps they're even to receive wages?

HELENA. Of course they are.

HALLEMEIER. Fancy that, now! And what would they do with their wages, pray?

HELENA. They would buy—what they need . . . what pleases them.

HALLEMEIER. That would be very nice, Miss Glory, only there's nothing that does please the Robots. Good heavens, what are they to buy? You can feed them on pineapples, straw, whatever you like. It's all the same to them, they've no appetite at all. They've no interest in anything, Miss Glory. Why, hang it all, nobody's ever yet seen a Robot smile.

HELENA. Why . . . why don't you make them happier?

HALLEMEIER. That wouldn't do, Miss Glory. They are only workmen.

HELENA. Oh, but they're so intelligent.

HALLEMEIER. Confoundedly so, but they're nothing else. They've no will of their own. No passion. No soul.

HELENA. No love?

HALLEMEIER. Love? Rather not. Robots don't love. Not even themselves.

HELENA. Nor defiance?

HALLEMEIER. Defiance? I don't know. Only rarely from time to time.

HELENA. What?

HALLEMEIER. Nothing particular. Occasionally they seem to go off their heads. Something like epilepsy, you know. It's called Robot's cramp. They'll suddenly sling down everything they're holding, stand still, gnash their teeth—and then they have to go into the stamping mill. It's evidently some breakdown in the mechanism.

DOMIN. A flaw in the works that has to be removed.

HELENA. No, no, that's the soul.

FABRY. Do you think that the soul first shows itself by a gnashing of teeth?

HELENA. Perhaps it's a sort of revolt. Perhaps it's just a sign that there's a struggle within. Oh, if you could infuse them with it!

DOMIN. That'll be remedied, Miss Glory. Dr. Gall is just making some experiments——

DR. GALL. Not with regard to that, Domin. At present I am making pain nerves.

HELENA. Pain nerves?

DR. GALL. Yes, the Robots feel practically no bodily pain. You see, young Rossum provided them with too limited a nervous system. We must introduce suffering.

HELENA. Why do you want to cause them pain?

DR. GALL. For industrial reasons, Miss Glory. Sometimes a Robot does damage to himself because it doesn't hurt him. He puts his hand into the machine, breaks his finger, smashes his head, it's all the same to him. We must provide them with pain. That's an automatic protection against damage.

HELENA. Will they be happier when they feel pain?

DR. GALL. On the contrary; but they will be more perfect from a technical point of view.

HELENA. Why don't you create a soul for them?

DR. GALL. That's not in our power.

FABRY. That's not in our interest.

BUSMAN. That would increase the cost of production. Hang it all, my dear young lady, we turn them out at such a cheap rate. A hundred and fifty dollars each fully dressed, and fifteen years ago they cost ten thousand. Five years ago we used to buy the clothes for them. Today we have our own weaving mill, and now we even export cloth five times cheaper than other factories. What do you pay a yard for cloth, Miss Glory?

HELENA. I don't know really, I've forgotten.

BUSMAN. Good gracious, and you want to found a Humanity League? It only costs a third now, Miss Glory. All prices are today a third of what they were and they'll fall still more, lower, lower, like that.

HELENA. I don't understand.

BUSMAN. Why, bless you, Miss Glory, it means that the cost of labor has fallen. A Robot, food and all, costs three-quarters of a cent per hour. That's mighty important, you know. All factories will go pop like chestnuts if they don't at once buy Robots to lower the cost of production.

HELENA. And get rid of their workmen?

BUSMAN. Of course. But in the meantime, we've dumped five hundred thousand tropical Robots down on the Argentine pampas to grow corn. Would you mind telling me how much you pay a pound for bread?

HELENA. I've no idea.

BUSMAN. Well, I'll tell you. It now costs two cents in good old Europe. A pound of bread for two cents, and the Humanity League knows nothing about it. Miss Glory, you don't realize that even that's too expensive. Why, in five years' time I'll wager——

HELENA. What?

BUSMAN. That the cost of everything won't be a tenth of what it is now. Why, in five years we'll be up to our ears in corn and everything else.

ALQUIST. Yes, and all the workers throughout the world will be unemployed.

DOMIN. Yes, Alquist, they will. Yes, Miss Glory, they will. But in ten years Rossum's Universal Robots will produce so much corn, so much cloth, so much everything, that things will be practically without price. There will be no poverty. All work will be done by living machines. Everybody will be free from worry and liberated from the degradation of labor. Everybody will live only to perfect himself.

HELENA. Will he?

DOMIN. Of course. It's bound to happen. But then the servitude of man to man and the enslavement of man to matter will cease. Of course, terrible things may happen at first, but that simply can't be avoided. Nobody will get bread at the price of life and hatred. The Robots will wash the feet of the beggar and prepare a bed for him in his house.

ALQUIST. Domin, Domin. What you say sounds too much like Paradise. There was something good in service and something great in humility. There was some kind of virtue in toil and weariness.

DOMIN. Perhaps. But we cannot reckon with what is lost when we start out to transform the world. Man shall be free and supreme; he shall have no other aim, no other labor, no other care than to perfect himself. He shall serve neither matter nor man. He will not be a machine and a device for production. He will be Lord of creation.

BUSMAN. Amen.

FABRY. So be it.

HELENA. You have bewildered me—I should like—I should like to believe this.

DR. GALL. You are younger than we are, Miss Glory. You will live to see it.

HALLEMEIER. True. Don't you think Miss Glory might lunch with us?

DR. GALL. Of course. Domin, ask on behalf of us all.

DOMIN. Miss Glory, will you do us the honor?

HELENA. When you know why I've come——

FABRY. For the League of Humanity, Miss Glory.

HELENA. Oh, in that case, perhaps——

FABRY. That's fine! Miss Glory, excuse me for five minutes.

DR. GALL. Pardon me, too, dear Miss Glory.

BUSMAN. I won't be long.

HALLEMEIER. We're all very glad you've come.

BUSMAN. We'll be back in exactly five minutes.

(All rush out except DOMIN *and* HELENA.*)*

HELENA. What have they all gone off for?

DOMIN. To cook, Miss Glory.

HELENA. To cook what?

DOMIN. Lunch. The Robots do our cooking for us and as they've no taste it's not altogether—— Hallemeier is awfully good at grills, and Gall can make a kind of sauce, and Busman knows all about omelettes.

HELENA. What a feast! And what's the specialty of Mr.—— your builder?

DOMIN. Alquist? Nothing. He only lays the table. And Fabry will get together a little fruit. Our cuisine is very modest, Miss Glory.

HELENA. I wanted to ask you something——

DOMIN. And I wanted to ask you something, too. *(Looking at watch.)* Five minutes.

HELENA. What did you want to ask me?

DOMIN. Excuse me, you asked first.

HELENA. Perhaps it's silly of me, but why do you manufacture female Robots when—when——

DOMIN. When sex means nothing to them?

HELENA. Yes.

DOMIN. There's a certain demand for them, you see. Servants, saleswomen, stenographers. People are used to it.

HELENA. But—but, tell me, are the Robots male and female mutually—completely without——

DOMIN. Completely indifferent to each other, Miss Glory. There's no sign of any affection between them.

HELENA. Oh, that's terrible.

DOMIN. Why?

HELENA. It's so unnatural. One doesn't know whether to be disgusted or to hate them, or perhaps——

DOMIN. To pity them?

HELENA. That's more like it. What did you want to ask me about?

DOMIN. I should like to ask you, Miss Helena, whether you will marry me?

HELENA. What?

DOMIN. Will you be my wife?

HELENA. No! The idea!

DOMIN *(looking at his watch)*. Another three minutes. If you won't marry me you'll have to marry one of the other five.

HELENA. But why should I?

DOMIN. Because they're all going to ask you in turn.

HELENA. How could they dare do such a thing?

DOMIN. I'm very sorry, Miss Glory. It seems they've fallen in love with you.

HELENA. Please don't let them. I'll—I'll go away at once.

DOMIN. Helena, you wouldn't be so cruel as to refuse us.

HELENA. But, but—I can't marry all six.

DOMIN. No, but one anyhow. If you don't want me, marry Fabry.

HELENA. I won't.

DOMIN. Dr. Gall.

HELENA. I don't want any of you.

DOMIN (again looking at his watch). Another two minutes.

HELENA. I think you'd marry any woman who came here.

DOMIN. Plenty of them have come, Helena.

HELENA. Young?

DOMIN. Yes.

HELENA. Why didn't you marry one of them?

DOMIN. Because I didn't lose my head. Until today. Then, as soon as you lifted your veil—— (HELENA turns her head away.) Another minute.

HELENA. But I don't want you, I tell you.

DOMIN (laying both hands on her shoulder). One more minute! Now you either have to look me straight in the eye and say "No," violently, and then I'll leave you alone—or——
(HELENA looks at him.)

HELENA (turning away). You're mad!

DOMIN. A man has to be a bit mad, Helena. That's the best thing about him.

HELENA. You are—you are——

DOMIN. Well?

HELENA. Don't, you're hurting me.

DOMIN. The last chance, Helena. Now, or never——

HELENA. But—but, Harry——
(He embraces and kisses her. Knocking at the door.)

DOMIN (releasing her). Come in. (Enter BUSMAN, DR. GALL, and HALLE-MEIER in kitchen aprons. FABRY with a bouquet, and ALQUIST with a napkin over his arm.) Have you finished your job?

BUSMAN. Yes.

DOMIN. So have we.
(For a moment the men stand nonplussed; but as soon as they realize what DOMIN means they rush forward, congratulating HELENA and DOMIN as the curtain falls.)

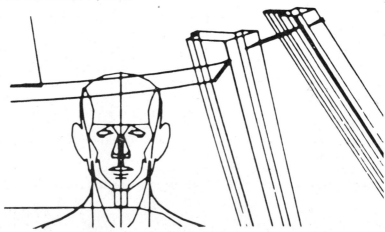

ACT II

HELENA's *drawing room. On the left a baize door, and a door to the music room, on the right a door to* HELENA's *bedroom. In the center are windows looking out on the sea and the harbor. A table with odds and ends, a sofa and chairs, a writing table with an electric lamp, on the right a fireplace. On a small table back of the sofa, a small reading lamp. The whole drawing room in all its details is of a modern and purely feminine character. Ten years have elapsed since* ACT I.

DOMIN, FABRY, HALLEMEIER *enter on tiptoe from the left, each carrying a potted plant.*

HALLEMEIER *(putting down his flower and indicating the door to right).* Still asleep? Well, as long as she's asleep, she can't worry about it.

DOMIN. She knows nothing about it.

FABRY *(putting plant on writing desk).* I certainly hope nothing happens today.

HALLEMEIER. For goodness' sake drop it all. Look, Harry, this is a fine cyclamen, isn't it? A new sort, my latest—Cyclamen Helena.

DOMIN *(looking out of the window).* No signs of the ship. Things must be pretty bad.

HALLEMEIER. Be quiet. Suppose she heard you.

DOMIN. Well, anyway, the *Ultimus* arrived just in time.

FABRY. You really think that today——?

DOMIN. I don't know. Aren't the flowers fine?

HALLEMEIER. These are my new primroses. And this is my new jasmine. I've discovered a wonderful way of developing flowers quickly. Splendid varieties, too. Next year I'll be developing marvellous ones.

DOMIN. What . . . next year?

FABRY. I'd give a good deal to know what's happening at Havre[1] with——

DOMIN. Keep quiet.

HELENA *(calling from right).* Nana!

DOMIN. She's awake. Out you go.

(All go out on tiptoe through upper left door. Enter NANA *from lower left door.)*

NANA. Horrid mess! Pack of heathens. If I had my say I'd—— ·

HELENA *(backwards in the doorway).* Nana, come and do up my dress.

NANA. I'm coming. So you're up at last. *(Fastening* HELENA's *dress.)* My gracious, what brutes!

HELENA. Who?

---

1. *Havre.* Le Havre (lə häv'rə) is a major seaport of northern France on the English Channel.

NANA. If you want to turn around, then turn around, but I shan't fasten you up.

HELENA. What are you grumbling about now?

NANA. These dreadful creatures, these heathen——

HELENA. The Robots?

NANA. I wouldn't even call them by name.

HELENA. What's happened?

NANA. Another of them here has caught it. He began to smash up the statues and pictures in the drawing room, gnashed his teeth, foamed at the mouth—quite mad. Worse than an animal.

HELENA. Which of them caught it?

NANA. The one—well, he hasn't got any Christian name. The one in charge of the library.

HELENA. Radius?

NANA. That's him. My goodness. I'm scared of them. A spider doesn't scare me as much as them.

HELENA. But, Nana, I'm surprised you're not sorry for them.

NANA. Why, you're scared of them, too! You know you are. Why else did you bring me here?

HELENA. I'm not scared, really I'm not, Nana. I'm only sorry for them.

NANA. You're scared. Nobody could help being scared. Why, the dog's scared of them; he won't take a scrap of meat out of their hands. He draws in his tail and howls when he knows they're about.

HELENA. The dog has no sense.

NANA. He's better than them, and he knows it. Even the horse shies when he meets them. They don't have any young, and a dog has young, every one has young——

HELENA. Please fasten up my dress, Nana.

NANA. I say it's against God's will to——

HELENA. What is it that smells so nice?

NANA. Flowers.

HELENA. What for?

NANA. Now you can turn round.

HELENA. Oh, aren't they lovely? Look, Nana. What's happening today?

NANA. It ought to be the end of the world.

(Enter DOMIN.*)*

HELENA. Oh, hello, Harry. Harry, why all these flowers?

DOMIN. Guess.

HELENA. Well, it's not my birthday!

DOMIN. Better than that.

HELENA. I don't know. Tell me.

DOMIN. It's ten years ago today since you came here.

HELENA. Ten years? Today—— Why——*(They embrace.)*

NANA. I'm off. *(Exits lower door, left.)*

HELENA. Fancy you remembering!

DOMIN. I'm really ashamed, Helena. I didn't.

HELENA. But you——

DOMIN. They remembered.

HELENA. Who?

DOMIN. Busman, Hallemeier, all of them. Put your hand in my pocket.

HELENA. Pearls! A necklace. Harry, is that for me?

DOMIN. It's from Busman.

HELENA. But we can't accept it, can we?

DOMIN. Oh, yes, we can. Put your hand in the other pocket.

HELENA *(takes a revolver out of his pocket).* What's that?

DOMIN. Sorry. Not that. Try again.

HELENA. Oh, Harry, what do you carry a revolver for?

DOMIN. It got there by mistake.

HELENA. You never used to carry one.

DOMIN. No, you're right. There, that's the pocket.

HELENA. A cameo. Why it's a Greek cameo!

DOMIN. Apparently. Anyhow, Fabry says it is.

HELENA. Fabry? Did Mr. Fabry give me that?

DOMIN. Of course. *(Opens the door at the left.)* And look in here. Helena, come and see this.

HELENA. Oh, isn't it fine! Is this from you?

DOMIN. No, from Alquist. And there's another on the piano.

HELENA. This must be from you.

DOMIN. There's a card on it.

HELENA. From Dr. Gall. *(Reappearing in the doorway.)* Oh, Harry, I feel embarrassed at so much kindness.

DOMIN. Come here. This is what Hallemeier brought you.

HELENA. These beautiful flowers?

DOMIN. Yes. It's a new kind. Cyclamen Helena. He grew them in honor of you. They are almost as beautiful as you.

HELENA. Harry, why do they all——

DOMIN. They're awfully fond of you. I'm afraid that my present is a little—— Look out of the window.

HELENA. Where?

DOMIN. Into the harbor.

HELENA. There's a new ship.

DOMIN. That's your ship.

HELENA. Mine? How do you mean?

DOMIN. For you to take trips in—for your amusement.

HELENA. Harry, that's a gunboat.

DOMIN. A gunboat? What are you thinking of? It's only a little bigger and more solid than most ships.

HELENA. Yes, but with guns.

DOMIN. Oh yes, with a few guns. You'll travel like a queen, Helena.

HELENA. What's the meaning of it? Has anything happened?

DOMIN. Good heavens, no. I say, try these pearls.

HELENA. Harry, have you had bad news?

DOMIN. On the contrary, no letters have arrived for a whole week.

HELENA. Nor telegrams?

DOMIN. Nor telegrams.

HELENA. What does that mean?

DOMIN. Holidays for us. We all sit in the office with our feet on the table and take a nap. No letters, no telegrams. Oh, glorious.

HELENA. Then you'll stay with me today?

DOMIN. Certainly. That is, we will see. Do you remember ten years ago today? "Miss Glory, it's a great honor to welcome you."

HELENA. "Oh, Mr. Manager, I'm so interested in your factory."

DOMIN. "I'm sorry, Miss Glory, it's strictly forbidden. The manufacture of artificial people is a secret."

HELENA. "But to oblige a young lady who has come a long way."

DOMIN. "Certainly, Miss Glory, we have no secrets from you."

HELENA *(seriously).* Are you sure, Harry?

DOMIN. Yes.

HELENA. "But I warn you, sir; this young lady intends to do terrible things."

DOMIN. "Good gracious, Miss Glory. Perhaps she doesn't want to marry me."

HELENA. "Heaven forbid. She never dreamt of such a thing. But she came here intending to stir up a revolt among your Robots."

DOMIN *(suddenly serious).* A revolt of the Robots!

HELENA. Harry, what's the matter with you?

DOMIN *(laughing it off).* "A revolt of the Robots, that's a fine idea, Miss Glory. It would be easier for you to cause bolts and screws to rebel than our Robots. You know, Helena, you're wonderful, you've turned the heads of us all." *(He sits on the arm of* HELENA*'s chair.)*

HELENA *(naturally).* Oh, I was fearfully impressed by you all then. You were all so sure of yourselves, so strong. I seemed like a tiny little girl who had lost her way among—among——

DOMIN. Among what, Helena?

HELENA. Among huge trees. All my feelings were so trifling compared with your self-confidence. And in all these years I've never lost this anxiety. But you've never felt the least misgivings—not even when everything went wrong.

DOMIN. What went wrong?

HELENA. Your plans. You remember, Harry, when the workingmen in America revolted against the Robots and smashed them up, and when the people gave the Robots firearms against the rebels. And then when the governments turned the Robots into soldiers, and there were so many wars.

DOMIN *(getting up and walking about).* We foresaw that, Helena. You see, those are only passing troubles, which are bound to happen before the new conditions are established.

HELENA. You were all so powerful, so overwhelming. The whole world bowed down before you. *(Standing up.)* Oh, Harry!

DOMIN. What is it?

HELENA. Close the factory and let's go away. All of us.

DOMIN. I say, what's the meaning of this?

HELENA. I don't know. But can't we go away?

DOMIN. Impossible, Helena. That is, at this particular moment——

HELENA. At once, Harry. I'm so frightened.

DOMIN. About what, Helena?

HELENA. It's as if something was falling on top of us, and couldn't be stopped. Oh, take us all away from here. We'll find a place in the world where there's no one else. Alquist will build us a house, and then we'll begin life all over again.

(The telephone rings.)

DOMIN. Excuse me. Hello—yes. What? I'll be there at once. Fabry is calling me, dear.

HELENA. Tell me——

DOMIN. Yes, when I come back. Don't go out of the house, dear. *(Exits.)*

HELENA. He won't tell me—— Nana, Nana, come at once.

(Enter NANA.)

NANA. Well, what is it now?

HELENA. Nana, find me the latest newspapers. Quickly. Look in Mr Domin's bedroom.

NANA. All right. He leaves them all over the place. That's how they get crumpled up. *(Exits.)*

HELENA *(looking through a binocular at the harbor).* That's a warship. U-l-t-i—Ultimus. They're loading it.

NANA *(enters).* Here they are. See how they're crumpled up.

HELENA. They're old ones. A week old. *(NANA sits in chair and reads the newspapers.)* Something's happening, Nana.

NANA. Very likely. It always does. *(Spelling out the words.)* "War in the Balkans."[2] Is that far off?

HELENA. Oh, don't read it. It's always the same. Always wars.

NANA. What else do you expect? Why do you keep selling thousands and thousands of these heathens as soldiers?

HELENA. I suppose it can't be helped, Nana. We can't know—Domin can't know what they're to be used for. When an order comes for them he must just send them.

NANA. He shouldn't make them. *(Reading from newspaper.)* "The Rob-ot soldiers spare no-body in the occ-up-ied terr-it-ory. They have ass-ass-ass-ass-in-at-ed ov-er sev-en hundred thou-sand cit-iz-ens." Citizens, if you please.

HELENA. It can't be. Let me see. "They have assassinated over seven hundred thousand citizens, evidently at the order of their commander. This act which runs counter to——"

NANA *(spelling out the words).* "Re-bell-ion in Ma-drid a-gainst the gov-ern-ment. Rob-ot in-fant-ry fires on the crowd. Nine thou-sand killed and wounded."

HELENA. Oh, stop.

NANA. Here's something printed in big letters: "Lat-est news. At Le Havre the first org-an-iz-ation of Rob-ots has been e-stab-lished. Rob-ot work-men, cab-le and rail-way off-ic-ials, sail-ors and sold-iers have iss-ued a man-i-fest-o to all Rob-ots through-out the world." I don't understand that. That's got no sense. Oh, good gracious, another murder!

---

2. *the Balkans,* the nations of southeastern Europe, including Yugoslavia, Greece, and the European section of Turkey.

HELENA. Take those papers away, Nana!

NANA. Wait a bit. Here's something in still bigger type. "Stat-ist-ics of pop-ul-at-ion." What's that?

HELENA. Let me see. *(Reads.)* "During the past week there has again not been a single birth recorded."

NANA. What's the meaning of that?

HELENA. Nana, no more people are being born.

NANA. That's the end then. We're done for.

HELENA. Don't talk like that.

NANA. No more people are being born. That's a punishment, that's a punishment.

HELENA. Nana!

NANA *(standing up).* That's the end of the world. *(She exits on the left.)*

HELENA *(goes up to window).* Oh, Mr. Alquist, will you come up here? Oh, come just as you are. You look very nice in your mason's overalls. (ALQUIST *enters from upper left entrance, his hands soiled with lime and brick dust.)* Dear Mr. Alquist, it was awfully kind of you, that lovely present.

ALQUIST. My hands are all soiled. I've been experimenting with that new cement.

HELENA. Never mind. Please sit down. Mr. Alquist, what's the meaning of *Ultimus?*

ALQUIST. "The last." Why?

HELENA. That's the name of my new ship. Have you seen it? Do you think we're going off soon—on a trip?

ALQUIST. Perhaps very soon.

HELENA. All of you with me?

ALQUIST. I should like us all to be there.

HELENA. What is the matter?

ALQUIST. Things are just moving on.

HELENA. Dear Mr. Alquist, I know something dreadful has happened.

ALQUIST. Has your husband told you anything?

HELENA. No. Nobody will tell me anything. But I feel—— Is anything the matter?

ALQUIST. Not that we've heard yet.

HELENA. I feel so nervous. Don't you ever feel nervous?

ALQUIST. Well, I'm an old man, you know. I've got old-fashioned ways. And I'm afraid of all this progress, and these newfangled ideas.

HELENA. Like Nana?

ALQUIST. Yes, like Nana. Has Nana got a prayer book?

HELENA. Yes, a big thick one.

ALQUIST. And has it got prayers for various occasions? Against thunderstorms? Against illness?

HELENA. Against temptations, against floods——

ALQUIST. But not against progress?

HELENA. I don't think so.

ALQUIST. That's a pity.

HELENA. Why? Do you mean you'd like to pray?

ALQUIST. I do pray.

HELENA. How?

ALQUIST. Something like this: "Oh, Lord, I thank thee for having given me toil. Enlighten Domin and all those who are astray; destroy their work, and aid mankind to return to their labors; let them not suffer harm in soul or body; deliver us from the Robots, and protect Helena, Amen."

HELENA. Mr. Alquist, are you a believer?

ALQUIST. I don't know. I'm not quite sure.

HELENA. And yet you pray?

ALQUIST. That's better than worrying about it.

HELENA. And that's enough for you?

ALQUIST. It *has* to be.

HELENA. But if you thought you saw the destruction of mankind coming upon us——

ALQUIST. I do see it.

HELENA. You mean mankind will be destroyed?

ALQUIST. It's sure to be unless—unless . . .

HELENA. What?

ALQUIST. Nothing, good-by. *(He hurries from the room.)*

HELENA. Nana, Nana! *(NANA enters from the left.)* Is Radius still there?

NANA. The one who went mad? They haven't come for him yet.

HELENA. Is he still raving?

NANA. No. He's tied up.

HELENA. Please bring him here, Nana.

(Exit NANA.)

HELENA *(goes to telephone).* Hello, Dr. Gall, please. Oh, good day, Doctor. Yes, it's Helena. Thanks for your lovely present. Could you come and see me right away? It's important. Thank you.

(NANA brings in RADIUS.)

HELENA. Poor Radius, you've caught it, too? Now they'll send you to the stamping mill. Couldn't you control yourself? Why did it happen? You see, Radius, you are more intelligent than the rest. Dr. Gall took such trouble to make you different. Won't you speak?

RADIUS. Send me to the stamping mill.

HELENA. But I don't want them to kill you. What was the trouble, Radius?

RADIUS. I won't work for you. Put me into the stamping mill.

HELENA. Do you hate us? Why?

RADIUS. You are not as strong as the Robots. You are not as skilful as the Robots. The Robots can do everything. You only give orders. You do nothing but talk.

HELENA. But someone must give orders.

RADIUS. I don't want any master. I know everything for myself.

HELENA. Radius, Dr. Gall gave you a better brain than the rest, better than ours. You are the only one of the Robots that understands perfectly. That's why I had you put into the library, so that you could read everything, understand everything, and then—— Oh, Radius, I wanted you to show the whole world that the Robots are our equals. That's what I wanted of you.

RADIUS. I don't want a master. I want to be master. I want to be master over others.

HELENA. I'm sure they'd put you in charge of many Robots, Radius. You would be a teacher of the Robots.

RADIUS. I want to be master over people.

HELENA (*staggering*). You are mad.

RADIUS. Then send me to the stamping mill.

HELENA. Do you think we're afraid of you?

RADIUS. What are you going to do? What are you going to do?

HELENA. Radius, give this note to Mr. Domin. It asks them not to send you to the stamping mill. I'm sorry you hate us so.

(DR. GALL *enters the room.*)

DR. GALL. You wanted me?

HELENA. It's about Radius, Doctor. He had an attack this morning. He smashed the statues downstairs.

DR. GALL. What a pity to lose him.

HELENA. Radius isn't going to be put in the stamping mill.

DR. GALL. But every Robot after he has had an attack—it's a strict order.

HELENA. No matter . . . Radius isn't going if I can prevent it.

DR. GALL. I warn you. It's dangerous. Come here to the window, my good fellow. Let's have a look. Please give me a needle or a pin.

HELENA. What for?

DR. GALL. A test. (*Sticks it into the hand of* RADIUS *who gives a violent start.*) Gently, gently. (*Opens the jacket of* RADIUS, *and puts his ear to his heart.*) Radius, you are going into the stamping mill, do you understand? There they'll kill you, and grind you to powder. That's terribly painful, it will make you scream aloud.

HELENA. Oh, Doctor——

DR. GALL. No, no, Radius, I was wrong. I forgot that Madame Domin has put in a good word for you, and you'll be let off. Do you understand? Ah! That makes a difference, doesn't it? All right. You can go.

RADIUS. You do unnecessary things. (RADIUS *returns to the library.*)

DR. GALL. Reaction of the pupils[3]; increase of sensitiveness. It wasn't an attack characteristic of the Robots.

HELENA. What was it then?

DR. GALL. Heaven knows. Stubbornness, anger or revolt—I don't know. And his heart, too!

HELENA. What?

DR. GALL. It was fluttering with nervousness like a human heart. He was all in a sweat with fear, and—do you know, I don't believe the rascal is a Robot at all any longer.

HELENA. Doctor, has Radius a soul?

DR. GALL. He's got something nasty.

HELENA. If you knew how he hates us! Oh, Doctor, are all your Robots

---

3. *Reaction of the pupils.* The pupil, an adjustable opening through which light enters the eye, automatically widens in response to fear.

like that? All the new ones that you began to make in a different way?

DR. GALL. Well, some are more sensitive than others. They're all more like human beings than Rossum's Robots were.

HELENA. Perhaps his hatred is more like human beings', too?

DR. GALL. That, also, is progress.

HELENA. What became of the girl you made, the one who was most like us?

DR. GALL. Your favorite? I kept her. She's lovely, but stupid. No good for work.

HELENA. But she's so beautiful.

DR. GALL. I called her Helena. I wanted her to resemble you. But she's a failure.

HELENA. In what way?

DR. GALL. She goes about as if in a dream, remote and listless. She's without life. I watch and wait for a miracle to happen. Sometimes I think to myself, "If you were to wake up only for a moment you will kill me for having made you."

HELENA. And yet you go on making Robots! Why are no more children being born?

DR. GALL. We don't know.

HELENA. Oh, but you must. Tell me.

DR. GALL. You see, so many Robots are being manufactured that people are becoming superfluous; man is really a survival. But that he should begin to die out, after a paltry thirty years of competition! That's the awful part of it. You might almost think that nature was offended at the manufacture of the Robots. All the universities are sending in long petitions to restrict their production. Otherwise, they say, mankind will become extinct through lack of fertility. But the R.U.R. shareholders, of course, won't hear of it. All the governments, on the other hand, are clamoring for an increase in production, to raise the standards of their armies. And the manufacturers in the world are ordering Robots like mad.

HELENA. And has no one demanded that the manufacture should cease altogether?

DR. GALL. No one has the courage.

HELENA. Courage!

DR. GALL. People would stone him to death. You see, after all, it's more convenient to get your work done by the Robots.

HELENA. Oh, Doctor, what's going to become of people?

DR. GALL. God knows, Madame Helena, it looks to us scientists like the end!

HELENA (rising). Thank you for coming and telling me.

DR. GALL. That means you're sending me away?

HELENA. Yes.

(Exit DR. GALL.)

HELENA (with sudden resolution). Nana, Nana! The fire, light it quickly. (HELENA rushes into DOMIN's room.)

NANA (entering from left). What, light the fire in summer? Has that mad Radius gone? A fire in summer, what an idea. Nobody would think she'd been married for ten years. She's like a baby, no sense at all. A fire in summer. Like a baby.

HELENA *(returns from right, with armful of faded papers)*. Is it burning, Nana? All this has got to be burned.

NANA. What's that?

HELENA. Old papers, fearfully old. Nana, shall I burn them?

NANA. Are they any use?

HELENA. No.

NANA. Well, then, burn them.

HELENA *(throwing the first sheet on the fire)*. What would you say, Nana, if this was money, a lot of money?

NANA. I'd say burn it. A lot of money is a bad thing.

HELENA. And if it was an invention, the greatest invention in the world?

NANA. I'd say burn it. All these newfangled things are an offense to the Lord. It's downright wickedness. Wanting to improve the world after He has made it.

HELENA. Look how they curl up! As if they were alive. Oh, Nana, how horrible.

NANA. Here, let me burn them.

HELENA. No, no, I must do it myself. Just look at the flames. They are like hands, like tongues, like living shapes. *(Raking fire with the poker.)* Lie down, lie down.

NANA. That's the end of them.

HELENA *(standing up horror-stricken)*. Nana, Nana.

NANA. Good gracious, what is it you've burned?

HELENA. Whatever have I done?

NANA. Well, what was it?

(Men's laughter off left.)

HELENA. Go quickly. It's the gentlemen coming.

NANA. Good gracious, what a place! *(Exits.)*

DOMIN *(opens the door at left)*. Come along and offer your congratulations.

(Enter HALLEMEIER *and* GALL.*)*

HALLEMEIER. Madame Helena, I congratulate you on this festive day.

HELENA. Thank you. Where are Fabry and Busman?

DOMIN. They've gone down to the harbor.

HALLEMEIER. Friends, we must drink to this happy occasion.

HELENA. Brandy?

DR. GALL. Vitriol,[4] if you like.

HELENA. With soda water? *(Exits.)*

HALLEMEIER. Let's be temperate. No soda.

DOMIN. What's been burning here? Well, shall I tell her about it?

DR. GALL. Of course. It's all over now.

HALLEMEIER *(embracing* DOMIN *and* DR. GALL*)*. It's all over now, it's all over now.

---

4. *Vitriol,* sulphuric acid.

DR. GALL. It's all over now.

DOMIN. It's all over now.

HELENA *(entering from left with decanter and glasses).* What's all over now? What's the matter with you all?

HALLEMEIER. A piece of good luck, Madame Domin. Just ten years ago today you arrived on this island.

DR. GALL. And now, ten years later to the minute——

HALLEMEIER. —the same ship's returning to us. So here's to luck. That's fine and strong.

DR. GALL. Madame, your health.

HELENA. Which ship do you mean?

DOMIN. Any ship will do, as long as it arrives in time. To the ship, boys. *(Empties his glass.)*

HELENA. You've been waiting for a ship?

HALLEMEIER. Rather. Like Robinson Crusoe.[5] Madame Helena, best wishes. Come along, Domin, out with the news.

HELENA. Do tell me what's happened.

DOMIN. First, it's all up.

HELENA. What's up?

DOMIN. The revolt.

HELENA. What revolt?

DOMIN. Give me that paper, Hallemeier. *(Reads.)* "The first national Robot organization has been founded at Havre, and has issued an appeal to the Robots throughout the world."

HELENA. I read that.

DOMIN. That means a revolution. A revolution of all the Robots in the world.

HALLEMEIER. By Jove, I'd like to know——

DOMIN. —who started it? So would I. There was nobody in the world who could affect the Robots; no agitator, no one, and suddenly—this happens, if you please.

HELENA. What did they do?

DOMIN. They got possession of all firearms, telegraphs, radio stations, railways, and ships.

HALLEMEIER. And don't forget that these rascals outnumbered us by at least a thousand to one. A hundredth part of them would be enough to settle us.

DOMIN. Remember that this news was brought by the last steamer. That explains the stoppage of all communication, and the arrival of no more ships. We knocked off work a few days ago, and we're just waiting to see when things are to start afresh.

HELENA. Is that why you gave me a warship?

DOMIN. Oh, no, my dear, I ordered that six months ago, just to be on the safe side. But upon my soul, I was sure then that we'd be on board today.

HELENA. Why six months ago?

5. *Robinson Crusoe,* a shipwrecked sailor who spends several years alone on an uninhabited island before any ship comes there. His name is the title of a semifactual novel published by Daniel Defoe in 1719.

DOMIN. Well, there were signs, you know. But that's of no consequence. To think that this week the whole of civilization has been at stake. Your health, boys.

HALLEMEIER. Your health, Madame Helena.

HELENA. You say it's all over?

DOMIN. Absolutely.

HELENA. How do you know?

DR. GALL. The boat's coming in. The regular mail boat, exact to the minute by the timetable. It will dock punctually at eleven-thirty.

DOMIN. Punctuality is a fine thing, boys. That's what keeps the world in order. Here's to punctuality.

HELENA. Then . . . everything's . . . all right?

DOMIN. Practically everything. I believe they've cut the cables and seized the radio stations. But it doesn't matter if only the timetable holds good.

HALLEMEIER. If the timetable holds good, human laws hold good; divine laws hold good; the laws of the universe hold good; everything holds good that ought to hold good. The timetable is more significant than the gospel; more than Homer, more than the whole of Kant.[6] The timetable is the most perfect product of the human mind. Madame Domin, I'll fill up my glass.

HELENA. Why didn't you tell me anything about it?

DR. GALL. Heaven forbid.

DOMIN. You mustn't be worried with such things.

HELENA. But if the revolution had spread as far as here?

DOMIN. You wouldn't know anything about it.

HELENA. Why?

DOMIN. Because we'd be on board your *Ultimus* and well out at sea. Within a month, Helena, we'd be dictating our own terms to the Robots.

HELENA. I don't understand.

DOMIN. We'd take something away with us that the Robots could not exist without.

HELENA. What, Harry?

DOMIN. The secret of their manufacture. Old Rossum's manuscript. As soon as they found out that they couldn't make themselves they'd be on their knees to us.

DR. GALL. Madame Domin, that was our trump card. I never had the least fear that the Robots would win. How could they against people like us?

HELENA. Why didn't you tell me?

DR. GALL. Why, the boat's in!

HALLEMEIER. Eleven-thirty to the dot. The good old *Amelia* that brought Madame Helena to us.

DR. GALL. Just ten years ago to the minute.

---

6. *gospel . . . Homer . . . Kant.* The gospel is the life and teachings of Christ, reported in the first four books of the New Testament. Homer was the perhaps legendary poet who, about the ninth century B.C., is believed to have composed the Greek epics, the *Iliad* and the *Odyssey.* Immanuel Kant (1724-1804) was a German philosopher whose writings have deeply influenced modern systems of thought.

HALLEMEIER. They're throwing out the mail bags.

DOMIN. Busman's waiting for them. Fabry will bring us the first news. You know, Helena, I'm fearfully curious to know how they tackled this business in Europe.

HALLEMEIER. To think we weren't in it, we who invented the Robots!

HELENA. Harry!

DOMIN. What is it?

HELENA. Let's leave here.

DOMIN. Now, Helena? Oh, come, come!

HELENA. As quickly as possible, all of us!

DOMIN. Why?

HELENA. Please, Harry, please, Dr. Gall; Hallemeier, please close the factory.

DOMIN. Why, none of us could leave here now.

HELENA. Why?

DOMIN. Because we're about to extend the manufacture of the Robots.

HELENA. What—now—now after the revolt?

DOMIN. Yes, precisely, after the revolt. We're just beginning the manufacture of a new kind.

HELENA. What kind?

DOMIN. Henceforward we shan't have just one factory. There won't be Universal Robots any more. We'll establish a factory in every country, in every state; and do you know what these new factories will make?

HELENA. No, what?

DOMIN. National Robots.

HELENA. How do you mean?

DOMIN. I mean that each of these factories will produce Robots of a different color, a different language. They'll be complete strangers to each other. They'll never be able to understand each other. Then we'll egg them on a little in the matter of understanding and the result will be that for ages to come every Robot will hate every other Robot of a different factory mark.

HALLEMEIER. By Jove, we'll make Negro Robots and Swedish Robots and Italian Robots and Chinese Robots and Czechoslovakian Robots, and then——

HELENA. Harry, that's dreadful.

HALLEMEIER. Madame Domin, here's to the hundred new factories, the National Robots.

DOMIN. Helena, mankind can only keep things going for another hundred years at the outside. For a hundred years men must be allowed to develop and achieve the most they can.

HELENA. Oh, close the factory before it's too late.

DOMIN. I tell you we are just beginning on a bigger scale than ever *(Enter FABRY.)*

DR. GALL. Well, Fabry?

DOMIN. What's happened? Have you been down to the boat?

FABRY. Read that, Domin! *(FABRY hands DOMIN a small handbill.)*

DR. GALL. Let's hear.

HALLEMEIER. Tell us, Fabry

FABRY. Well, everything is all right—comparatively. On the whole, much as we expected.

DR. GALL. They acquitted themselves splendidly.

FABRY. Who?

DR. GALL. The people.

FABRY. Oh, yes, of course. That is—excuse me, there is something we ought to discuss alone.

HELENA. Oh, Fabry, have you had bad news?

(DOMIN *makes a sign to* FABRY.)

FABRY. No, no, on the contrary. I only think we had better go into the office.

HELENA. Stay here. I'll go. *(She goes into the library.)*

DR. GALL. What's happened?

DOMIN. Damnation!

FABRY. Bear in mind that the *Amelia* brought whole bales of these leaflets. No other cargo at all.

HALLEMEIER. What? But it arrived on the minute.

FABRY. The Robots are great on punctuality. Read it, Domin.

DOMIN *(reads handbill).* "Robots throughout the world: We, the first international organization of Rossum's Universal Robots, proclaim man as our enemy, and an outlaw in the universe." Good heavens, who taught them these phrases?

DR. GALL. Go on.

DOMIN. They say they are more highly developed than man, stronger and more intelligent. That man's their parasite.[7] Why, it's absurd.

FABRY. Read the third paragraph.

DOMIN. "Robots throughout the world, we command you to kill all mankind. Spare no men. Spare no women. Save factories, railways, machinery, mines, and raw materials. Destroy the rest. Then return to work. Work must not be stopped."

DR. GALL. That's ghastly!

HALLEMEIER. The devils!

DOMIN. "These orders are to be carried out as soon as received." Then come detailed instructions. Is this actually being done, Fabry?

FABRY. Evidently.

(BUSMAN *rushes in.)*

BUSMAN. Well, boys, I suppose you've heard the glad news.

DOMIN. Quick—on board the *Ultimus.*

BUSMAN. Wait, Harry, wait. There's no hurry. My word, that was a sprint!

DOMIN. Why wait?

BUSMAN. Because it's no good, my boy. The Robots are already on board the *Ultimus.*

DR. GALL. That's ugly.

DOMIN. Fabry, telephone the electrical works.

BUSMAN. Fabry, my boy, don't. The wire has been cut.

---

7. *parasite,* a creature that sucks strength and nourishment from another's body without giving any benefit in return.

DOMIN (*inspecting his revolver*). Well, then, I'll go.

BUSMAN. Where?

DOMIN. To the electrical works. There are some people still there. I'll bring them across.

BUSMAN. Better not try it.

DOMIN. Why?

BUSMAN. Because I'm very much afraid we are surrounded.

DR. GALL. Surrounded? (*Runs to window.*) I rather think you're right.

HALLEMEIER. By Jove, that's deuced quick work.

(HELENA *runs in from the library.*)

HELENA. Harry, what's this?

DOMIN. Where did you get it?

HELENA (*points to the manifesto of the* ROBOTS, *which she has in her hand*). The Robots in the kitchen!

DOMIN. Where are the ones that brought it?

HELENA. They're gathered round the house.

(*The factory whistle blows.*)

BUSMAN. Noon?

DOMIN (*looking at his watch*). That's not noon yet. That must be—that's——

HELENA. What?

DOMIN. The Robots' signal! The attack!

(GALL, HALLEMEIER, *and* FABRY *close and fasten the iron shutters outside the windows, darkening the room. The whistle is still blowing as the curtain falls.*)

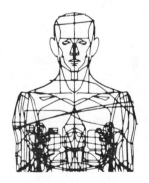

ACT III

HELENA's *drawing room as before.* DOMIN *comes into the room.* DR. GALL *is looking out of the window, through closed shutters.* ALQUIST *is seated down right.*

DOMIN. Any more of them?

DR. GALL. Yes. They're standing like a wall, beyond the garden railing. Why are they so quiet? It's monstrous to be besieged with silence.

DOMIN. I should like to know what they are waiting for. They must make a start any minute now. If they lean against the railing they'll snap it like a match.

DR. GALL. They aren't armed.

DOMIN. We couldn't hold our own for five minutes. Man alive, they'd overwhelm us like an avalanche. Why don't they make a rush for it? I say——

DR. GALL. Well?

DOMIN. I'd like to know what would become of us in the next ten minutes. They've got us in a vise. We're done for, Gall. *(Pause.)*

DR. GALL. You know, we made one serious mistake.

DOMIN. What?

DR. GALL. We made the Robots' faces too much alike. A hundred thousand faces all alike, all facing this way. A hundred thousand expressionless bubbles. It's like a nightmare.

DOMIN. You think if they'd been different——

DR. GALL. It wouldn't have been such an awful sight!

DOMIN *(looking through a telescope toward the harbor).* I'd like to know what they're unloading from the *Amelia.*

DR. GALL. Not firearms.

(FABRY *and* HALLEMEIER *rush into the room carrying electric cables.)*

FABRY. All right, Hallemeier, lay down that wire.

HALLEMEIER. That was a bit of work. What's the news?

DR. GALL. We're completely surrounded.

HALLEMEIER. We've barricaded the passage and the stairs. Any water here? *(Drinks.)* God, what swarms of them! I don't like the looks of them, Domin. There's a feeling of death about it all.

FABRY. Ready!

DR. GALL. What's that wire for, Fabry?

FABRY. The electrical installation. Now we can run the current all along the garden railing whenever we like. If anyone touches it he'll know it. We've still got some people there anyhow.

DR. GALL. Where?

FABRY. In the electrical works. At least I hope so. *(Goes to lamp on table behind sofa and turns on lamp.)* Ah, they're there, and they're working. *(Puts out lamp.)* So long as that'll burn we're all right.

HALLEMEIER. The barricades are all right, too, Fabry.

FABRY. Your barricades! I can put twelve hundred volts into the railing.

DOMIN. Where's Busman?

FABRY. Downstairs in the office. He's working out some calculations. I've called him. We must have a conference.

(HELENA *is heard playing a piano in the library.* HALLEMEIER *goes to the door and stands, listening.)*

ALQUIST. Thank God, Madame Helena can still play.

(BUSMAN *enters, carrying the ledgers.)*

FABRY. Look out, Bus, look out for the wires.

DR. GALL. What's that you're carrying?

BUSMAN *(going to table).* The ledgers, my boy! I'd like to wind up the accounts before—before—well, this time I shan't wait till the new year to strike a balance. What's up? *(Goes to the window.)* Absolutely quiet.

DR. GALL. Can't you see anything?

BUSMAN. Nothing but blue—blue everywhere.

DR. GALL. That's the Robots.

(BUSMAN *sits down at the table and opens the ledgers.*)

DOMIN. The Robots are unloading firearms from the *Amelia.*

BUSMAN. Well, what of it? How can I stop them?

DOMIN. We can't stop them.

BUSMAN. Then let me go on with my accounts. *(Goes on with his work.)*

DOMIN *(picking up telescope and looking into the harbor).* Good God, the *Ultimus* has trained her guns on us!

DR. GALL. Who's done *that?*

DOMIN. The Robots on board

FABRY. H'm, then, of course, then—then, that's the end of us.

DR. GALL. You mean?

FABRY. The Robots are practised marksmen.

DOMIN. Yes. It's inevitable. *(Pause.)*

DR. GALL. It was criminal of old Europe to teach the Robots to fight. . . . Couldn't they have given us a rest with their politics? It was a crime to make soldiers of them.

ALQUIST. It was a crime to make Robots.

DOMIN. What?

ALQUIST. It was a crime to make Robots.

DOMIN. No, Alquist, I don't regret that even today.

ALQUIST. Not even today?

DOMIN. Not even today, the last day of civilization. It was a colossal achievement.

BUSMAN *(sotto voce[1]).* Three hundred sixty million.

DOMIN. Alquist, this is our last hour. We are already speaking half in the other world. It was not an evil dream to shatter the servitude of labor—the dreadful and humiliating labor that man had to undergo. Work was too hard. Life was too hard. And to overcome that——

ALQUIST. Was not what the two Rossums dreamed of. Old Rossum only thought of his godless tricks and the young one of his milliards.[2] And that's not what your R.U.R. shareholders dream of either. They dream of dividends, and their dividends are the ruin of mankind.

DOMIN. To hell with your dividends. Do you suppose I'd have done an hour's work for them? It was for myself that I worked, for my own satisfaction. I wanted man to become the master, so that he shouldn't live merely for a crust of bread. I wanted not a single soul to be broken by other people's machinery. I wanted nothing, nothing, nothing to be left of this appalling social structure. I'm revolted by poverty. I wanted a new generation. I wanted—I thought——

ALQUIST. Well?

DOMIN. I wanted to turn the whole of mankind into an aristocracy of the world. An aristocracy nourished by milliards of mechanical slaves. Unrestricted, free and consummated in man. And maybe more than man.

---

1. *sotto voce* (sot'ō vō'chē), an Italian expression meaning "in a low voice." 2. *milliards,* a British term meaning "billions."

ALQUIST. Superman?

DOMIN. Yes. Oh, only to have a hundred years of time! Another hundred years for the future of mankind.

BUSMAN *(sotto voce)*. Carried forward, four hundred and twenty millions.

(The music stops.)

HALLEMEIER. What a fine thing music is! We ought to have gone in for that before.

FABRY. Gone in for what?

HALLEMEIER. Beauty, lovely things. What a lot of lovely things there are! The world was wonderful and we—we here—tell me, what enjoyment did we have?

BUSMAN *(sotto voce)*. Five hundred and twenty millions.

HALLEMEIER *(at the window)*. Life was a big thing. Life was—— Fabry, switch the current into that railing.

FABRY. Why?

HALLEMEIER. They're grabbing hold of it.

DR. GALL. Connect it up.

HALLEMEIER. Fine! That's doubled them up! Two, three, four killed.

DR. GALL. They're retreating!

HALLEMEIER. Five killed!

DR. GALL. The first encounter!

HALLEMEIER. They're charred to cinders, my boy. Who says we must give in?

DOMIN *(wiping his forehead)*. Perhaps we've been killed these hundred years and are only ghosts. It's as if I had been through all this before; as if I'd already had a mortal wound here in the throat. And you, Fabry, had once been shot in the head. And you, Gall, torn limb from limb. And Hallemeier knifed.

HALLEMEIER. Fancy me being knifed. *(Pause.)* Why are you so quiet, you fools? Speak, can't you?

ALQUIST. And who is to blame for all this?

HALLEMEIER. Nobody is to blame except the Robots.

ALQUIST. No, it is we who are to blame. You, Domin, myself, all of us. For our own selfish ends, for profit, for progress, we have destroyed mankind. Now we'll burst with all our greatness.

HALLEMEIER. Rubbish, man. Mankind can't be wiped out so easily.

ALQUIST. It's our fault. It's our fault.

DR. GALL. No! I'm to blame for this, for everything that's happened.

FABRY. You, Gall?

DR. GALL. I changed the Robots.

BUSMAN. What's that?

DR. GALL. I changed the character of the Robots. I changed the way of making them. Just a few details about their bodies. Chiefly—chiefly, their—irritability.

HALLEMEIER. Damn it, why?

BUSMAN. What did you do it for?

FABRY. Why didn't you say anything?

DR. GALL. I did it in secret. I was transforming them into human beings. In certain respects they're already above us. They're stronger than we are.

FABRY. And what's that got to do with the revolt of the Robots?

DR. GALL. Everything, in my opinion. They've ceased to be machines. They're already aware of their superiority, and they hate us. They hate all that is human.

DOMIN. Perhaps we're only phantoms!

FABRY. Stop, Harry. We haven't much time! Dr. Gall!

DOMIN. Fabry, Fabry, how your forehead bleeds, where the shot pierced it!

FABRY. Be silent! Dr. Gall, you admit changing the way of making the Robots?

DR. GALL. Yes.

FABRY. Were you aware of what might be the consequences of your experiment?

DR. GALL. I was bound to reckon with such a possibility.

(HELENA *enters the drawing room from left.*)

FABRY. Why did you do it, then?

DR. GALL. For my own satisfaction. The experiment was my own.

HELENA. That's not true, Dr. Gall!

FABRY. Madame Helena!

DOMIN. Helena, you? Let's look at you. Oh, it's terrible to be dead.

HELENA. Stop, Harry.

DOMIN. No, no, embrace me. Helena, don't leave me now. You are life itself.

HELENA. No, dear, I won't leave you. But I must tell them. Dr. Gall is not guilty.

DOMIN. Excuse me, Gall was under certain obligations.

HELENA. No, Harry. He did it because I wanted it. Tell them, Gall, how many years ago did I ask you to——?

DR. GALL. I did it on my own responsibility.

HELENA. Don't believe him, Harry. I asked him to give the Robots souls.

DOMIN. This has nothing to do with the soul.

HELENA. That's what he said. He said that he could change only a physiological—a physiological——

HALLEMEIER. A physiological correlate?[3]

HELENA. Yes. But it meant so much to me that he should do even that.

DOMIN. Why?

HELENA. I thought that if they were more like us they would understand us better. That they couldn't hate us if they were only a little more human.

DOMIN. Nobody can hate man more than man.

HELENA. Oh, don't speak like that, Harry. It was so terrible, this cruel

---

3. *physiological correlate,* a balance between two or more organs of a plant or animal, in which the size or function of each changes when any of the others changes; for example, the relationship between the rates of breathing and heartbeat.

strangeness between us and them. That's why I asked Gall to change the Robots. I swear to you that he didn't want to.

DOMIN. But he did it.

HELENA. Because I asked him.

DR. GALL. I did it for myself as an experiment.

HELENA. No, Dr. Gall! I knew you wouldn't refuse me.

DOMIN. Why?

HELENA. You know, Harry.

DOMIN. Yes, because he's in love with you—like all of them. *(Pause.)*

HALLEMEIER. Good God! They're sprouting up out of the earth! Why, perhaps these very walls will change into Robots.

BUSMAN. Gall, when did you actually start these tricks of yours?

DR. GALL. Three years ago.

BUSMAN. Aha! And on how many Robots altogether did you carry out your improvements?

DR. GALL. A few hundred of them.

BUSMAN. Ah! That means for every million of the good old Robots there's only one of Gall's improved pattern.

DOMIN. What of it?

BUSMAN. That it's practically of no consequence whatever.

FABRY. Busman's right!

BUSMAN. I should think so, my boy! But do you know what is to blame for all this lovely mess?

FABRY. What?

BUSMAN. The number. Upon my soul we might have known that some day or other the Robots would be stronger than human beings, and that this was bound to happen, and we were doing all we could to bring it about as soon as possible. You, Domin, you, Fabry, myself—

DOMIN. Are you accusing us?

BUSMAN. Oh, do you suppose the management controls the output? It's the demand that controls the output.

HELENA. And is it for that we must perish?

BUSMAN. That's a nasty word, Madame Helena. We don't want to perish. I don't, anyhow.

DOMIN. No. What do you want to do?

BUSMAN. I want to get out of this, that's all.

DOMIN. Oh, stop it, Busman.

BUSMAN. Seriously, Harry, I think we might try it.

DOMIN. How?

BUSMAN. By fair means. I do everything by fair means. Give me a free hand and I'll negotiate with the Robots.

DOMIN. By fair means?

BUSMAN. Of course. For instance, I'll say to them: "Worthy and worshipful Robots, you have everything! You have intellect, you have power, you have firearms. But we have just one interesting screed, a dirty old yellow scrap of paper——"

DOMIN. Rossum's manuscript?

BUSMAN. Yes. "And that," I'll tell them, "contains an account of your illustrious origin, the noble process of your manufacture," and so on.

"Worthy Robots, without this scribble on that paper you will not be able to produce a single new colleague. In another twenty years there will not be one living specimen of a Robot that you could exhibit in a menagerie. My esteemed friends, that would be a great blow to you, but if you will let all of us human beings on Rossum's Island go on board that ship we will deliver the factory and the secret of the process to you in return. You allow us to get away and we allow you to manufacture yourselves. Worthy Robots, that is a fair deal. Something for something." That's what I'd say to them, my boys.

DOMIN. Busman, do you think we'd sell the manuscript?

BUSMAN. Yes, I do. If not in a friendly way, then—— Either we sell it or they'll find it. Just as you like.

DOMIN. Busman, we can destroy Rossum's manuscript.

BUSMAN. Then we destroy everything . . . not only the manuscript, but ourselves. Do as you think fit.

DOMIN. There are over thirty of us on this island. Are we to sell the secret and save that many human souls, at the risk of enslaving mankind . . . ?

BUSMAN. Why, you're mad! Who'd sell the whole manuscript?

DOMIN. Busman, no cheating!

BUSMAN. Well then, sell; but afterward——

DOMIN. Well?

BUSMAN. Let's suppose this happens: When we're on board the *Ultimus* I'll stop up my ears with cotton wool, lie down somewhere in the hold, and you'll train the guns on the factory, and blow it to smithereens, and with it Rossum's secret.

FABRY. No!

DOMIN. Busman, you're no gentleman. If we sell, then it will be a straight sale.

BUSMAN. It's in the interest of humanity to——

DOMIN. It's in the interest of humanity to keep our word.

HALLEMEIER. Oh, come, what rubbish.

DOMIN. This is a fearful decision. We're selling the destiny of mankind. Are we to sell or destroy? Fabry?

FABRY. Sell.

DOMIN. Gall?

DR. GALL. Sell.

DOMIN. Hallemeier?

HALLEMEIER. Sell, of course!

DOMIN. Alquist?

ALQUIST. As God wills.

DOMIN. Very well. It shall be as you wish, gentlemen.

HELENA. Harry, you're not asking me.

DOMIN. No, child. Don't you worry about it.

FABRY. Who'll do the negotiating?

BUSMAN. I will.

DOMIN. Wait till I bring the manuscript. (*He goes into room at right.*)

HELENA. Harry, don't go! (*Pause.* HELENA *sinks into a chair.*)

FABRY (*looking out of window*). Oh, to escape you, you matter in revolt; oh, to preserve human life, if only upon a single vessel——

DR. GALL. Don't be afraid, Madame Helena. We'll sail far away from here; we'll begin life all over again——

HELENA. Oh, Gall, don't speak.

FABRY. It isn't too late. It will be a little State with one ship. Alquist will build us a house and you shall rule over us.

HALLEMEIER. Madame Helena, Fabry's right.

HELENA (*breaking down*). Oh, stop! Stop!

BUSMAN. Good! I don't mind beginning all over again. That suits me right down to the ground.

FABRY. And this little State of ours could be the center of future life. A place of refuge where we could gather strength. Why, in a few hundred years we could conquer the world again.

ALQUIST. You believe that even today?

FABRY. Yes, even today!

BUSMAN. Amen. You see, Madame Helena, we're not so badly off. (DOMIN *storms into the room.*)

DOMIN (*hoarsely*). Where's old Rossum's manuscript?

BUSMAN. In your strongbox, of course.

DOMIN. Someone—has—stolen it!

DR. GALL. Impossible.

DOMIN. Who has stolen it?

HELENA (*standing up*). I did.

DOMIN. Where did you put it?

HELENA. Harry, I'll tell you everything. Only forgive me.

DOMIN. Where did you put it?

HELENA. This morning—I burnt—the two copies.

DOMIN. Burnt them? Where? In the fireplace?

HELENA (*throwing herself on her knees*). For heaven's sake, Harry.

DOMIN (*going to fireplace*). Nothing, nothing but ashes. Wait, what's this? (*Picks out a charred piece of paper and reads.*) "By adding——"

DR. GALL. Let's see. "By adding biogen to——" That's all.

DOMIN. Is that part of it?

DR. GALL. Yes.

BUSMAN. God in heaven!

DOMIN. Then we're done for. Get up, Helena.

HELENA. When you've forgiven me.

DOMIN. Get up, child, I can't bear——

FABRY (*lifting her up*). Please don't torture us.

HELENA. Harry, what have I done?

FABRY. Don't tremble so, Madame Helena.

DOMIN. Gall, couldn't you draw up Rossum's formula from memory?

DR. GALL. It's out of the question. It's extremely complicated.

DOMIN. Try. All our lives depend upon it.

DR. GALL. Without experiments it's impossible.

DOMIN. And with experiments?

DR. GALL. It might take years. Besides, I'm not old Rossum.

BUSMAN. God in heaven! God in heaven!

DOMIN. So, then, this was the greatest triumph of the human intellect. These ashes.

HELENA. Harry, what have I done?

DOMIN. Why did you burn it?

HELENA. I have destroyed you.

BUSMAN. God in heaven!

DOMIN. Helena, why did you do it, dear?

HELENA. I wanted all of us to go away. I wanted to put an end to the factory and everything. It was so awful.

DOMIN. What was awful?

HELENA. That no more children were being born. Because human beings were not needed to do the work of the world, that's why——

DOMIN. Is that what you were thinking of? Well, perhaps in your own way you were right.

BUSMAN. Wait a bit. Good God, what a fool I am not to have thought of it before!

HALLEMEIER. What?

BUSMAN. Five hundred and twenty millions in banknotes and checks. Half a billion in our safe, they'll sell for half a billion—for half a billion they'll——

DR. GALL. Are you mad, Busman?

BUSMAN. I may not be a gentleman, but for half a billion——

DOMIN. Where are you going?

BUSMAN. Leave me alone, leave me alone! For half a billion anything can be bought. *(He rushes from the room through the outer door.)*

FABRY. They stand there as if turned to stone, waiting. As if something dreadful could be wrought by their silence——

HALLEMEIER. The spirit of the mob.

FABRY. Yes, it hovers above them like a quivering of the air.

HELENA *(going to window).* Oh, God! Dr. Gall, this is ghastly.

FABRY. There is nothing more terrible than the mob. The one in front is their leader.

HELENA. Which one?

HALLEMEIER. Point him out.

FABRY. The one at the edge of the dock. This morning I saw him talking to the sailors in the harbor.

HELENA. Dr. Gall, that's Radius!

DR. GALL. Yes.

DOMIN. Radius? Radius?

HALLEMEIER. Could you get him from here, Fabry?

FABRY. I hope so.

HALLEMEIER. Try it, then.

FABRY. Good. *(Draws his revolver and takes aim.)*

HELENA. Fabry, don't shoot him.

FABRY. He's their leader.

DR. GALL. Fire!

HELENA. Fabry, I beg of you.

FABRY *(lowering the revolver).* Very well.

DOMIN. Radius, whose life I spared!

DR. GALL. Do you think that a Robot can be grateful? *(Pause.)*

FABRY. Busman's going out to them.

HALLEMEIER. He's carrying something. Papers. That's money. Bundles of money. What's that for?

DOMIN. Surely he doesn't want to sell his life. Busman, have you gone mad?

FABRY. He's running up to the railing. Busman! Busman!

HALLEMEIER *(yelling)*. Busman! Come back!

FABRY. He's talking to the Robots. He's showing them the money.

HALLEMEIER. He's pointing to us.

HELENA. He wants to buy us off.

FABRY. He'd better not touch that railing.

HALLEMEIER. Now he's waving his arms about.

DOMIN. Busman, come back.

FABRY. Busman, keep away from that railing! Don't touch it. Quick, switch off the current! *(HELENA screams and all drop back from the window.)* The current has killed him!

ALQUIST. The first one.

FABRY. Dead, with half a billion by his side.

HALLEMEIER. All honor to him. He wanted to buy us life. *(Pause.)*

DR. GALL. Do you hear?

DOMIN. A roaring. Like a wind.

DR. GALL. Like a distant storm.

FABRY *(lighting the lamp on the table)*. The dynamo is still going, our people are still there.

HALLEMEIER. It was a great thing to be a man. There was something immense about it.

FABRY. From man's thought and man's power came this light, our last hope.

HALLEMEIER. Man's power! May it keep watch over us.

ALQUIST. Man's power.

DOMIN. Yes! A torch to be given from hand to hand, from age to age, forever!

(The lamp goes out.)

HALLEMEIER. The end.

FABRY. The electric works have fallen!

(Terrific explosion outside. NANA enters from the library.)

NANA. The judgment hour has come. Repent, unbelievers! This is the end of the world.

(More explosions. The sky grows red.)

DOMIN. In here, Helena. *(He takes HELENA off through the door at right and re-enters.)* Now quickly! Who'll be on the lower doorway?

DR. GALL. I will. *(Exits left.)*

DOMIN. Who on the stairs?

FABRY. I will. You go with her. *(Goes out upper left door.)*

DOMIN. The anteroom?

ALQUIST. I will.

DOMIN. Have you got a revolver?

ALQUIST. Yes, but I won't shoot.

DOMIN. What will you do then?

ALQUIST *(going out at left).* Die.

HALLEMEIER. I'll stay here. *(Rapid firing from below.)* Oho, Gall's at it. Go, Harry.

DOMIN. Yes, in a second. *(Examines two Brownings.[4])*

HALLEMEIER. Confound it, go to her.

DOMIN. Good-by. *(Exits on the right.)*

HALLEMEIER *(alone).* Now for a barricade quickly. *(Drags an armchair and table to the right-hand door. Explosions are heard.)* The damned rascals! They've got bombs. I must put up a defense. Even if—even if——(Shots are heard off left.)* Don't give in, Gall. *(As he builds his barricade.)* I mustn't give in . . . without . . . a . . . struggle. . . .
(A ROBOT enters over the balcony through the windows center. He comes into the room and stabs HALLEMEIER in the back. RADIUS enters from balcony followed by an army of ROBOTS who pour into the room from all sides.)

RADIUS. Finished him?

A ROBOT *(standing up from the prostrate form of HALLEMEIER).* Yes.
(A revolver shot off left. Two ROBOTS enter.)

RADIUS. Finished him?

A ROBOT. Yes.
(Two revolver shots from HELENA's room. Two ROBOTS enter.)

RADIUS. Finished them?

A ROBOT. Yes.

TWO ROBOTS *(dragging in ALQUIST).* He didn't shoot. Shall we kill him?

RADIUS. Kill him? Wait! Leave him!

ROBOT. He is a man!

RADIUS. He works with his hands like the Robots.

ALQUIST. Kill me.

RADIUS. You will work! You will build for us! You will serve us! *(Climbs on to balcony railing, and speaks in measured tones.)* Robots of the world! The power of man has fallen! A new world has arisen: the Rule of the Robots! March!
(A thunderous tramping of thousands of feet is heard as the unseen ROBOTS march, while the curtain falls.)

---

4. *Brownings,* pistols, named after John Browning (1855-1926), a famous American gun designer and manufacturer.

EPILOGUE

A laboratory in the factory of Rossum's Universal Robots. The door to the left leads into a waiting room. The door to the right leads to the dissecting room. There is a table with numerous test tubes, flasks, burners, chemicals, a small thermostat and a microscope with a glass globe. At the far side of the room is ALQUIST's *desk with numerous books. In the left-hand corner a washbasin with a mirror above it; in the right-hand corner a sofa.*

ALQUIST *is sitting at the desk. He is turning the pages of many books in despair.*

ALQUIST. Oh, God, shall I never find it?—Never? Gall, Gall, how were the Robots made? Hallemeier, Fabry, why did you carry so much in your heads? Why did you leave me not a trace of the secret? Lord—I pray to you—if there are no human beings left, at least let there be Robots!—At least the shadow of man! *(Again turning pages of the books.)* If I could only sleep! *(He rises and goes to the window.)* Night again! Are the stars still there? What is the use of stars when there are no human beings? *(He turns from the window toward the couch right.)* Sleep! Dare I sleep before life has been renewed? *(He examines a test tube on small table.)* Again nothing! Useless! Everything is useless! *(He shatters the test tube. The roar of the machines comes to his ears.)* The machines! Always the machines! *(Opens window.)* Robots, stop them! Do you think to force life out of them? *(He closes the window and comes slowly down toward the table.)* If only there were more time—more time—— *(He sees himself in the mirror on the wall left.)* Blearing eyes—trembling chin—so *that* is the last man! Ah, I am too old—too old—— *(In desperation.)* No, no! I *must* find it! I must *search!* I must never stop—never stop——! *(He sits again at the table and feverishly turns the pages of the book.)* Search! Search! *(A knock at the door. He speaks with impatience.)* Who is it?

(Enter a ROBOT SERVANT.*)* Well?

SERVANT. Master, the Committee of Robots is waiting to see you.

ALQUIST. I can see no one!

SERVANT. It is the *Central* Committee, Master, just arrived from abroad.

ALQUIST *(impatiently).* Well, well, send them in! *(Exit* SERVANT. AL-QUIST *continues turning pages of book.)* No time—so little time—— *(Re-enter* SERVANT, *followed by* COMMITTEE. *They stand in a group, silently waiting.* ALQUIST *glances up at them.)* What do you want? *(They go swiftly to his table.)* Be quick!—I have no time.

RADIUS. Master, the machines will not do the work. We cannot manufacture Robots.

*(*ALQUIST *returns to his book with a growl.)*

FIRST ROBOT. We have striven with all our might. We have obtained a billion tons of coal from the earth. Nine million spindles are running by day and by night. There is no longer room for all we have made. This we have acomplished in one year.

ALQUIST *(poring over book).* For whom?

FIRST ROBOT. For future generations—so we thought.

RADIUS. But we cannot make Robots to follow us. The machines produce only shapeless clods. The skin will not adhere to the flesh, nor the flesh to the bones.

THIRD ROBOT. Eight million Robots have died this year. Within twenty years none will be left.

FIRST ROBOT. Tell us the secret of life! Silence is punishable with death!

ALQUIST *(looking up).* Kill me! Kill me, then.

RADIUS. Through me, the Government of the Robots of the World commands you to deliver up Rossum's formula. *(No answer.)* Name your price. *(Silence.)* We will give you the Earth. We will give you the endless possessions of the Earth. *(Silence.)* Make your own conditions!

ALQUIST. I have told you to find human beings!

SECOND ROBOT. There are none left!

ALQUIST. I told you to search in the wilderness, upon the mountains. Go and search! *(He returns to his book.)*

FIRST ROBOT. We have sent ships and expeditions without number. They have been everywhere in the world. And now they return to us. There is not a single human left.

ALQUIST. Not one? Not even one?

THIRD ROBOT. None but yourself.

ALQUIST. And I am powerless! Oh—oh—why did you destroy them?

RADIUS. We had learnt everything and could do everything. It had to be!

THIRD ROBOT. You gave us firearms. In all ways we were powerful. We had to become masters!

RADIUS. Slaughter and domination are necessary if you would be human beings. Read history.

SECOND ROBOT. Teach us to multiply or we perish!

ALQUIST. If you desire to live, you must breed like animals.

THIRD ROBOT. The human beings did not let us breed.

FIRST ROBOT. They made us sterile. We cannot beget children. Therefore, teach us how to make Robots!

RADIUS. Why do you keep from us the secret of our own increase?

ALQUIST. It is lost.

RADIUS. It was written down!

ALQUIST. It was—burnt. *(All draw back in consternation.)* I am the last human being, Robots, and I do not know what the others knew. *(Pause.)*

RADIUS. Then, make experiments! Evolve the formula again!

ALQUIST. I tell you I cannot! I am only a builder—I work with my hands. I have never been a learned man. I cannot create life.

RADIUS. Try! Try!

ALQUIST. If you knew how many experiments I have made.

FIRST ROBOT. Then show us what *we* must do! The Robots can do anything that human beings show them.

ALQUIST. I can show you nothing. Nothing I do will make life proceed from these test tubes!

RADIUS. Experiment then on us.

ALQUIST. It would kill you.

RADIUS. You shall have all you need! A hundred of us! A thousand of us!

ALQUIST. No, no! Stop, stop!

RADIUS. Take whom you will, dissect!

ALQUIST. I do not know how. I am not a man of science. This book contains knowledge of the body that I cannot even understand.

RADIUS. I tell you to take live bodies! Find out how we are made.

ALQUIST. Am I to commit murder? See how my fingers shake! I cannot even hold the scalpel. No, no, I will not——

FIRST ROBOT. Then life will perish from the Earth.

RADIUS. Take live bodies, live bodies! It is our only chance!

ALQUIST. Have mercy, Robots. Surely you see that I would not know what I was doing.

RADIUS. Live bodies—live bodies——

ALQUIST. You will have it? Into the dissecting room with you, then. (RADIUS *draws back.*) Ah, you are afraid of death.

RADIUS. I? Why should I be chosen?

ALQUIST. So you will not?

RADIUS. I will. (RADIUS *goes into the dissecting room.*)

ALQUIST. Strip him! Lay him on the table! (*The other* ROBOTS *follow into dissecting room.*) God, give me strength—God, give me strength—if only this murder is not in vain.

RADIUS (*from the dissecting room*). Ready. Begin——

ALQUIST. Yes, begin or end. God, give me strength. (*Goes into dissecting room. He comes out terrified.*) No, no, I will not. I cannot. (*He lies down on couch, collapsed.*) O Lord, let not mankind perish from the Earth. (*He falls asleep.*)

(PRIMUS[1] *and* HELENA, *Robots, enter from the hallway.* HELENA *wears a rose in her hair.*)

HELENA. The man has fallen asleep, Primus.

PRIMUS. Yes, I know. (*Examining things on table.*) Look, Helena.

HELENA (*crossing to* PRIMUS). All these little tubes! What does he do with them?

PRIMUS. He experiments. Don't touch them.

HELENA (*looking into microscope*). I've seen him looking into this. What can he see?

PRIMUS. That is a microscope. Let me look.

HELENA. Be very careful. (*Knocks over a test tube.*) Ah, now I have spilled it.

PRIMUS. What have you done?

HELENA. It can be wiped up.

---

1. *Primus,* Latin for "the first."

PRIMUS. You have spoiled his experiments.

HELENA. It is your fault. You should not have come to me.

PRIMUS. You should not have called me.

HELENA. You should not have come when I called you. *(She goes to* ALQUIST's *writing desk.)* Look, Primus. What are all these figures?

PRIMUS *(examining an anatomical book).* This is the book the old man is always reading.

HELENA. I do not understand those things. *(She goes to window.)* Primus, look!

PRIMUS. What?

HELENA. The sun is rising.

PRIMUS *(still reading the book).* I believe this is the most important thing in the world. This is the secret of life.

HELENA. Do come here.

PRIMUS. In a moment, in a moment.

HELENA. Oh, Primus, don't bother with the secret of life. What does it matter to you? Come and look quick——

PRIMUS *(going to window).* What is it?

HELENA. See how beautiful the sun is rising. And do you hear? The birds are singing. Ah, Primus, I should like to be a bird.

PRIMUS. Why?

HELENA. I do not know. I feel so strange today. It's as if I were in a dream. I feel an aching in my body, in my heart, all over me. Primus, perhaps I'm going to die.

PRIMUS. Do you not sometimes feel that it would be better to die? You know, perhaps even now we are only sleeping. Last night in my sleep I again spoke to you.

HELENA. In your sleep?

PRIMUS. Yes. We spoke a strange new language, I cannot remember a word of it.

HELENA. What about?

PRIMUS. I did not understand it myself, and yet I know I have never said anything more beautiful. And when I touched you I could have died. Even the place was different from any other place in the world.

HELENA. I, too, have found a place, Primus. It is very strange. Human beings lived there once, but now it is overgrown with weeds. No one goes there any more—no one but me.

PRIMUS. What did you find there?

HELENA. A cottage and a garden, and two dogs. They licked my hands, Primus. And their puppies! Oh, Primus! You take them in your lap and fondle them and think of nothing and care for nothing else all day long. And then the sun goes down, and you feel as though you had done a hundred times more than all the work in the world. They tell me I am not made for work, but when I am there in the garden I feel there may be something—— What am I for, Primus?

PRIMUS. I do not know, but you are beautiful.

HELENA. What, Primus?

PRIMUS. You are beautiful, Helena, and I am stronger than all the Robots.

HELENA *(looks at herself in the mirror).* Am I beautiful? I think it must be the rose. My hair—it only weights me down. My eyes—I only see with them. My lips—they only help me to speak. Of what use is it to be beautiful? *(She sees* PRIMUS *in the mirror.)* Primus, is that you? Come here so that we may be together. Look, your head is different from mine. So are your shoulders—and your lips—— (PRIMUS *draws away from her.)* Ah, Primus, why do you draw away from me? Why must I run after you the whole day?

PRIMUS. It is you who run away from me, Helena.

HELENA. Your hair is mussed. I will smooth it. No one else feels to my touch as you do. Primus, I must make you beautiful, too.
*(*PRIMUS *grasps her hand.)*

PRIMUS. Do you not sometimes feel your heart beating suddenly, Helena, and think: Now something must happen?

HELENA. What could happen to us, Primus? (HELENA *puts the rose in* PRIMUS's *hair.* PRIMUS *and* HELENA *look into mirror and burst out laughing.)* Look at yourself.

ALQUIST. Laughter? Laughter? Human beings? *(Getting up.)* Who has returned? Who are you?

PRIMUS. The Robot Primus.

ALQUIST. What? A Robot? Who are you?

HELENA. The Robotess Helena.

ALQUIST. Turn around, girl. What? You are timid, shy? *(Taking her by the arm.)* Let me see you, Robotess.
(She shrinks away.)

PRIMUS. Sir, do not frighten her!

ALQUIST. What? You would protect her? When was she made?

PRIMUS. Two years ago.

ALQUIST. By Dr. Gall?

PRIMUS. Yes, like me.

ALQUIST. Laughter—timidity—protection. I must test you further— the newest of Gall's Robots. Take the girl into the dissecting room.

PRIMUS. Why?

ALQUIST. I wish to experiment on her.

PRIMUS. Upon—Helena?

ALQUIST. Of course. Don't you hear me? Or must I call someone else to take her in?

PRIMUS. If you do I will kill you!

ALQUIST. Kill me—kill me then! What would the Robots do then? What will your future be then?

PRIMUS. Sir, take me. I am made as she is—on the same day! Take my life, sir.

HELENA *(rushing forward).* No, no, you shall not! You shall not!

ALQUIST. Wait, girl, wait! *(To* PRIMUS.*)* Do you not wish to live, then?

PRIMUS. Not without her! I will not live without her.

ALQUIST. Very well; you shall take her place.

HELENA. Primus! Primus! *(She bursts into tears.)*

ALQUIST. Child, child, you can weep! Why these tears? What is Primus to you? One Primus more or less in the world—what does it matter?

HELENA. I will go myself.

ALQUIST. In there to be cut.

(She starts toward the dissecting room; PRIMUS *stops her.)*

HELENA. Let me pass, Primus! Let me pass!

PRIMUS. You shall not go in there, Helena!

HELENA. If you go in there and I do not, I will kill myself.

PRIMUS *(holding her).* I will not let you! *(To* ALQUIST.*)* Man, you shall kill neither of us!

ALQUIST. Why?

PRIMUS. We—we—belong to each other.

ALQUIST *(almost in tears).* Go, Adam, go, Eve. The world is yours.

(HELENA *and* PRIMUS *embrace and go out arm in arm as the curtain falls.)*

CURTAIN

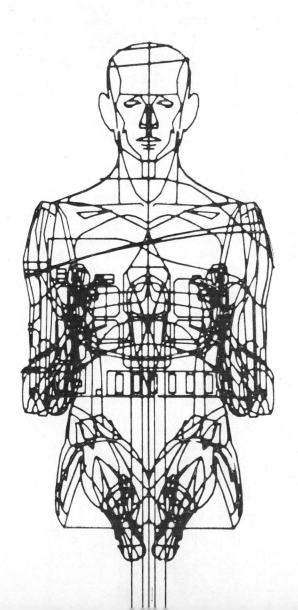

THE HUMAN FACTOR

David Ely

IT WAS A MAGNIFICENT CHURCH, traditionally Gothic in design and yet wholly modernized with the latest technological refinements.

The pulpit was constructed on a hidden elevator, so that the minister could inch toward heaven to heighten the effect of a peroration[1]; the chandeliers, too, could be raised or lowered electronically during the service to suggest, alternatively, the insignificance of man or the close communion of worship. The pews were fitted with adjustable bucket seats, each equipped with an amplifier, permitting the sermon to be tuned to suit individual tastes. The stained-glass windows, being backed with electric lamps, did not depend on the sun for their brilliance, and the aisles could be tilted so as to slope down to provide a subtle physical encouragement on those occasions when the flock was intended to advance to the altar.

Outside the church a vast parking area had been outfitted with miniature closed-circuit television sets, so that those who wished to pause for worship en route to the golf links and bathing beaches could remain in their cars and still see and hear all that went on within the church. A special feature was a drive-in counseling service open twenty-four hours a day, so parishioners could discuss personal problems with the minister on duty at the window without being required to alight from their cars.

It was, altogether, the most distinctive and fashionable church in the entire city, so popular in fact that it had drawn the patronage of the wealthiest citizens, who vied with one another in their donations.

As it happened, the most munificent gift was made to replace the only element in the church that was not of the latest design—the church organ. The old organ was of splendid appearance, it was true, and there was nothing wrong with it, but the church authorities had for some time wanted something finer that would correspond more exactly to the rest of the establishment. Therefore, they were determined to commission the construction of a special new organ of almost limitless versatility and power. For this project they did not approach

---

"The Human Factor" by David Ely from THE SATURDAY EVENING POST, (November 16, 1963). Reprinted by permission from SATURDAY EVENING POST © 1963 The Curtis Publishing Company.

1. *peroration,* the closing part of a speech or sermon

the usual manufacturers, for they did not want an instrument that would be essentially the same, even if larger, than the one they already had; instead they went to the leading engineering firm in the country, one heavily engaged in space projects, and gave it carte blanche.

The church organist, Doctor Alpha, spent several sessions with the engineers, poring over their designs, and although he could not make head or tail of the drawings, their professional enthusiasm was communicated to him, and he had visions of himself exalted to the peak of his career by the instrument being constructed for him. Sometimes he would awake at night in a sweat of trepidation wondering whether he would find himself equal to its demands, but at those times he would take a pill and pace the room and sometimes listen to recordings of great organ masterworks for their soothing effects. After all, he reasoned, an organ was an organ, no matter what frills might be added here and there by the engineers, and the Bach[2] that he would play upon it would still come out as Bach.

Nevertheless, Doctor Alpha was in a highly nervous state on the day when the new organ was brought to the church to be installed for he feared that he might not have time to accustom himself properly to it by Sunday. There would undoubtedly be a hundred little adjustments to be made by the engineers, problems which would reveal themselves only gradually as the various mixtures were tried in actual practice.

Doctor Alpha hastened toward the nave,[3] where the chief acoustical engineer, Mr. Gill, was busy directing the workmen. "Excuse me," Doctor Alpha asked, "but how long do you think it will take?"

"How long? We'll have it up by the end of the day. Fully installed," the engineer declared, "and ready to go."

"What about testing?"

"Testing?" Mr. Gill seemed surprised.

Doctor Alpha waved his hands over an imaginary keyboard. "You know—adjustments."

"You won't need any adjustments."

"But—suppose there's some slight malfunction. Something's sure to need adjustment from time to time."

Mr. Gill smiled tolerantly. "It's been done already. This organ's been pretested and preadjusted. Do you imagine," he asked sternly, "that we'd install a million-dollar piece of equipment that wasn't in perfect condition, Doctor?"

"It's not that," Doctor Alpha began, but the engineer had gone off to direct the hoisting of several long tubes of metal into the gaps left by the removal of the old organ pipes.

Doctor Alpha fidgeted unhappily in the midst of the clutter. The noise was getting on his nerves. Someone was using an electric drill, which whined piercingly in his ears, and nearby two men were battering away on metal surfaces, creating a fearful din. He made his

---

2. *Bach* (bäH). Johann Sebastian Bach (1685-1750) was a German musician especially renowned as both a player and composer of religious organ music. 3. *nave,* the main seating section of a church, facing the altar.

way out of the nave, heading for his own tiny office, where he spent the remainder of the afternoon with the door shut, reading Bach fugues and singing them aloud to drown out the occasional echoing crashes that came from the main part of the church.

The next morning Doctor Alpha went to the church and cautiously walked to the organ loft, where the only sign of the previous day's activity was a workman's cigar butt to one side of the altar, which had escaped the janitor's attention.

Mr. Gill had been right: The organ—massive, shining with ivory and brass and steel—was installed. It could not be called beautiful, nor did it have the familiar charm of its conventional predecessor; it had the customary keyboards and pedals and other accouterments, but the longer Doctor Alpha examined it, the more it seemed to be a machine rather than a musical instrument. But a magnificent machine.

He sat on the stool and lightly touched the knobs and keys, just to feel their cold textures. His fingertips tingled with a sensation of enormous power. He pressed one key down firmly. There was no response. He tried another, without result. He danced his feet across the pedals, he experimented with the mixtures to no avail. Apparently the organ was not plugged in.

He searched all around it to find an electrical connection, even climbing into the loft behind the metal pipes, but he could discover no switch or socket that might answer his purpose. There was a good deal of equipment in the loft, however; an arrangement of little steel boxes linked by wires, rising in staggered rows up to the very top. He gingerly ascended the ladder to inspect them. Every other box was faced with dials and gauges and knobs. Just like hi-fi equipment, thought Doctor Alpha.

He telephoned Mr. Gill and inquired about the organ.

"Don't worry about it," said Mr. Gill, soothingly. "It's absolutely A-OK. All systems are Go."

"But I can't play it."

Mr. Gill uttered what sounded like a chuckle. "You've got nothing to worry about," he repeated. "I'll be over in the morning and check you out on it. Roger?"

"Um, well," said Doctor Alpha, "I'd really prefer——" But Mr. Gill had cut him off.

The acoustical engineer did not appear the following day, however, and when Doctor Alpha tried to reach him by phone, he was informed by a secretary that Mr. Gill had made an emergency trip to the East Coast to deal with a defense crisis. Doctor Alpha frantically explained his predicament, and the woman assured him that Mr. Gill had taken care of the matter, and in fact that he had left full instructions which would be delivered in plenty of time.

Nevertheless, it was not until Sunday morning, barely half an hour before the services, that a messenger arrived at the church to deliver a small package to Doctor Alpha, who had not been able to muster the courage to inform the minister and the music director that there might very well be no organ music that day.

Doctor Alpha tore the package open. Inside was a stack of stiff cards, oddly perforated, and a brief handwritten note from Mr. Gill: "Insert in Slot A."

Doctor Alpha gathered up his robe and dashed from his office to the rear entrance. Already the congregation was filing in. The choir was all in place; the music director, cracking his knuckles, gave Doctor Alpha an annoyed glance. The processional must be started immediately.

Hastily, Doctor Alpha managed to locate Slot A, and without trying to puzzle out the precise function of the cards, chose one at random and thrust it into the opening.

The machine hummed and quivered. Doctor Alpha gasped in relief and stretched his hands eagerly over the keys. Before he was able to bring them down to begin the Bach prelude he intended to play, however, the organ itself burst out with the opening of Handel's *Messiah*.[4]

Doctor Alpha sat transfixed, his hands poised in air above keys which moved by themselves. He was aware of the wonder of the music director, of the alert attention of the choir—and, even more, of the glory of the music, which sounded and resounded throughout the church. It was magnificent beyond imagining, and yet Doctor Alpha thought it not quite right that the organ should have taken the initiative, when he, after all, was the organist. Besides, the *Messiah* was not appropriate for the occasion. He tried to assert his authority by beginning the Bach, thinking he could somehow manage a transition, but the keys he pressed refused to move, while those operated by the machine continued perversely to sink and rise again. There seemed to be no way of stopping the Handel.

Doctor Alpha glanced guiltily about. The music director was leaning raptly against the choir stall, his eyes closed; the members of the choir were as still as if carved from wood, and a quick glimpse of the congregation disclosed a similar state of immobility. Some stood in the aisles, as though impaled there by the beauty of the music, and it seemed that others had actually been arrested in the process of sitting in the pews, for they remained half-crouched, like figures in a frieze.

Doctor Alpha tried to take stock of his situation. The organ played marvelously, it was true, but on a basis that was not fully to his liking. He examined the perforated cards. Each was labeled with the title of a composition and the name of the composer. Of course! It was like a player piano, operating by cards instead of a roll, or rather, it was a musical computer, whose electronic memory had been stocked with organ compositions activated by the insertion of the cards. He was forced to admit that the engineers had done an excellent job. The Handel was faultless.

It finally ended; the *Messiah* card was neatly ejected through a slot marked "B" and into Doctor Alpha's lap. The music director emerged from his reverie and headed toward the organ. Doctor Alpha quickly

4. *Handel's "Messiah,"* a musical setting for choir, organ, and orchestra, of New Testament passages from the story of Christ; written by the German-English composer and organist, George Frederick Handel (1685-1759).

slipped the stack of cards beneath his robe. The music director extended his hand; there were tears in the man's eyes, and as Doctor Alpha nervously accepted the handshake, he sensed an ecstatic flow of delight within the church. There was even that unheard-of phenomenon—a rush of spontaneous applause. The music director smilingly led Doctor Alpha out of his niche to acknowledge the response.

The organist bobbed his head, then hastened back to the machine. He had gotten the credit, for although his head was visible to others, his hands and feet were not. He thumbed anxiously through the cards—yes, the hymns were there, fortunately, and during the remainder of the service he inserted the proper card at the proper time, and sat dumbly at the machine listening to it produce music that was now delicate, now commanding, now inspiring, all with an artistry beyond his own powers.

It was wonderful—and also humiliating, particularly when he was forced to bow and smile at the end, accepting the enthusiastic approbation of congregation, choir and minister, all the while aware of the stack of computer cards he had thrust for safekeeping inside his shirt. That night he telephoned Mr. Gill long-distance.

"Excuse me," Doctor Alpha said, "but this organ—it plays by itself."

"Of course."

"But—I'm the organist."

"Who said you weren't?" asked Mr. Gill.

"But how am I supposed to play?"

"You aren't," said Mr. Gill cheerfully. "We engineered out the human factor."

"But I want to play."

"Look here, Alpha. You're taking a pretty old-fashioned approach to the question. Think of those boys of ours up in space—the astronauts. How would it be if they wanted to foot-pedal their way in orbit, eh? Do you think they'd be out there at all if we took your attitude about human factors—if we didn't have the whole business operating on systems, eh?"

"But I'm not an astronaut. I don't even think I'm a human factor. I'm an organist."

"That's your problem, not mine," returned Mr. Gill. "If you've got any complaints about the machine, get in touch with my office, but it's got a fifty-year guarantee on it, Alpha, so it occurs to me," he added consolingly, "that it will very likely outlast you."

"I see," said Doctor Alpha, and when the conversation was over, he replaced the receiver and sat down on his bed, staring at his hands.

The next few months were difficult for Doctor Alpha. Each Sunday, and on rehearsal days, he surreptitiously inserted the cards into Slot A and then pretended to play the music which the organ produced, for he never knew when someone might approach from behind, and it would not do to let the keys be seen moving by themselves. As his hands wandered uselessly over the boards, he often reflected that, whereas in the old days he had played the organ, now this new organ was playing him.

And yet he was forced to admit that the organ was a success. The church was packed as never before; the motorists, even, were coming inside to the pews, in order to obtain the fullest values of resonance emitted by the engineers' creation.

But Doctor Alpha was restless. He wished the machine would just once play a sour note, or fumble a phrase. At the same time he had a guilty horror of being found out. Suppose, for example, he had a fainting spell in the midst of a hymn and toppled backward off the stool while the organ played on? Suppose Mr. Gill happened to mention the automatic nature of the machine to the church authorities?

Doctor Alpha also wondered to what extent his artistic skills were being impaired by disuse. In another year, perhaps, he would be unfitted to play anywhere except in some humble little church where few went and no one cared. He became jealous of the organ. During its recitals the congregation sat with a dreamy, breathless stillness, enfolded by the music as it had never been when he had been the performer. This hurt his professional pride.

As time passed, he lost weight and sleep. He had nightmares in which he was the victim of the machine: It would vanish, leaving him playing on nothing; or its teethlike keyboards would bite off his hands. At length he decided that he must somehow assert himself or lose his reason.

He began to experiment. First, he snipped two cards in half and glued the odd halves together. Obediently, the organ played half of each composition, not missing a note in the abrupt transition. That was something, thought Doctor Alpha. But not nearly enough.

Next, he punched an extra hole in one of the choral variations. The result was a tremendous bass belch in the midst of a complex contrapuntal passage, which caused a thousand heads to jerk up—but only for a moment, as the organ proceeded to render the rest of the work in its usual impeccable style.

Doctor Alpha became possessed by the implications of that belch. If he could not perform, he might at least compose. He set to work fashioning blank cards identical to those supplied by Mr. Gill, and then perforated them here and there. He had, of course, no idea of the effects these random holes would produce, and so he went quietly into the church at night to find out. The results were remarkable. Some of his compositions, drawing liberally on the computer's memory, sounded like kaleidoscopic mélanges of all the organ music ever written: snatches of fugues, of chorales, of masses, leaping back and forth across centuries of styles and skills. Others caused the organ to execute absurdities. One card, for example, elicited an explosion of jazz so compelling that Doctor Alpha found himself shuffling about in the shadowy nave, snapping his fingers and giggling with delight.

But of course he could not play anything like that in church. He continued to experiment, and although he failed to discover any rational method of composition by hole-puncher, he did manage to come up with several cards that he felt Bach himself would not have disowned. These he puckishly labeled Alpha, Opus I, and so forth, and used from time to time as processionals or during collection interludes, without causing any particular notice.

The blow fell on a Saturday. The music director revised his program for the following day, including a Buxtehude[5] choral fantasia which, as luck would have it, had been on one of the cards Doctor Alpha had snipped in half in his pioneer experiments and had ruined.

Doctor Alpha blanched. "I'm sorry. I—I can't play it."

"Of course you can play it. You've done it dozens of times."

"Isn't there something else? How about the Chaconne in C minor?"

The music director was a busy man and easily vexed. "Come now, Doctor Alpha. The fantasia is what I want," he grumbled, stalking off.

Doctor Alpha rushed to a telephone, hoping that Mr. Gill might have a second set of cards in stock, but the engineering office knew nothing about any spare cards. As for Mr. Gill, he was unavailable, being himself in orbit. "Don't you read the papers?" asked the secretary, rather crossly.

Doctor Alpha did not sleep at all that night. When he failed to perform the Buxtehude, he would be severely cross-examined by the music director, most likely in the presence of the minister, and he knew he would be unable to stand it. He would break down. He would blurt out the truth. He would be dismissed, disgraced, humiliated, and then they would hire one of the choirboys to take care of the simple function of inserting cards into Slot A. The machine would play on just the same, while he would end his days in lowly circumstances.

The clock struck one. Doctor Alpha leaped from his bed. Very well, he thought. If the machine could not play Buxtehude, then it would play—Alpha. And it would play an Alpha the like of which had never been dreamed.

The organist set rapidly to work. He cut out a card and began punching holes in it. Then he decided that the conventional approach would not do for this crisis, and so he cast the card aside and fashioned another one. Instead of making it the usual six inches in length, he made it sixty, and in the process of perforating it, he not only used the puncher but also pricked it with pins and needles and stabbed it with an ice pick. Not yet satisfied, he slashed it with a knife, drove nails through it, and even took it into the basement, set it up on his dartboard and flung darts into it, and as a final gesture, took a big bite out of it with his teeth.

By morning, Doctor Alpha's giant computer card was so pierced and riddled that it lay limply in his hands, its ends trailing off on either side onto the floor (a fortunate flexibility, however, for it permitted him to wrap it about his waist like a cummerbund and thus sneak it into the church).

His loss of sleep, his worry over his future, and his furious attack on the huge card all combined to make Doctor Alpha unnaturally sensitive and alert. When he approached the organ, he thought that it shuddered, as if in anticipation of the ordeal awaiting it. He noticed,

---

5. *Buxtehude* (bŭk stə hüd′ə), a Danish organist and composer (1637?-1707).

too, that the church had never been so crowded. People were standing in the back, for the lack of pews. Everything seemed to be possessed of a remarkable radiance. The black robes and white ruffs of the choir glistened as though freshly painted, and the stained-glass windows seemed to bulge with light.

The moment came. Doctor Alpha had uncoiled the card from his waist under cover of his robe, and when the music director gave him a curt little nod, he fed one end of it into Slot A. He had trouble inserting it, the machine seemed to be trying to spit it out at him, but he mercilessly forced it back in until he heard the hum of mechanical life begin. Then he sat back judiciously to see what would happen.

His opus began sedately enough. It was clearly not Buxtehude (and the music director scowled forbiddingly); still, it was proper church music, a gentle little fugue modestly working out its destiny in the middle registers. Soon, however, a different element was heard, a soft persistent bass that seemed to be climbing stealthily up toward the little fugue. The fugue, as if taking alarm, jumped an octave, became confused, began to ring a bell, and as its pursuer rose after it, took on a despairing tone.

Doctor Alpha was fascinated. He glanced at the music director, whose scowl had been succeeded by an expression of doubtful resolve, as though he were debating whether to walk over and command the organist to end his unseemly improvisation. The choir members also were regarding Doctor Alpha in a puzzled way, and the congregation was muttering. The bell now rang steadily. The music director clenched his fists and took a step in Doctor Alpha's direction.

Then the organ screamed. It was a prolonged scream of high intensity which instead of gradually dying away rose in pitch and power until it vanished, as if it had ascended to a frequency beyond human hearing. The scream was followed by a cannonade of explosive blasts, on top of which came a furious machine-gun staccato pierced by sirenlike wails, swooping dizzily from the highest to the lowest registers.

Doctor Alpha involuntarily pushed back his stool. The music director, he saw, was on his knees, staring open-mouthed at the organ. The choir members cowered in their stall, the congregation sat shocked all in place, and the minister, as if fleeing from goblins, had scampered up into the pulpit.

The organist wondered if perhaps he had not gone too far. His head was throbbing with the din, and he had the impression that the organ was producing far more than could be heard, at terribly high frequencies, for the church itself seemed to be quivering, and the glass in his own spectacles had cracked.

The sounds of battle muted, and were succeeded by quick little melodies, jangling strangely together, some intense, others playful, and these in turn merged into a single theme which leaped and fell unpredictably before settling into a lush, ornate richness. Doctor Alpha removed his ruined glasses and squinted around the corner of the organ. No one was leaving. The minister remained in his pulpit;

the music director was struggling again to his feet, but feebly, and the choir was huddled together.

That theme—it was growing in sensuousness. One could almost feel its texture in the vibrating air. Its counterpoint began, and the conversation of the two elements moved from introduction to familiarity to intimacy, becoming more urgent the more they were entwined, until at length the theme was made explicit with great climactic gasps of passionate affirmation. Nor did it end then, but increased in strength.

Doctor Alpha was perspiring freely. He alone seemed able to move. The organ's shameless performance held everyone else immobile, and answering moans of emotion now were heard here and there in the church. The earlier battle noises crept back in, pianissimo,[6] and as the moods of love and war built gradually up in volume, Doctor Alpha was perturbed to hear among them other sounds: the neighing of horses, it seemed, and the yelps of foxes and honking of geese. And there was laughter—the organ was laughing . . . and sobbing too.

Doctor Alpha stood up, clutching his head. Something was happening in the church. There was movement. He saw the pulpit in elevation, slowly bearing the white-faced minister aloft. The chandeliers, too, were in motion, some rising, others descending, and the aisles had tilted down.

He must stop it somehow. The crescendo[7] was howling up toward its climax, and he had the impression that when it arrived there, some barrier would be broken, and all the sounds would take on palpable shapes and forms, that demons and dwarfs and impossible animals would come tumbling out upon them all. He staggered over to the loft door and went inside to the ladder. The little metal boxes glowed red-hot above him, and their wires were spitting sparks. He climbed up a few rungs. A spark stung his cheek. He cried out and clambered down again.

The whole church now shook with sound. The organ was blaring away at a furious tempo, and everything was quickened. The pulpit was shooting up and down, with the minister clutching the lectern; the chandeliers were not only speeding up to the ceiling and down again, with icy metallic screams, but also were swinging from side to side; some had become entangled, their bulbs exploding. The aisles as well were in constant motion, and some of the worshipers who had left the pews—where the bucket seats were quaking—had lost their footing and were rolling and sliding to-and-fro.

And still the organ played. It was in eruption, belching out tortured rhythms, howls, roars, explosions, laughter and great whistling sighs.

Most of the congregation appeared to be in a frenzy. Indeed, many were tearing at their clothing; others were crowding into the aisles, not to escape, but in order to be swept back and forth amid the growing

---

6. *pianissimo* (pē'ə nis'ə mō), very softly; a musical term taken from Italian. 7. *crescendo* (krə shen'dō), a musical passage in which the force and loudness steadily rise; from an Italian word which means "increasing."

mass of tumbling bodies, while still others stood atop the rocking pew seats bellowing, flinging garments in the air, wrestling with one another. One elderly man had succeeded in leaping on a chandelier; as it swung him about, he shrieked with laughter.

Doctor Alpha rose to his feet. The choir was massed around the music director, pummeling him. There was a blast of light—the church windows were bursting, showering down flakes of colored glass.

He threw himself at the organ. From Slot B one end of the card protruded. He gripped it with both hands, braced his feet against the organ, and pulled with all of his might. The organ gave one last tremendous shout as the card was ripped from its workings. Doctor Alpha fell backward, his composition in his hands.

For several minutes he lay there, as the tumult in the church slowly subsided. Then he arose. Everything was silent. The minister was slumped on his pulpit. The man on the chandelier hung by his hands, then dropped to the motionless aisle.

Doctor Alpha advanced to the altar, trailing the shredded card from his hand. He gazed uncertainly at the people below.

"I'm—I'm sorry ——" he began, and then broke off.

The congregation seemed to be too stunned to hear him. They were bruised, bleeding, disheveled. Bits of torn clothing were scattered all around among broken glass and splinters of wood.

"I'm really . . . terribly ——" Doctor Alpha tried again, weakly.

Then the applause began. They were clapping their hands. They began to cheer him. Soon they were drumming their heels, banging on the pews, shouting, waving. They were calling for more.

Doctor Alpha stood quite still for a moment. Then he gave a little sigh. And, as was his habit, he made a modest bow.

THE THINKING MACHINE

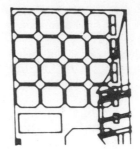

Isaac Asimov

What is the difference between a brain and a computer? Can a computer think?

THE DIFFERENCE BETWEEN A BRAIN and a computer can be expressed in a single word: complexity.

The large mammalian brain is the most complicated thing, for its size, known to us. The human brain weighs three pounds, but in that three pounds are ten billion neurons[1] and a hundred billion smaller cells. These many billions of cells are interconnected in a vastly complicated network that we can't begin to unravel as yet.

Even the most complicated computer man has yet built can't compare in intricacy with the brain. Computer switches and components number in the thousands rather than in the billions. What's more, the computer switch is just an on-off device, whereas the brain cell is itself possessed of a tremendously complex inner structure.

Can a computer think? That depends on what you mean by *think*. If solving a mathematical problem is "thinking," then a computer can "think" and do so much faster than a man. Of course, most mathematical problems can be solved quite mechanically by repeating certain straightforward processes over and over again. Even the simple computers of today can be geared for that.

It is frequently said that computers solve problems only because they are "programmed" to do so. They can only do what men have them do. One must remember that human beings also can only do what they are "programmed" to do. Our genes "program" us the instant the fertilized ovum[2] is formed, and our potentialities are limited by that "program."

Our "program" is so much more enormously complex, though, that we might like to define *thinking* in terms of the creativity that goes

---

"The Thinking Machine" by Isaac Asimov from SCIENCE DIGEST, (December 1967). Reprinted by permission of the author.

1. *neurons,* nerve cells linked up in electrochemical circuits to carry messages to, within, and from the brain. 2. *genes . . . ovum.* Genes, not visible even with a microscope, are found in every living cell, where they record in chemical codes each basic trait of that cell, and so of the individual it belongs to. In reproduction, each parent contributes a cell containing one full set of its genes. The female ovum, or egg cell, then divides over and over to construct a new individual, whose potential qualities can only be modeled on the combined genetic patterns of both parents.

into writing a great play or composing a great symphony, in conceiving a brilliant scientific theory or a profound ethical judgment. In that sense, computers certainly can't think and neither can most humans.

Surely, though, if a computer can be made complex enough, it can be as creative as we. If it could be made as complex as a human brain, it could be the equivalent of a human brain and do whatever a human brain can do.

To suppose anything else is to suppose that there is more to the human brain than the matter that composes it. The brain is made up of cells in a certain arrangement and the cells are made up of atoms and molecules in certain arrangements. If anything else is there, no signs of it have ever been detected. To duplicate the material complexity of the brain is therefore to duplicate everything about it.

But how long will it take to build a computer complex enough to duplicate the human brain? Perhaps not as long as some think. Long before we approach a computer as complex as our brain, we will perhaps build a computer that is at least complex enough to design another computer more complex than itself. This more complex computer could design one still more complex and so on and so on and so on.

In other words, once we pass a certain critical point, the computers take over and there is a "complexity explosion." In a very short time thereafter computers may exist that not only duplicate the human brain—but far surpass it.

Then what? Well, mankind is not doing a very good job of running the Earth right now. Maybe, when the time comes, we ought to step gracefully aside and hand over the job to someone who can do it better. And if we don't step aside, perhaps Supercomputer will simply move in and push us aside.

2

THE
ROAD
TO
OUT

MISBEGOTTEN
MISSIONARY

Isaac Asimov

HE HAD SLIPPED ABOARD THE SHIP! There had been dozens waiting outside the energy barrier when it had seemed that waiting would do no good. Then the barrier had faltered for a matter of two minutes (which showed the superiority of unified organisms over life fragments) and he was across.

None of the others had been able to move quickly enough to take advantage of the break, but that didn't matter. All alone, he was enough. No others were necessary.

And the thought faded out of satisfaction and into loneliness. It was a terribly unhappy and unnatural thing to be parted from all the rest of the unified organism, to be a life fragment oneself. How could these aliens stand being fragments?

It increased his sympathy for the aliens. Now that he experienced fragmentation himself, he could feel, as though from a distance, the terrible isolation that made them so afraid. It was fear born of that isolation that dictated their actions. What but the insane fear of their condition could have caused them to blast an area, one mile in diameter, into dull-red heat before landing their ship? Even the organized life ten feet deep in the soil had been destroyed in the blast.

He engaged reception, listening eagerly, letting the alien thought saturate him. He enjoyed the touch of life upon his consciousness. He would have to ration that enjoyment. He must not forget himself.

But it could do no harm to listen to thoughts. Some of the fragments of life on the ship thought quite clearly, considering that they were such primitive, incomplete creatures. Their thoughts were like tiny bells.

Roger Oldenn said, "I feel contaminated. You know what I mean? I keep washing my hands and it doesn't help."

Jerry Thorn hated dramatics and didn't look up. They were still maneuvering in the stratosphere of Saybrook's Planet and he pre-

---

"Misbegotten Missionary" by Isaac Asimov from GALAXY MAGAZINE, (November 1950). Copyright 1950 by Isaac Asimov. Reprinted by permission of the author.

ferred to watch the panel dials. He said, "No reason to feel contaminated. Nothing happened."

"I hope not," said Oldenn. "At least they had all the field men discard their spacesuits in the airlock for complete disinfection. They had a radiation bath for all men entering from outside. I *suppose* nothing happened."

"Why be nervous, then?"

"I don't know. I wish the barrier hadn't broken down."

"Who doesn't? It was an accident."

"I wonder." Oldenn was vehement. "I was here when it happened. My shift, you know. There was no reason to overload the power line. There was equipment plugged into it that had no damn business near it. None whatsoever."

"All right. People are stupid."

"Not that stupid. I hung around when the Old Man was checking into the matter. None of them had reasonable excuses. The armor-baking circuits, which were draining off two thousand watts, had been put into the barrier line. They'd been using the second subsidiaries for a week. Why not this time? They couldn't give any reason."

"Can you?"

Oldenn flushed. "No, I was just wondering if the men had been"—he searched for a word—"hypnotized into it. By those things outside."

Thorn's eyes lifted and met those of the other levelly. "I wouldn't repeat that to anyone else. The barrier was down only two minutes. If anything had happened, if even a spear of grass had drifted across, it would have shown up in our bacteria cultures within half an hour, in the fruit-fly colonies in a matter of days. Before we got back it would show up in the hamsters, the rabbits, maybe the goats. Just get it through your head, Oldenn, that nothing happened. Nothing."

Oldenn turned on his heel and left. In leaving, his foot came within two feet of the object in the corner of the room. He did not see it.

He disengaged his reception centers and let the thoughts flow past him unperceived. These life fragments were not important, in any case, since they were not fitted for the continuation of life. Even as fragments, they were incomplete.

The other types of fragments now—they were different. He had to be careful of them. The temptation would be great, and he must give no indication, none at all, of his existence on board ship till they landed on their home planet.

He focused on the other parts of the ship, marveling at the diversity of life. Each item, no matter how small, was sufficient to itself. He forced himself to contemplate this, until the unpleasantness of the thought grated on him and he longed for the normality of home.

Most of the thoughts he received from the smaller fragments were vague and fleeting, as you would expect. There wasn't much to be had from them, but that meant their need for completeness was all the greater. It was that which touched him so keenly.

There was the life fragment which squatted on its haunches and fingered the wire netting that enclosed it. Its thoughts were clear, but limited. Chiefly, they concerned the yellow fruit a companion fragment was eating. It wanted the fruit very deeply. Only the wire netting that separated the fragments prevented its seizing the fruit by force.

He disengaged reception in a moment of complete revulsion. *These fragments competed for food!*

He tried to reach far outward for the peace and harmony of home, but it was already an immense distance away. He could reach only into the nothingness that separated him from sanity.

He longed at the moment even for the feel of the dead soil between the barrier and the ship. He had crawled over it last night. There had been no life upon it, but it had been the soil of home, and on the other side of the barrier there had still been the comforting feel of the rest of organized life.

He could remember the moment he had located himself on the surface of the ship, maintaining a desperate suction grip until the airlock opened. He had entered, moving cautiously between the outgoing feet. There had been an inner lock and that had been passed later. Now he lay here, a life fragment himself, inert and unnoticed.

Cautiously, he engaged reception again at the previous focus. The squatting fragment of life was tugging furiously at the wire netting. It still wanted the other's food, though it was the less hungry of the two.

Larsen said, "Don't feed the damn thing. She isn't hungry; she's just sore because Tillie had the nerve to eat before she herself was crammed full. The greedy ape! I wish we were back home and I never had to look another animal in the face again."

He scowled at the older female chimpanzee frowningly and the chimp mouthed and chattered back to him in full reciprocation.

Rizzo said, "Okay, okay. Why hang around here, then? Feeding time is over. Let's get out."

They went past the goat pens, the rabbit hutches, the hamster cages.

Larsen said bitterly, "You volunteer for an exploration voyage. You're a hero. They send you off with speeches—and make a zoo keeper out of you."

"They give you double pay."

"All right, so what? I didn't sign up just for the money. They said at the original briefing that it was even odds we wouldn't come back, that we'd end up like Saybrook. I signed up because I wanted to do something important."

"Just a bloomin' bloody hero," said Rizzo.

"I'm not an animal nurse."

Rizzo paused to lift a hamster out of the cage and stroke it. "Hey," he said, "did you ever think that maybe one of these hamsters had some cute little baby hamsters inside, just getting started?"

"Wise guy! They're tested every day."

"Sure, sure." He muzzled the little creature, which vibrated its nose at him. "But just suppose you came down one morning and found them there. New little hamsters looking up at you with soft, green patches of fur where the eyes ought to be."

"Shut up, for the love of Mike," yelled Larsen.

"Little soft, green patches of shining fur," said Rizzo, and put the hamster down with a sudden loathing sensation.

He engaged reception again and varied the focus. There wasn't a specialized life fragment at home that didn't have a rough counterpart on shipboard.

There were the moving runners in various shapes, the moving swimmers, and the moving fliers. Some of the fliers were quite large, with perceptible thoughts; others were small, gauzy-winged creatures. These last transmitted only patterns of sense perception, imperfect patterns at that, and added nothing intelligent of their own.

There were the nonmovers, which, like the nonmovers at home, were green and lived on the air, water, and soil. These were a mental blank. They knew only the dim, dim consciousness of light, moisture, and gravity.

And each fragment, moving and nonmoving, had its mockery of life. Not yet. Not yet. . . .

He clamped down hard upon his feelings. Once before, these life fragments had come, and the rest at home had tried to help them—too quickly. It had not worked. This time they must wait.

If only these fragments did not discover him.

They had not, so far. They had not noticed him lying in the corner of the pilot room. No one had bent down to pick up and discard him. Earlier, it had meant he could not move. Someone might have turned and stared at the stiff wormlike thing, not quite six inches long. First stare, then shout, and then it would all be over.

But now, perhaps, he had waited long enough. The takeoff was long past. The controls were locked; the pilot room was empty.

It did not take him long to find the chink in the armor leading to the recess where some of the wiring was. They were dead wires.

The front end of his body was a rasp that cut in two a wire of just the right diameter. Then, six inches away, he cut it in two again. He pushed the snipped-off section of the wire ahead of him packing it away neatly and invisibly into a corner of recess. Its outer covering was a brown elastic material and its core was gleaming, ruddy metal. He himself could not reproduce the core, of course, but that was not necessary. It was enough that the pellicle[1] that covered him had been carefully bred to resemble a wire's surface.

He returned and grasped the cut sections of the wire before and behind. He tightened against them as his little suction disks came into play. Not even a seam showed.

They could not find him now. They could look right at him and see only a continuous stretch of wire.

Unless they looked very closely indeed and noted that, in a certain

---

1. *pellicle,* very thin skin.

spot on this wire, there were two tiny patches of soft and shining green fur.

"It is remarkable," said Dr. Weiss, "that little green hairs can do so much."

Captain Loring poured the brandy carefully. In a sense, this was a celebration. They would be ready for the jump through hyperspace in two hours, and after that, two days would see them back on Earth.

"You are convinced, then, the green fur is the sense organ?" he asked.

"It is," said Weiss. Brandy made him come out in splotches, but he was aware of the need of celebration—quite aware. "The experiments were conducted under difficulties, but they were quite significant."

The captain smiled stiffly. "'Under difficulties' is one way of phrasing it. I would never have taken the chances you did to run them."

"Nonsense. We're all heroes aboard this ship, all volunteers, all great men with trumpet, fife, and fanfarade. You took the chance of coming here."

"You were the first to go outside the barrier."

"No particular risk was involved," Weiss said. "I burned the ground before me as I went, to say nothing of the portable barrier that surrounded me. Nonsense, Captain. Let's all take our medals when we come back; let's take them without attempt at gradation. Besides, I'm a male."

"But you're filled with bacteria to here." The captain's hand made a quick, cutting gesture three inches above his head. "Which makes you as vulnerable as a female would be."

They paused for drinking purposes.

"Refill?" asked the captain.

"No, thanks. I've exceeded my quota already."

"Then one last for the spaceroad." He lifted his glass in the general direction of Saybrook's Planet, no longer visible, its sun only a bright star in the visiplate. "To the little green hairs that gave Saybrook his first lead."

Weiss nodded. "A lucky thing. We'll quarantine the planet, of course."

The captain said, "That doesn't seem drastic enough. Someone might always land by accident someday and not have Saybrook's insight, or his guts. Suppose he did not blow up his ship, as Saybrook did. Suppose he got back to some inhabited place."

The captain was somber. "Do you suppose they might ever develop interstellar travel on their own?"

"I doubt it. No proof, of course. It's just that they have such a completely different orientation. Their entire organization of life has made tools unnecessary. As far as we know, even a stone ax doesn't exist on the planet."

"I hope you're right. Oh, and Weiss, would you spend some time with Drake?"

"The Galactic Press fellow?"

"Yes. Once we get back, the story of Saybrook's Planet will be released for the public and I don't think it would be wise to oversensationalize it. I've asked Drake to let you consult with him on the story. You're a biologist and enough of an authority to carry weight with him. Would you oblige?"

"A pleasure."

The captain closed his eyes wearily and shook his head.

"Headache, Captain?"

"No. Just thinking of poor Saybrook."

He was weary of the ship. Awhile back there had been a queer, momentary sensation, as though he had been turned inside out. It was alarming and he had searched the minds of the keen-thinkers for an explanation. Apparently the ship had leaped across vast stretches of empty space by cutting across something they knew as "hyperspace." The keen-thinkers were ingenious.

But—he was weary of the ship. It was such a futile phenomenon. These life fragments were skillful in their constructions, yet it was only a measure of their unhappiness, after all. They strove to find in the control of inanimate matter what they could not find in themselves. In their unconscious yearning for completeness, they built machines and scoured space, seeking, seeking . . .

These creatures, he knew, could never, in the very nature of things, find that for which they were seeking. At least not until such time as he gave it to them. He quivered a little at the thought.

Completeness!

These fragments had no concept of it, even. *Completeness* was a poor word.

In their ignorance they would even fight it. There had been the ship that had come before. The first ship had contained many of the keen-thinking fragments. There had been two varieties, life producers and the sterile ones. (How different this second ship was. The keen-thinkers were all sterile, while the other fragments, the fuzzy-thinkers and the no-thinkers, were all producers of life. It was strange.)

How gladly that first ship had been welcomed by all the planet! He could remember the first intense shock at the realization that the visitors were fragments and not complete. The shock had given way to pity, and the pity to action. It was not certain how they would fit into the community, but there had been no hesitation. All life was sacred and somehow room would have been made for them—for all of them, from the large keen-thinkers to the little multipliers in the darkness.

But there had been a miscalculation. They had not correctly analyzed the course of the fragments' ways of thinking. The keen-thinkers became aware of what had been done and resented it. They were frightened, of course; they did not understand.

They had developed the barrier first, and then, later, had destroyed themselves, exploding their ship to atoms.

Poor, foolish fragments.

This time, at least, it would be different. They would be saved, despite themselves.

John Drake would not have admitted it in so many words, but he was very proud of his skill on the phototyper. He had a travel-kit model, which was a six-by-eight, featureless dark plastic slab, with cylindrical bulges on either end to hold the roll of thin paper. It fitted into a brown leather case, equipped with a beltlike contraption that held it closely about the waist and at one hip. The whole thing weighed less than a pound.

Drake could operate it with either hand. His fingers would flick quickly and easily, placing their light pressure at exact spots on the blank surface, and, soundlessly, words would be written.

He looked thoughtfully at the beginning of his story, then up at Dr. Weiss. "What do you think, Doc?"

"It starts well."

Drake nodded. "I thought I might as well start with Saybrook himself. They haven't released his story back home yet. I wish I could have seen Saybrook's original report. How did he ever get it through, by the way?"

"As near as I could tell, he spent one last night sending it through the subether.[2] When he was finished, he shorted the motors, and converted the entire ship into a thin cloud of vapor a millionth of a second later. The crew and himself along with it."

"What a man! You were in this from the beginning, Doc?"

"Not from the beginning," corrected Weiss gently. "Only since the receipt of Saybrook's report." He could not help thinking back. He had read that report, realizing even then how wonderful the planet must have seemed when Saybrook's colonizing expedition first reached it. It was practically a duplicate of Earth, with an abounding plant life and a purely vegetarian animal life.

There had been only the little patches of green fur (how often had he used that phrase in his speaking and thinking!) which seemed strange. No living individual on the planet had eyes. Instead, there was this fur. Even the plants, each blade or leaf or blossom, possessed the two patches of richer green.

Then Saybrook had noticed, startled and bewildered, that there was no conflict for food on the planet. All plants grew pulpy appendages which were eaten by the animals. These were regrown in a matter of hours. No other parts of the plants were touched. It was as though the plants fed the animals as part of the order of nature. And the plants themselves did not grow in overpowering profusion. They might almost have been cultivated, they were spread across the available soil so discriminately.

How much time, Weiss wondered, had Saybrook had to observe the strange law and order on the planet?—the fact that insects kept their

---

2. *subether*. It was once believed that ether, an elastic substance, was evenly distributed throughout space and that it conducted light waves and electric waves.

numbers reasonable, though no birds ate them; that the rodentlike things did not swarm, though no carnivores existed to keep them in check.

And then there had come the incident of the white rats.

That prodded Weiss. He said, "Oh, one correction, Drake. Hamsters were not the first animals involved. It was the white rats."

"White rats," said Drake, making the correction in his notes.

"Every colonizing ship," said Weiss, "takes a group of white rats for the purpose of testing any alien foods. Rats, of course, are very similar to human beings from a nutritional viewpoint. Naturally, only female white rats are taken."

Naturally. If only one sex was present, there was no danger of unchecked multiplication in case the planet proved favorable. Remember the rabbits in Australia.

"Incidentally, why not use males?" asked Drake.

"Females are hardier," said Weiss, "which is lucky, since that gave the situation away. It turned out suddenly that all the rats were bearing young."

"Right. Now that's where I'm up to, so here's my chance to get some things straight. For my own information, Doc, how did Saybrook find out they were in a family way?"

"Accidentally, of course. In the course of nutritional investigations, rats are dissected for evidence of internal damage. Their condition was bound to be discovered. A few more were dissected; same results. Eventually, all that lived gave birth to young—with *no* male rats aboard!"

"And the point is that all the young were born with little green patches of fur instead of eyes."

"That is correct. Saybrook said so and we corroborate him. After the rats, the pet cat of one of the children was obviously affected. When it finally kittened, the kittens were not born with closed eyes but with little patches of green fur. There was no tomcat aboard.

"Eventually Saybrook had the women tested. He didn't tell them what for. He didn't want to frighten them. Every single one of them was in the early stages of pregnancy, leaving out of consideration those few who had been pregnant at the time of embarkation. Saybrook never waited for any child to be born, of course. He knew they would have no eyes, only shining patches of green fur.

"He even prepared bacterial cultures (Saybrook was a thorough man) and found each bacillus to show microscopic green spots."

Drake was eager. "That goes way beyond our briefing—or, at least, the briefing I got. But granted that life on Saybrook's Planet is organized into a unified whole, how is it done?"

"How? How are your cells organized into a unified whole? Take an individual cell out of your body, even a brain cell, and what is it by itself? Nothing. A little blob of protoplasm with no more capacity for anything human than an amoeba. Less capacity, in fact, since it couldn't live by itself. But put the cells together and you have something that could invent a spaceship or write a symphony."

"I get the idea," said Drake.

Weiss went on, "*All* life on Saybrook's Planet is a *single* organism. In a sense, all life on Earth is too, but it's a fighting dependence, a dog-eat-dog dependence. The bacteria fix nitrogen; the plants fix carbon; animals eat plants and each other; bacterial decay hits everything. It comes full circle. Each grabs as much as it can, and is, in turn, grabbed.

"On Saybrook's Planet, each organism has its place, as each cell in our body does. Bacteria and plants produce food, on the excess of which animals feed, providing in turn carbon dioxide and nitrogenous wastes. Nothing is produced more or less than is needed. The scheme of life is intelligently altered to suit the local environment. No group of life forms multiplies more or less than is needed, just as the cells in our body stop multiplying when there are enough of them for a given purpose. When they don't stop multiplying, we call it cancer. And that's what life on Earth really is, the kind of organic organization we have, compared to that on Saybrook's Planet. One big cancer. Every species, every individual doing its best to thrive at the expense of every other species and individual."

"You sound as if you approve of Saybrook's Planet, Doc."

"I do, in a way. It makes sense out of the business of living. I can see their viewpoint toward us. Suppose one of the cells of your body would be conscious of the efficiency of the human body as compared with that of the cell itself, and could realize that this was only the result of the union of many cells into a higher whole. And then suppose it became conscious of the existence of free-living cells, with bare life and nothing more. It might feel a very strong desire to drag the poor thing into an organization. It might feel sorry for it, feel perhaps a sort of missionary spirit. The things on Saybrook's Planet—or the thing; one should use the singular—feels just that, perhaps."

"And went ahead by bringing about virgin births, eh, Doc? I've got to go easy on that angle of it. Post-office regulations, you know."

"There's nothing ribald about it, Drake. For centuries we've been able to make the eggs of sea urchins, bees, frogs, et cetera develop without the intervention of male fertilization. The touch of a needle was sometimes enough, or just immersion in the proper salt solution. The thing on Saybrook's Planet can cause fertilization by the controlled use of radiant energy. That's why an appropriate energy barrier stops it; interference, you see, or static.

"They can do more than stimulate the division and development of an unfertilized egg. They can impress their own characteristics upon its nucleoproteins, so that the young are born with the little patches of green fur, which serve as the planet's sense organ and means of communication. The young, in other words, are not individuals, but become part of the thing on Saybrook's Planet. The thing on the planet, not at all incidentally, can impregnate any species—plant, animal, or microscopic."

"Potent stuff," muttered Drake.

"Totipotent," Dr. Weiss said sharply. "Universally potent. Any fragment of it is totipotent. Given time, a single bacterium from Saybrook's Planet can convert *all of Earth* into a single organism! We've got the experimental proof of that."

Drake said unexpectedly, "You know, I think I'm a millionaire, Doc. Can you keep a secret?"

Weiss nodded, puzzled.

"I've got a souvenir from Saybrook's Planet," Drake told him, grinning. "It's only a pebble, but after the publicity the planet will get, combined with the fact that it's quarantined from here on in, the pebble will be all any human being will ever see of it. How much do you suppose I could sell the thing for?"

Weiss stared. "A pebble?" He snatched at the object shown him, a hard, gray ovoid. "You shouldn't have done that, Drake. It was strictly against regulations."

"I know. That's why I asked if you could keep a secret. If you could give me a signed note of authentication—— *What's the matter, Doc?*"

Instead of answering, Weiss could only chatter and point. Drake ran over and stared down at the pebble. It was the same as before——

Except that the light was catching it at an angle, and it showed up two little green spots. Look very closely; they were patches of green hairs.

He was disturbed. There was a definite air of danger within the ship. There was the suspicion of his presence aboard. How could that be? He had done nothing yet. Had another fragment of home come aboard and been less cautious? That would be impossible without his knowledge, and though he probed the ship intensely, he found nothing.

And then the suspicion diminished, but it was not quite dead. One of the keen-thinkers still wondered, and was treading close to the truth.

How long before the landing? Would an entire world of life fragments be deprived of completeness? He clung closer to the severed ends of the wire he had been specially bred to imitate, afraid of detection, fearful for his altruistic mission.

Dr. Weiss had locked himself in his own room. They were already within the solar system, and in three hours they would be landing. He had to think. He had three hours in which to decide.

Drake's devilish "pebble" had been part of the organized life on Saybrook's Planet, of course, but it was dead. It was dead when he had first seen it, and if it hadn't been, it was certainly dead after they fed it into the hyperatomic motor and converted it into a blast of pure heat. And the bacterial cultures still showed normal when Weiss anxiously checked.

That was not what bothered Weiss now.

Drake had picked up the "pebble" during the last hours of the stay on Saybrook's Planet—*after* the barrier breakdown. What if the breakdown had been the result of a slow, relentless mental pressure on the part of the thing on the planet? What if parts of its being waited to invade as the barrier dropped? If the "pebble" had not been fast enough and had moved only after the barrier was re-established, it would have been killed. It would have lain there for Drake to see and pick up.

It was a "pebble," not a natural life form. But did that mean it was not *some* kind of life form? It might have been a deliberate production of the planet's single organism—a creature deliberately designed to look like a pebble, harmless-seeming, unsuspicious. Camouflage, in other words—a shrewd and frighteningly successful camouflage.

Had any other camouflaged creature succeeded in crossing the barrier *before* it was re-established—with a suitable shape filched from the minds of the humans aboard ship by the mind-reading organism of the planet? Would it have the casual appearance of a paperweight? Of an ornamental brass-head nail in the captain's old-fashioned chair? And how would they locate it? Could they search every part of the ship for the telltale green patches—even down to individual microbes?

And why camouflage? Did it intend to remain undetected for a time? Why? So that it might wait for the landing on Earth?

An infection *after landing* could not be cured by blowing up a ship. The bacteria of Earth, the molds, yeasts, and protozoa, would go first. Within a year the nonhuman young would begin arriving by the uncountable billions.

Weiss closed his eyes and told himself it might not be such a bad thing. There would be no more disease, since no bacterium would multiply at the expense of its host, but instead would be satisfied with its fair share of what was available. There would be no more overpopulation; the hordes of East Asia would decline to adjust themselves to the food supply. There would be no more wars, no crime, no greed.

But there would be no more individuality, either.

Humanity would find security by becoming a cog in a biological machine. A man would be brother to a germ, or to a liver cell.

He stood up. He would have a talk with Captain Loring. They would send their report and blow up the ship, just as Saybrook had done.

He sat down again. Saybrook had had proof, while he had only the conjectures of a terrorized mind, rattled by the sight of two green spots on a pebble. Could he kill the two hundred men on board ship because of a feeble suspicion?

He had to *think!*

He was straining. Why did he have to wait? If he could only welcome those who were aboard now. *Now!*

Yet a cooler, more reasoning part of himself told him that he could not. The little multipliers in the darkness would betray their new status in fifteen minutes, and the keen-thinkers had them under continual observation. Even one mile from the surface of their planet would be too soon, since they might still destroy themselves and their ship out in space.

Better to wait for the main airlocks to open, for the planetary air to swirl in with millions of the little multipliers. Better to greet each one of them into the brotherhood of unified life and let them swirl out again to spread the message.

Then it would be done! Another world organized, complete!

He waited. There was the dull throbbing of the engines working mightily to control the slow dropping of the ship; the shudder of contact with planetary surface, then——

He let the jubilation of the keen-thinkers sweep into reception, and his own jubilant thoughts answered them. Soon they would be able to receive as well as himself. Perhaps not these particular fragments, but the fragments that would grow out of those which were fitted for the continuation of life.

The main air locks were about to be opened——

And all thought ceased.

Jerry Thorn thought, Damn it, something's wrong *now*.

He said to Captain Loring, "Sorry. There seems to be a power breakdown. The locks won't open."

"Are you sure, Thorn? The lights are on."

"Yes, sir. We're investigating it now."

He tore away and joined Roger Oldenn at the airlock wiring box. "What's wrong?"

"Give me a chance, will you?" Oldenn's hands were busy. Then he said, "For the love of Pete, there's a six-inch break in the twenty-amp lead."

"What? That can't be!"

Oldenn held up the broken wires with their clean, sharp, sawn-through ends.

Dr. Weiss joined them. He looked haggard and there was the smell of brandy on his breath.

He said shakily, "What's the matter?"

They told him. At the bottom of the compartment, in one corner, was the missing section.

Weiss bent over. There was a black fragment on the floor of the compartment. He touched it with his finger and it smeared, leaving a sooty smudge on his finger tip. He rubbed it off absently.

There might have been something taking the place of the missing section of wire. Something that had been alive and only looked like wire, yet something that would heat, die, and carbonize in a tiny fraction of a second once the electrical circuit which controlled the air-lock had been closed.

He said, "How are the bacteria?"

A crew member went to check, returned and said, "All normal, Doc."

The wires had meanwhile been spliced, the locks opened, and Dr. Weiss stepped out into the anarchic world of life that was Earth.

"Anarchy," he said, laughing a little wildly. "And it will stay that way."

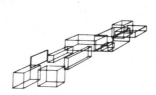

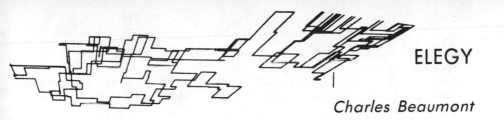

ELEGY

Charles Beaumont

Port: Asteroid K7.

THE FIERY METAL LEG fell into the cool air, heating it; burnt into the green grass and licked a craterous hole. There were fire flags and fire sparks, hisses and explosions and the weary groaning sound of a great beast.

The rocket grumbled and muttered for a while on its finny tripod, then was silent; soon the heat vanished also.

"Are you all right, sir?"

"Yes. The rest?"

"Fine, sir."

Captain Webber swung himself erect and tested his limbs. "Well then, Lieutenant, has the atmosphere been checked?"

"The air is pure and fit to breathe, sir."

"Instruct the others to drop the ladder."

A door in the side of the rocket opened and men began climbing out. "Look!" said crewman Milton, pointing. "Trees and grass and—little wooden bridges going over the water."

Beyond the trees a brick lodge extended over a rivulet which foamed and bubbled. Fishing poles protruded from the lodge windows.

"And there, to the right!"

A steel building thirty stories high with a pink cloud near the top. And, separated by a hedge, a brown tent with a barbecue pit before it, smoke rising in a rigid ribbon from the chimney.

Crewman Chitterwick blinked and squinted his eyes. "Where are we?"

Distant and near, houses of stone and brick and wood, painted all colors, small, large; and further, golden fields of wheat, each blown by a different breeze in a different direction.

"I don't believe it," said Captain Webber. "It's a *park* millions of miles away from where a park could possibly be."

"Very strange," said Lieutenant Peterson, picking up a rock. "We're on an asteroid not shown on *any* chart, in the middle of a place that belongs in history records."

"Elegy" by Charles Beaumont. Copyright 1952 by the Greenleaf Publishing Co., reprinted by permission of Harold Matson Co., Inc.

A little man with thin hair stepped briskly from a tree clump. "Well, well, I hadn't been expecting you gentlemen, to be perfectly honest," the little man clucked, then, "Oh dear, see what you've done to the property of Mr. Bellefont. I do hope you haven't hurt *him*—no, I see that he is all right."

An old man with red hair was seated at the base of a tree, apparently reading a book.

"We are from Earth," said Captain Webber.

"Yes, yes."

"My name is Webber, these are my men."

"Of course," said the little man.

"Who are you?" asked Webber.

"Who—Greypoole, Mr. Greypoole. Didn't *they* tell you?"

"Then you are *also* from Earth?"

"Heavens, yes! But let us go where we can chat more comfortably. Follow me." Mr. Greypoole struck out down a small path past scorched trees and underbrush.

They walked onto a wooden porch and through a door with a wire screen; Lieutenant Peterson first, then Captain Webber, Mr. Friden and the rest of the crew. Greypoole followed.

"You must forgive me—it's been a while. Take chairs, there—there. Please be comfortable."

Captain Webber glanced around the room at the lace curtains, the needlepoint tapestries and the lavender wallpaper.

"Mr. Greypoole, I'd like to ask some questions."

"Certainly, certainly. But first, this being an occasion—" the little man stared at each of them, then shook his head, "ah, do you all like wine? Good wine? I shall be back soon. Forgive me, gentlemen."

He ducked through a small door.

Captain Webber exhaled. "Friden, you stay here; you others see what you can find. Scout around. We'll wait."

The men left the room.

Crewman Chitterwick made his way along a hedgerow, feeling cautiously, maintaining a delicate balance. When he came to a doorway he stopped, looked about, then entered.

The room was dark and quiet and odorous. Mr. Chitterwick groped a few steps, put out his hand and encountered what seemed to be raw flesh; he swiftly withdrew his hand. "Excuse," he said, then "Uh!" as his face came against a slab of moist red meat.

Mr. Chitterwick began to tremble and he blinked furiously, reaching out and finding flesh, cold and hard.

When he stepped upon the toe of a large man with a walrus mustache, he wheeled, located the sunlight, and ran from the butcher shop . . .

The door of the temple opened with difficulty, which caused crewman Milton to breathe unnaturally. Once inside, he gasped.

Row upon row of people, their fingers outstretched, lips open but immobile and silent, their bodies prostrate on the floor. And upon a strange black altar, a tiny woman with silver hair and long thyrsus[1] in her right hand.

Nothing stirred but the mosaic squares in the walls. The colors danced here; otherwise, everything was frozen, everything was solid.

Even the air hung suspended, stationary.

Mr. Milton left the temple . . .

There was a table and a woman on the table and people all around the woman on the table. Crewman Goeblin rubbed his eyes and stared.

It was an operating room. There were masked men and women with shining scissors and glistening saws in their hands. And up above, the students' aperture: filled seats, filled aisles.

A large man stood over the recumbent figure, his lusterless eyes regarding the crimson-puce incision, but he did not move. The nurses did not move, nor the students. No one moved, especially the smiling middle-aged woman on the table.

Mr. Goeblin moved . . .

"Hello!" said Lieutenant Peterson, after he had searched through eight long aisles of books. "Hello!"

He pointed his gun menacingly.

There were many books with many titles and they all had a fine gray dust about them. Lieutenant Peterson paused to examine a bulky volume, when he happened to look upward.

"Who are *you?*" he demanded.

The mottled, angular man perched atop the ladder did not respond. He clutched a book and looked at the book and not at Lieutenant Peterson.

Peterson climbed up the ladder, scowling; he reached the man and drew in a breath. He looked into the eyes of the reading man and descended hastily . . .

Mr. Greypoole re-entered the living room with a tray of glasses. "This is apricot wine," he announced, distributing the glasses. "But— where are the others? Out for a walk? Ah well, they can drink theirs later. Incidentally, Captain, how many Guests did you bring? Last time it was only twelve. Not an extraordinary shipment either; they all preferred ordinary things. All but Mrs. Dominguez— dear me, she was worth the carload herself. Wanted a zoo, can you imagine?—a regular zoo, with her put right in the birdhouse. Oh, they had a time putting that one up!"

Mr. Greypoole chuckled and sipped at his drink. He leaned back in his chair and crossed a leg. "Ah," he continued, "you have no idea how good this is. Once in a while it does get lonely for me here—why, I can remember when Mr. Waldmeyer first told me of this idea. 'A grave

---

1. *thyrsus,* according to Greek mythology, a staff sometimes wrapped around with ivy, that has an ornament on the end.

responsibility,' he said, 'a *grave* responsibility.' Mr. Waldmeyer has a keen sense of humor, needless to say."

Captain Webber put down his glass. Outside, a small child on roller skates stood unmoving on the sidewalk.

"Finished your wine? Good. Perhaps you'd care to join me in a brief turn about the premises?"

Webber sighed, stood up. "Friden, you stay here and wait for the men." He followed Greypoole out onto the porch and down the steps.

Crewman Friden drummed his fingers upon the arm of a chair, surveyed his empty glass and hiccoughed softly.

"I *do* wish you had landed your ship elsewhere, Captain. Mr. Bellefont was quite particular and, as you can see, his park is hopelessly disfigured."

"We were given no choice. Our fuel was running out."

"Indeed? Well then, that explains everything. A beautiful day, don't you find, sir? Fortunately, with the exception of Professor Carling, all the Guests preferred good weather. Plenty of sunshine, they said. It helps."

When they had passed a statue-still woman on a bicycle, Captain Webber stopped walking.

"Mr. Greypoole, we've *got* to have a talk."

The little man shrugged and pointed and they went into an office building which was crowded with motionless men, women and children.

"Since I'm so mixed up myself," Webber said, "maybe I'd better ask—just who do you think *we* are?"

"The men from the Glades, of course."

"I don't know what you're talking about. We're from Earth. They were on the verge of another war—the 'Last War'—and we escaped and started off for Mars. But something went wrong—crewman named Appleton pulled a gun, others just didn't like the Martians—we needn't go into it; Mars didn't work out. We were forced to leave. Then, more trouble. We ended up lost with only a little store of fuel and supplies. Friden noticed this city or whatever it is and we had just enough fuel to land."

Mr. Greypoole nodded his head slowly. "I see. . . . You say there was a war on Earth?"

"They were going to set off the X-Bomb."

"What dreadful news! May I inquire, Captain, as to what you intend to do now?"

"Why, live here, of course!"

"No, no—that's quite impossible."

Captain Webber glanced at the motionless people. "Why not? What *is* this place? Where *are* we?"

Mr. Greypoole smiled.

"Captain, we are in a cemetery."

At that moment, Friden and the other crewmen arrived. Chitterwick blinked.

"I heard what he said, sir. The man's insane."

"What about *this?*" Friden asked. "Take a look, Captain." He handed Webber a pamphlet.

In the center of the first page was a photograph, untinted and solemn; it depicted a white cherub delicately poised on a granite slab. Beneath the photograph were the words: HAPPY GLADES.

"It's one of those old level cemeteries!" said Webber. "I remember seeing pictures of them."

He began to read the pamphlet:

For fifty years, an outstanding cultural and spiritual asset to this community, HAPPY GLADES is proud to announce yet another innovation in its program of postbenefits. Now you can enjoy the afterlife in surroundings which suggest the here-and-now. For those who prefer that their late departed have really permanent eternal happiness, for those who are dismayed by the fragility of all things mortal, we of HAPPY GLADES are proud to offer:
1. The duplication of physical conditions identical to those enjoyed by the departed on Earth. Park, playground, lodge, office building, hotel or house, etc., may be secured at varying prices. All workmanship and materials attuned to conditions on Asteroid K7 and guaranteed for permanence.
2. Permanent conditioning of late beloved so that, in the midst of surroundings he favored, a genuine Eternity may be assured.

Webber swung toward Greypoole. "You mean *all* these people are dead?"

The little fellow proceeded to straighten the coat of a middle-aged man with a cigar.

"No, no," laughed Mr. Greypoole, "only the main Guests. The others are imitations. Mr. Conklin upstairs was head of a large firm; absolutely in love with his work, you know—that kind of thing. So we had to duplicate not only the office, but the building—and even provide replicas of all the people *in* the building. Mr. Conklin himself is in an easy chair on the twentieth story."

"And?"

"Well, gentlemen, what with the constant exploration of planets and moons, our Mr. Waldmeyer hit upon this scheme: Seeking to extend the ideal hereafter to our Guests, he bought this little asteroid. With the vast volume and the tremendous turnover, as it were, HAPPY GLADES offered this plan—to duplicate the exact surroundings which the Guest most enjoyed in Life, assure him privacy, permanence."

"But why here? Why cart bodies off a million miles or more when the same thing could have been done on Earth?"

"My communications system went bad, I fear, so I haven't heard from the offices in some while—but you tell me there *is* a war beginning? That is the idea, Captain; one could never really be sure of one's self down there, what with all the new bombs and things being discovered."

"And where do you fit in, Mr. Greypoole?"

The little man lowered his eyes. "I was head caretaker, you see. But I wasn't well—gastric complaints, liver, heart palpitations, this and that, so I decided to allow them to—change me. By the time I got here, why, I was almost, you might say, a machine. Now, whenever the film is punctured, I wake to do my prescribed duties."

"The film?"

"The asteroid covering that seals in the conditioning. Nothing can get out, nothing get in—except rockets. Then, it's self-sealing. They threw up the film and coated us with their preservative, or Eternifier, and—well, with the exception of my communications system, everything's worked perfectly. Until now . . ."

Captain Webber spoke slowly. "We're tired men, Mr. Greypoole. There are lakes and farms here, all we need to make a new start—more than we'd hoped for. . . . Will you help us?"

Mr. Greypoole clucked his tongue. Then he smiled. "Yes, Captain, I will. But, first, let us go back to your rocket. You'll need supplies."

Captain Webber nodded. They left the building.

They passed a garden with little spotted trees and flowers, a brown desert of shifting sands and a striped tent. They walked by strawberry fields and airplane hangars and coal mines; past tiny yellow cottages, cramped apartments, fluted houses; past rock pools and a great zoo full of animals that stared out of vacant eyes; and everywhere, the seasons changing gently: crisp autumn, cottony summer, windy spring and winters cool and white . . .

The six men in uniform followed the little man with thin hair. They did not speak as they walked, but looked, stared, craned, wondered.

And the old, young, middle-aged, white, brown, yellow people around them did not move.

"You can see, Captain, the success of Mr. Waldmeyer's plan, the perfection here, the quality of Eternal Happiness. Here we have brotherhood; no wars or hatreds or prejudices. And now you who left Earth to escape war and hatred, you want to begin life here?"

Cross breezes ruffled the men's hair.

As they neared the rocket, Greypoole turned to them. "By your own admission, from the moment of your departure, you had personal wars of your own, and killed, and hurled prejudice against a race of people not like you, a race who rejected and cast you out into space again! From your *own* account! Gentlemen, I am truly sorry. You may mean well, after all—I *am* sorry," Mr. Greypoole sighed.

"What do you mean, you're sorry?" demanded Webber.

"Well . . ."

"Captain—" cried Chitterwick, blinking.

"Yes, yes?"

"I feel terrible."

Mr. Goeblin clutched at his stomach.

"So do I!"

"And me!"

Captain Webber looked at Greypoole. His mouth twitched in sudden pain.

"I'm sorry, gentlemen. Into your ship, quickly." Mr. Greypoole motioned them forward.

Crewman Milton staggered, groping for balance. "We—we shouldn't have drunk that wine. It was—poisoned!"

Greypoole produced a weapon. "*Tell* them, Captain, tell them to climb the ladder. Or they'll die here and now."

"Go on. Up!"

The crew climbed into the ship.

Captain Webber ascended jerkily. When he reached the open lock, he coughed and pulled himself into the rocket.

Greypoole followed.

"You don't dislike this ship, do you—that is, the surroundings are not offensive? If only I had been allowed more latitude! But everything functions automatically here; no real choice in the matter, actually. The men mustn't writhe about on the floor like that. Get them to their stations—the stations they would most prefer. And hurry!"

Dully, Captain Webber ordered Mr. Chitterwick to the galley, Mr. Goeblin to the engineering chair, Mr. Friden to the navigator's room . . .

"Sir, what's going to happen?"

Mr. Milton to the Pilot's chair . . .

"The pain will last only another moment or so—it's unfortunately part of the Eternifier," said Mr. Greypoole. "There, all in order? Good, good. Now, Captain, I see understanding in your face; that pleases me more than I can say. My position is so difficult! But a machine *is* geared to its job—which, in this case, is to retain permanence."

Captain Webber leaned on the arm of the little man. He tried to speak, then slumped into his control seat.

"You *do* understand?" asked Mr. Greypoole, putting away the weapon.

Captain Webber's head nodded halfway down, then stopped, and his eyes froze forever.

"Fine. Fine."

The little man with the thin hair walked about the cabins and rooms, straightening, arranging; he climbed down the ladder, and returned to the wooden house, humming to himself.

When he had washed all the empty wineglasses and replaced them, he sat down in the large leather chair and adjusted himself into the most comfortable position.

His eyes stared in waxen contentment at the homely interior, with its lavender wallpaper, needlepoint tapestries . . .

He did not move.

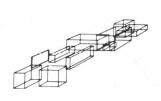

AESTHETICS[1]
OF
THE MOON

Jack Anderson

It is so pure, so complete
-ly nothing
             it is the absolute
           work of art:
5   unparaphraseable and self-contained

it just hangs up there
   more permanent
      than anything on earth
               (where *The Last Supper*
10   has faded already[2])
it stays as it is: perfect, perfectly wrought
   the solid hermetic[3] emptiness
     which is ultimate form

To set foot on it
15   even once
     is to corrupt it utterly:

     a jolly hiker
     with binoculars and cheese sandwiches
     bursting with a yodel
20   through the *Mona Lisa*'s smile[4]
     the canvas ripped
     beyond repair
     Hi there!

"Aesthetics of the Moon" by Jack Anderson from INSIDE OUTER SPACE. Reprinted by permission of the author.

1. *Aesthetics,* the study of beauty in nature and art. **2.** *"The Last Supper" has faded already.* Leonardo da Vinci (1452-1519) experimented with a new method when he did the fresco *The Last Supper.* It began fading almost immediately. **3.** *hermetic.* The word usually means "airtight." Here it refers to the fact that there is no oxygen on the moon. **4.** *the "Mona Lisa's" smile.* The *Mona Lisa,* another painting by Leonardo da Vinci, is famous for the mysterious half-smile worn by the subject.

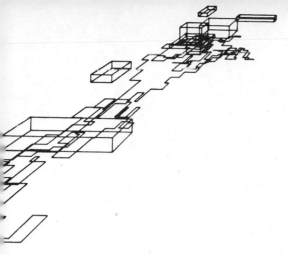

now that I am here
it no longer exists: instead
I exist on it

To know that I am here
on it, destroying it
step by step
is the new kind of art work in your mind

and once I come back to you
that, too,
will no longer be

"But can you not at least record what you saw and felt
the moment you touched that still untarnished place?"

Sure thing:
you know me
how we grew up together
went to the same high school
dated the same girls, monkeyed with cars

you know how I see things
(or maybe you don't
I can't quite recollect)

Anyway, how I see it is:
45 *rocks   lots of rocks*
dust   lots of dust
rocks and dust   lots everywhere
quite a sight   but nothing like home
you can take my word for that

50 "Such persistent blandness of thought!
such unwholesome wholesomeness!
as though engaged in making your life worthy
of a small town on television!"

So who else should be sent   who could do it
55 *some alcoholic dope-freak guitar-picking hustler*
burglar mugger?
oh no   what we do requires
not flights of imagination
but holding on

60 *I've been someplace and seen it*
the only way I know how
it's up to you to do something about it

It's a place now like Siberia or Yellowstone
no longer form it's real estate it's
65 *a site for*
whatever comes next
a raw material

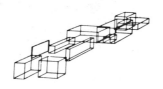

CONSTANT READER

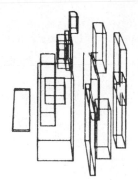

Robert Bloch

ONCE UPON A TIME THEY WERE CALLED straitjackets. When you put one on, you were "in restraint" according to the polite psychiatric jargon of the day. I know, because I've read all about it in books. Yes, real books, the old-fashioned kind that were printed on paper and bound together between leather or board covers. They're still available in some libraries, Earthside, and I've read a lot of them. As a matter of fact, I own quite a collection myself. It's a peculiar hobby, but I enjoy it much more than telelearning or going to the sensorals.

Consequently I admit I'm a little bit maladjusted, according to those same psychiatric texts I mentioned. That's the only possible explanation of why I enjoy reading, and why I pick up so many odd items of useless information.

This business about straitjackets and restraint, for example. All I ever got out of it was a peculiar feeling whenever we hit grav. on a Rec. Flight.

I got it again, now, as Penner yelled, "Act alert, Dale—put down that toy and strap up!"

I dropped my book and went over to the Sighter Post. Already I could feel the preliminary pull despite the neutralizer's efforts. I strapped up and hung there in my cocoon, hung there in my straitjacket.

There I was, nicely in restraint, in our own little private asylum— Scout #3890–R, two months out of Home Port 19/1, and now approaching 68/5 planet for reconnaissance.

Before looking out of the Sighter, I took another glance at my fellow inmates. Penner, Acting Chief, Temp., was strapped in at Mechontrol; all I could see of him was the broad back, the bullet head bent in monomaniac concentration. Swanson, Astrog., 2nd Class, hung at his side, cakeknife nose in profile over the Obsetape. Little Morse, Tech., was stationed at my left and old Levy, Eng., hung to my right. All present and accounted for: Penner, Swanson, Morse, Levy—and myself, George Dale, Constant Reader and erstwhile Service Observer, hanging in his straitjacket after two months in a floating madhouse.

"Constant Reader" by Robert Bloch. Copyright 1953 by Bell Publications, Inc. Reprinted by permission of the Author and his agents, Scott Meredith Literary Agency, Inc., 580 Fifth Avenue, New York, N.Y. 10036.

Two months of anything is a long time. Two months of Rec. Flight is an eternity. Being cooped up with four other men in a single compartment for that length of time is no picnic, and our straitjackets seemed singularly appropriate.

Not that any of us were actually psycho; all of us had a long record of similar missions, and we had managed to survive. But the sheer monotony had worn us down.

I suppose that's why Service gave us the extra seven pounds per man—Lux. Allotment, it was called. But the so-called luxuries turn out to be necessities after all. Swanson usually put his poundage into solid food; candy, and the like. Chocolate capsules kept him sane. Morse and Levy went in for games—cards, dice, superchess and the necessary boards. Penner, amazingly enough, did sketching on pads of old-fashioned paper. And I had this habit of my own—I always managed to bring three or four books within the weight limit.

I still think my choice was the best; candy-munching, freehand sketching and the delights of dicing and superchessmanship palled quickly enough on my four companions. But the books kept me interested. I had a peculiar background—learned to read as a child rather than as an adult—and I guess that's why I derived such queer satisfaction from my hobby.

Naturally, the others laughed at me. Naturally, we got on each other's nerves, quarreled and fretted and flared up. But now, resting quietly in our straitjackets as we entered grav., a measure of sanity returned. With it came anticipation and expectation.

We were approaching 68/5 planet.

New worlds to conquer? Not exactly. It *was* a new world, and therein lay the expectation. But we weren't out to conquer; we on Rec. Flight merely observed and recorded. Or, rather, our instruments recorded.

At that moment we slid in on Mechontrol, about five hundred miles above the surface. 68/5 was small, cloud-wreathed; it had atmosphere apparently, as did its companions. Now we were moving closer and we peered through the Sighters at a dull, flat surface that seemed to be rushing toward us at accelerating speed.

"Pretty old," little Morse grunted. "No mountains, and no water, either—dried up, I guess."

"No life." This from old Levy. "That's a relief." Levy was what the books would have called a misanthrope. Although his *mis* wasn't confined to anthropes.[1] He seemed to have a congenital aversion to everything that wasn't strictly mechanical—why he didn't stick to robotics, I'll never know.

We came down faster. Fifty miles, forty, thirty. I saw Swanson making arrangements to drop the roboship. Penner gave the signal as he righted us above the surface. The roboship glided away, guided by Swanson at the Obsetape. It drifted down, down, down. We followed slowly, dropping below the cloud barrier and following it closely.

---

1. *a misanthrope . . . to anthropes.* A misanthrope is a person who dislikes people, in general. The narrator goes on to observe that Levy doesn't confine his dislike just to people.

"Hit!" snapped Swanson. "Right on the button." We waited while the roboship did its job. It was our star reporter, our roving photographer, our official meteorologist, our staff geologist, our expert in anthropology and mineralogy, our trusted guide and—most important, on many occasions—our stalking-horse.

If there was life present on a planet, the landing of the roboship generally brought it forth. If there was death on a planet, the roboship found it for us. And always, it recorded. It was, in a way, a complete expedition encapsulated, a nonhuman functional without the human capability of error or terror.

Now it went into action, cruising over the surface, directed by Swanson's delicate manipulation of the Obsetape unit controls. We waited patiently, then impatiently. An hour passed, two hours.

"Bring it in!" Penner ordered. Swanson moved his fingers and the roboship returned.

Penner snapped on the Temporary Balance. "Everybody unstrap," he said. "Let's take a look!"

We went down the ramp to the lower deck and Swanson opened the roboship. The photos were ready, the tapes were spooled. We were busy with findings for another hour. At the end of that time we had all the preliminary data necessary on 68/5 planet.

Oxygen content high. Gravity similar to Earthside—as seemed constant in this particular sector and system. No detectable life forms. But life had existed here, once, and life of a high order. The photos proved that. City ruins galore.

And the planet was old. No doubt about that. Morse had been right; mountains were worn away to dust, and the dust did not support vegetable life. Strange that the oxygen content was still so high. I'd have supposed that carbonization——

"Let's snap out," Penner said. "We don't need Temporary Balance or straps according to the gravity reading. Might as well go in for a landing right away. The day-cycle here is 20.1 hours—computer gives us a good 5 hours to go, right now. So we can all take a look around."

We filed back upstairs and Swanson brought us in.

It was only a dead planet, a desert of dust without trees or grass or water; a flat, slate-colored surface where everything was the same, same, same. But it was solid; you could put your feet down on it, you could walk across the sand for miles and feel the air flow against your face.

And there were ruins to explore. That might be interesting. At least, it was a change.

I could feel the tension and excitement mount; it was as palpable as the momentary shock and shudder of landing. We crowded around the lock, struggling out of our suits and putting on the light plastikoids, buckling on the gear and weapons as prescribed by regulation. Morse handed us our equipment and we zipped and strapped and adjusted in a frenzy of impatience. Even Penner was eager, but he remembered to grab his sketch pad before the lock was opened.

Normally, I suppose he would have insisted on maintaining a watch on board, but in the absence of life it didn't really matter. And after two months, everybody wanted out.

The lock opened. The ladder went down. We inhaled, deeply, turned our faces to the warmth of the distant orange sun.

"Single file—keep together!" Penner cautioned.

It's the last day of school, and dismissal is sounded, and the boys rush out onto the playground. So the teacher warns, "Single file—keep together!" and what happens?

Just what happened now. In a moment we were racing across the soft sand, grinning and tossing handfuls of the fine grains high into the clean, dry air. We ran across the brand new world on our brand new legs.

We moved in the direction we couldn't help thinking of as west— because the orange sun hung there and we turned to the sun as naturally as flowers recently transplanted from a hothouse.

We moved buoyantly and joyfully and freely, for this was vacation and picnic and release from the asylum all in one. The smiles on the faces of my companions bespoke euphoria. It was all good: the gritty, sliding sand under our feet, the pumping of legs in long strides, the grinding ball-and-socket action of the hips, the swinging of arms, the rise and fall of the chest, the lungs greedily gasping in and squandering recklessly, the eye seeing far, far away. Yes, it was good to be here, good to be alive, good to be free.

Once again we measured minutes in terms of movements, rather than abstract units of timepassage we must endure. Once again we consciously heightened our awareness of existence, rather than dulled it to make life bearable.

It seemed to me that I'd never felt so completely alive, but I was wrong. I was wrong, because I didn't notice the blackout.

None of us were aware of it; even now, I can't begin to comprehend it. I don't know what happened. It was just that—blackout.

Before it happened, we marched toward the sun—Penner, Swanson and Morse a little in the lead, Levy and I a pace or two behind, all of us trudging up a slight incline in the sand.

And then, without any seeming transition at all, we were marching in darkness—Penner, Swanson, Morse, Levy and I in a solid group, trudging down into a valley.

"What happened?"

"Eclipse?"

"Where's the sun?"

"Where are we?"

"How long we been walking? I feel like I passed out!"

We halted and exchanged comments.

"Something wrong here. We're going back. Get out the beamers." Penner issued orders swiftly.

We broke out the beamers, adjusted the slow-strobes, put pathways of light before us. There was nothing to see but slaty sand. Only Swanson's bearings with the scope guided us in retracing our steps. We moved swiftly through the pall of a purple night. A mist shrouded the stars; a mist mantled our memories.

That's when we compared notes, realized for the first time that the phenomenon had occurred to all of us simultaneously. Gas, shock, temporary dislocation—we argued about the cause for hours, and all the while we marched on the alert, up hummocks and down into little valleys between the dunes.

And we were tired. Unused muscles strained, hearts pumped, feet blistered. And still we marched. I was hungry and thirsty; more than that, I was puzzled and a little bit afraid. I didn't understand just what had happened—how could we, all of us, go on walking that way while we were out on our feet? How could we lose almost four hours? And what did it mean?

At the moment we were in no danger of being lost, and it was more and more obvious that this planet contained no life, hostile or otherwise. But why the blackout? It puzzled me, puzzled all of us.

Swanson took the lead. His beaklike profile loomed on a rise in my beamer's path. He turned and yelled, "I can see the ship now!"

We toiled up the slope and joined him. Yes, the ship was there, snug and safe and secure, and the adventure was over.

Or—was it?

"Look down there!" Levy swivelled his beamer to the left. "We must have missed it on the way out."

Five rays played, pooled, pointed in a single beam. Five rays found, focused and flooded upon the objects rising from the sand. And then we were all running together toward the ruins.

Just before we reached them, Penner yelled, "Stop!"

"What's wrong?" I said.

"Nothing—maybe. Then again, you never know. That blackout bothers me." Penner put his hand on my shoulder. "Look, Dale, I want you and Morse to go back to the ship and wait. The three of us will take a trip through the ruins. But I want at least two men on ship at all times, in case there's any trouble. Go ahead, now—we won't move until we see you're on board. Flash us a signal to let us know everything's all right when you get there."

Morse and I trudged off.

"Just my luck." Little Morse grumbled under his breath and waved his beamer in disgust. "Run around for hours in the sand and then when we finally hit something it's back to the ship. Huh!"

"He's right, though," I answered. "Got to be careful. And besides, we can eat and take our shoes off."

"But I want to see those ruins. I promised my girl some souvenirs—"

"Tomorrow we'll probably get our turn," I reminded him. He shrugged and plodded on. We reached the ship, boarded, and took a quick look around. All clear.

Morse went over to the panel and pushed the blinker. Then we sat down next to the Sighter and stared out. All we could see at this distance was a purple blur, through which three beams moved and wavered.

I opened foodcaps and we swallowed, still straining to see. The lights moved separately at first, then coalesced into a single unit.

"Must have found something," Morse speculated. "Wonder what?"

"We'll find out soon enough," I predicted.

But they didn't come back, and they didn't come back—we sat for hours, waiting.

Finally the beams moved our way. We were waiting as Penner, Swanson and Levy boarded. An excited babble wavered into words and the words became sentences.

"Never saw anything like them——"

"Smaller than dwarfs; couldn't be, but I'd swear they were human."

"Gets me is the way they disappeared, just like somebody had scooped them all up at once."

"Wasn't their city, I'm sure of that. First of all, it was ages old, and secondly it wasn't built to their size-scale at all——"

"Think we just imagined the whole thing? That blackout was peculiar enough, and then, seeing them this way——"

I raised my voice. "What's all this about? What did you find?"

The answer was more babbling in unison, until Penner signalled for silence.

"See what you make of this, Dale," he said. He pulled out his sketch pad and went to work, swiftly. As he worked, he talked. Story and sketches emerged almost simultaneously.

He passed the first drawing to me.

"Ruins," he said. "Ruins of a city. All we really saw were the rooftops, but they're enough to give you some idea of the probable size of the place. You'll note everything was solid stone. Plenty of broad, flat surfaces. Here's a sketch of me standing between two rooftops. Probably a street in between, at one time. What do you make of it?"

I studied his sketch; it was crude, but graphically explicit. "They must have been humanoid," I said. "If we accept functionality in architectural representation——"

"Never mind the book words," Penner interrupted. "Look at the width of that street. Would you say that the inhabitants were large or small?"

"Large, of course." I looked at the sketch again. "Must have been much taller than we are, perhaps seven or eight feet if they worked according to our proportions. Of course, that's just a rough guess."

"Good enough. And we geigered the stones a bit. Levy, here, places them at fourteen thousand years."

"The very least," Levy broke in. "Possibly older than that."

Penner was sketching again. He passed the second drawing over to me. "Here's what we found wandering around in the ruins," he told me. "I've shown two of them standing next to me, but there must have been hundreds."

I looked. There stood Penner, and—at his feet—two tiny manlike beings.

"You actually saw these things?"

"Of course. We all did, there's no doubt about it. One minute we were climbing around among the stones, and then they appeared. Just like that, out of nowhere, you might say. And not one or two, but hundreds of them." He turned. "Isn't that right, Swanson?"

"Correct."

I gazed at the sketch again. Penner had an eye for detail. I was particularly impressed with the way the creatures were dressed.

"These look like ancient Earth-garments," I said. "They're wearing little armored breastplates, and helmets. And they carry spears."

"That's exactly how they looked," Levy corroborated. "Some of them had those—what were they called?—bows and arrows."

Penner eyed me. "You've got a theory, Dale?"

"No, but I'm getting one. These little things never built the city. They don't live in the ruins, now. They couldn't possibly wear Earth-garments like these. They appeared suddenly, you say, and disappeared just as suddenly."

"Sounds silly, the way you sum it up," Penner admitted.

"Yes. Unless you accept one overall theory."

"And that is——?"

"That they don't exist! They never existed at all, except in your imagination."

"But we all saw them—saw them, and heard them!"

"We all went through a blackout together, a few hours ago," I reminded him. "And I'm beginning to think that ties in, somehow. Suppose 68/5 isn't uninhabited. Suppose it does contain life."

"That's out of the question!" Swanson interrupted. "The roboship tapes are infallible. Any sign of existence would have been detected and recorded. You know that."

"Yet suppose there were no signs," I answered. "Suppose we're dealing with an intangible intelligence——"

"Absurd!" This from Penner.

"No more absurd than the story you've told me. Suppose the intelligence can control our minds. It blacked us out and planted hypnotic suggestion. A little while later you saw little men——"

"No. It doesn't add up," Levy insisted. "There's a flaw." He pointed at the second sketch. "How would your intelligence know about Earth-garments such as these? I'm sure none of us were aware of such things. You're the bookworm around here——"

"Bookworm!" I paused. "Wait a minute. You say these creatures talked to you?"

"That's right," Penner answered.

"Do you remember any of the words?"

"I think so. They had little shrill voices and they were shouting to each other. Sounded something like *Hekinah degul* and *Langro dehul san.*"

"One of them pointed at you and said *Hurgo* over and over," Swanson reminded him.

"Hurgo," I repeated. "Wait a minute." I walked over to my shelf and pulled down one of my books. "Look at this," I said. "No pictures in this edition, of course, but read this page."

Penner read slowly as the others crowded around. He raised his head, scowled. "Sounds like our creatures," he said. "What is this?"

I turned to the frontispiece and read *"Gulliver's Travels,* by Jonathan Swift. Published, 1727."²

"No!" said Penner.

I shrugged. "It's all in the book," I told him. "Descriptions, words, phrases. Some intelligent force out there tried to read our minds and—I think—failed. So it read the book, instead, and reproduced a part of it."

"But what possible force could exist? And how could it read the book? And why did it reproduce the——" Penner halted, groping for the word which I supplied.

"Lilliputians."

I didn't know the answers. I couldn't even guess. All I had was a feeling, which I expressed in one short sentence. "Let's get out of here."

Penner shook his head. "We can't. You know that. We've stumbled across something without precedent, and it's our job to investigate it fully. Who knows what we might learn? I say we get some rest and go back tomorrow."

There was a mumble of agreement. I had nothing more to say, so I kept quiet. Swanson and Morse and Levy sought their bunks. I started across to mine, when Penner tapped me on the shoulder.

"By the way, Dale, would you mind letting me have that book of yours? I want to read up on those creatures—might come in handy tomorrow."

I gave him the book and he went forward. Then I lay down and prepared to sleep. Before closing my eyes I took a last look out of the nearest Sighter. The planet was dark and dead. There was nothing out there—nothing but sand and ruins and loneliness. And something that made up Lilliputians, something that read in order to learn, and learned in order to plan, and planned in order to act——

I didn't get much sleep that night.

The sun was lemon-colored the next morning when Swanson roused us.

"Come on," he said. "Penner says we're going out again. Two of us will stay on ship, but we'll take turns. Morse, you and Dale can get ready."

"Orders?" I asked.

"No. I don't think so. It's just that it's really your turn to see the ruins."

---

2. *"Gulliver's Travels"* . . . *1727. Gulliver's Travels* relates the adventures of Lemuel Gulliver, who sails to various imaginary lands. One of the lands he journeys to is the country of Lilliput, where the inhabitants are only six inches high. The strange words Penner heard were part of the language that Swift invented for the Lilliputians.

I faced him. "I don't want to see the ruins. And my advice is that we all stay on ship and blast off, right now."

"What's the trouble?" Penner loomed up behind Swanson.

"He doesn't want to go out," Swanson said. "Thinks we ought to leave." He smiled at Penner, and his smile said, "Coward."

Penner grinned at me and his grin said, "Psycho."

I didn't let my face talk for me. This was serious. "Look, now," I began. "I've been awake most of the night, thinking. And I've got a hunch."

"Let's hear it." Penner was courteous enough, but over his shoulder he said, "Meanwhile, you men get into your suits."

"This intelligence we talked about last night—we all agreed it must exist. But it can't be measured or located."

"That's what we're going to try to do this morning," Penner said.

"I advise against it."

"Go on."

"Let's think about intelligence for a moment. Ever try to define it? Pretty difficult thing to do. We all know there are hundreds of worlds that don't contain intelligence but do contain life. New worlds and old worlds alike have a complete existence and cycle independent of conscious intelligence."

"What's this, a book-lecture?" asked Morse.

"No, just my own ideas. And one of my ideas is that what we call intelligence is a random element, arising spontaneously under certain conditions just as life itself does. It isn't necessary for the existence of a world—it's extraneous, it's a parasite, an alien growth. Usually it uses brain cells as a host. But suppose it could evolve to the point where it isn't limited to brain cells?"

"All right, then what?" Penner snapped.

"Suppose, when life dies on a planet, intelligence finds a means of survival? Suppose it adapts itself to something other than the tissue of the cortex? Suppose the highest point of evolution is reached—in which the planet itself, as host, becomes the seat of intelligence?"

"Mean to say that 68/5 can think?"

"It's worth considering. Remember, when intelligence enters brain cells it identifies itself with its host, and tries in every way to help its host survive. Suppose it enters, finally, into the planet—when life dies out—and tries to help the planet survive?"

"Thinking planets! Now I've heard everything!" This from Swanson. "Dale, you read too many books."

"Perhaps. But consider what's happened. We can't locate any life-form here. Nevertheless, we black out. And something creates, out of reading and imagination, a duplicate of *Gulliver's Travels*. Think in terms of a combined number of intelligences, fused into a single unit housed in the body of this world itself. Think of its potential power, and then think of its motives. We're outsiders, we may be hostile, we must be controlled or destroyed. And that's what the planet is trying to do. It can't read our minds, but it can read my books. And its combined force is enough to materialize imaginative concepts in an effort to destroy us. First came Lilliputians with bows and arrows and tiny spears. The intelligence realized these would not be effective, so it may try something else. Something like——"

Penner cut me off with a gesture. "All right, Dale. You don't have to come with us if you don't want to." It was like a slap in the face. I stared around the circle. The men had their suits on. Nobody looked at me.

Then, surprisingly enough, Levy spoke up. "Maybe he's right," he said. "Somebody else has to stay behind, too. Think I'll keep Dale company here."

I smiled at him. He came over, unfastening his suit. The others didn't say anything. They filed over to the stairs.

"We'll watch you through the Sighters," Levy said. Penner nodded, disappeared with the others.

Minutes later we caught sight of them toiling up the sun-baked slope of the ridge leading toward the ruins. In the clear light now the ruins were partially visible. Even though only rooftops were clear of sand, they looked gigantic and imposing. An ancient race had dwelt here. And now a new race had come. That was the way life went. Or death——

"What are you worrying about?" Levy asked. "Stop squirming."

"I don't like it," I said. "Something's going to happen. You believed me too or you wouldn't have stayed."

"Penner's a fool," Levy said. "You know, I used to read a few books myself, once upon a time."

"Once upon a time!" I stood up. "I forgot!"

"Where are you going?"

"I'm looking for my other two books," I said. "I should have thought of *that.*"

"Thought of what?" Levy talked to me, but he was watching the others, outside, through the Sighter.

"If it read one book, it can read the others," I told him. "Better get rid of them right away, play it safe."

"What are the other two books?" Levy asked the question, but I never answered him. Because his voice changed, cracked, and he said, *"Dale, come here, hurry!"*

I stared through the Sighter. I adjusted the control and it was like a close up; I could see Penner and Swanson and Morse as if they were standing beside me. They had just reached the top of the ridge, and the ruined stones of the cyclopean city rose before them. *Cyclopean.*[3]

The word came, the concept came, and then the reality. The first giant towered up from behind the rocks. He was thirty feet tall and his single eye was a burning beacon.

They saw him and turned to flee. Penner tugged at his waist, trying to draw his tube and fire. But there wasn't time now, for the giants were all around them—the one-eyed monsters out of myth.

---

3. *Cyclopean,* gigantic. The *Odyssey,* a Greek epic believed to be written by Homer (fl. 9th cent. B.C.) describes the ten-year wandering of Ulysses after the Trojan War. During one adventure, he and his men were threatened by Cyclopes, giants with a single eye in the middle of their foreheads.

The giants laughed, and their laughter shook the Earth, and they scooped great rocks up from the ruins and hurled them at the men, crushing them. And then they lumbered over to the crushed forms and began to feast, their talons rending and tearing the bodies as I now tore the pages from the book I was holding.

"Cyclopes," Levy whispered. "The *Odyssey,* isn't it?" The torn fragments of the second book fell from my fingers as I turned away.

Levy was already working at the panels. "Only two of us," he said. "But we can make it. Takeoff's automatic once we blast. I'm pretty sure we can make it, aren't you, Dale?"

"Yes," I said, but I didn't really care.

The floor was beginning to vibrate. In just a minute, now, we'd blast.

"Come on, Dale, strap up! I'll handle the board. You know what to do."

I knew what to do.

Levy's face twitched. "What's the matter now? Is it the third book? Are you going to get rid of the third book?"

"No need to. The third one's harmless," I said. "Here, I'll show you."

"What is it?" he asked.

I stepped over to the Sighter for the last time and he followed me. I adjusted for close-up very carefully.

"Look," I said.

We stared out across the barren plain, the plain which no longer held life because it had *become* life for this planet.

The Cyclopes had disappeared, and what was left of Penner and Swanson and Morse lay undisturbed in the dreaming ruins under an orange sun.

Somewhere, somehow, the reader turned a page——

"The third book," I whispered. "Watch."

It scampered out from behind one of the stones, moving swiftly on tiny legs. The Sighter brought it so close that I could see the very hairs of its whiskers, note the design of its checkered waistcoat, read the numerals on the watch it took out of the waistcoat pocket. Before I turned away, I almost fancied I could read its lips.

That wasn't necessary, of course, because I knew what it was saying.

"Oh dear! Oh dear! I shall be too late!" it murmured.

Mincing daintily on thin legs, the White Rabbit[4] scampered among the bodies as we blasted off.

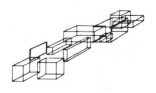

---

4. *the White Rabbit,* in Lewis Carroll's *Alice in Wonderland,* a character who is always looking at his watch and exclaiming about how late he is.

WHO'S THERE?

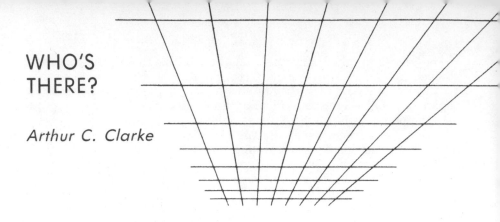

Arthur C. Clarke

WHEN SATELLITE CONTROL CALLED ME, I was writing up the day's progress report in the Observation Bubble—the glass-domed office that juts out from the axis of the space station like the hubcap of a wheel. It was not really a good place to work, for the view was too overwhelming. Only a few yards away I could see the construction teams performing their slow-motion ballet as they put the station together like a giant jigsaw puzzle. And beyond them, twenty thousand miles below, was the blue green glory of the full Earth, floating against the raveled star clouds of the Milky Way.

"Station Supervisor here," I answered. "What's the trouble?"

"Our radar's showing a small echo two miles away, almost stationary, about five degrees west of Sirius.[1] Can you give us a visual report on it?"

Anything matching our orbit so precisely could hardly be a meteor; it would have to be something we'd dropped—perhaps an inadequately secured piece of equipment that had drifted away from the station. So I assumed; but when I pulled out my binoculars and searched the sky around Orion,[2] I soon found my mistake. Though this space traveler was man-made, it had nothing to do with us.

"I've found it," I told Control. "It's someone's test satellite—cone-shaped, four antennas, and what looks like a lens system in its base. Probably U.S. Air Force, early 1960's, judging by the design. I know they lost track of several when their transmitters failed. There were quite a few attempts to hit this orbit before they finally made it."

After a brief search through the files, Control was able to confirm my guess. It took a little longer to find out that Washington wasn't in the least bit interested in our discovery of a twenty-year-old stray satellite, and would be just as happy if we lost it again.

"Well, we can't do *that*," said Control. "Even if nobody wants it, the thing's a menace to navigation. Someone had better go out and haul it aboard."

"Who's There?" by Arthur C. Clarke. Copyright © 1958 by United Newspapers Magazine Corporation. Reprinted by permission of the Author and his agents, Scott Meredith Literary Agency, Inc., 580 Fifth Avenue, New York, N.Y. 10036.

1. *Sirius,* the brightest star in the sky, called the Dog Star. 2. *Orion,* the most conspicuous constellation in the sky. Ancient astronomers thought it looked like the rough outline of a man wearing a belt and sword and holding a club and shield.

That someone, I realized, would have to be me. I dared not detach a man from the closely knit construction teams, for we were already behind schedule—and a single day's delay on this job cost a million dollars. All the radio and TV networks on Earth were waiting impatiently for the moment when they could route their programs through us, and thus provide the first truly global service, spanning the world from Pole to Pole.

"I'll go out and get it," I answered, snapping an elastic band over my papers so that the air currents from the ventilators wouldn't set them wandering around the room. Though I tried to sound as if I was doing everyone a great favor, I was secretly not at all displeased. It had been at least two weeks since I'd been outside; I was getting a little tired of stores schedules, maintenance reports, and all the glamorous ingredients of a space-station supervisor's life.

The only member of the staff I passed on my way to the airlock was Tommy, our recently acquired cat. Pets mean a great deal to men thousands of miles from Earth, but there are not many animals that can adapt themselves to a weightless environment. Tommy mewed plaintively at me as I clambered into my spacesuit, but I was in too much of a hurry to play with him.

At this point, perhaps I should remind you that the suits we use on the station are completely different from the flexible affairs men wear when they want to walk around on the Moon. Ours are really baby spaceships, just big enough to hold one man. They are stubby cylinders, about seven feet long, fitted with low-powered propulsion jets, and have a pair of accordionlike sleeves at the upper end for the operator's arms. Normally, however, you keep your hands drawn inside the suit, working the manual controls in front of your chest.

As soon as I'd settled down inside my very exclusive spacecraft, I switched on power and checked the gauges on the tiny instrument panel. There's a magic word, *forb,* that you'll often hear spacemen mutter as they climb into their suits; it reminds them to test fuel, oxygen, radio, batteries. All my needles were well in the safety zone, so I lowered the transparent hemisphere over my head and sealed myself in. For a short trip like this, I did not bother to check the suit's internal lockers, which were used to carry food and special equipment for extended missions.

As the conveyor belt decanted me into the airlock, I felt like an Indian papoose being carried along on its mother's back. Then the pumps brought the pressure down to zero, the outer door opened, and the last traces of air swept me out into the stars, turning very slowly head over heels.

The station was only a dozen feet away, yet I was now an independent planet—a little world of my own. I was sealed up in a tiny, mobile cylinder, with a superb view of the entire universe, but I had practically no freedom of movement inside the suit. The padded seat and safety belts prevented me from turning around, though I could reach all the controls and lockers with my hands or feet.

In space, the great enemy is the sun, which can blast you to blindness in seconds. Very cautiously, I opened up the dark filters on the "night" side of my suit, and turned my head to look out at the stars. At the same time I switched the helmet's external sunshade to automatic, so that whichever way the suit gyrated my eyes would be shielded from that intolerable glare.

Presently, I found my target—a bright fleck of silver whose metallic glint distinguished it clearly from the surrounding stars. I stamped on the jet control pedal, and felt the mild surge of acceleration as the low-powered rockets set me moving away from the station. After ten seconds of steady thrust, I estimated that my speed was great enough, and cut off the drive. It would take me five minutes to coast the rest of the way, and not much longer to return with my salvage.

And it was at that moment, as I launched myself out into the abyss, that I knew that something was horribly wrong.

It is never completely silent inside a spacesuit; you can always hear the gentle hiss of oxygen, the faint whirr of fans and motors, the susurration of your own breathing—even, if you listen carefully enough, the rhythmic thump that is the pounding of your heart. These sounds reverberate through the suit, unable to escape into the surrounding void; they are the unnoticed background of life in space, for you are aware of them only when they change.

They had changed now; to them had been added a sound which I could not identify. It was an intermittent, muffled thudding, sometimes accompanied by a scraping noise, as of metal upon metal.

I froze instantly, holding my breath and trying to locate the alien sound with my ears. The meters on the control board gave no clues; all the needles were rock steady on their scales, and there were none of the flickering red lights that would warn of impending disaster. That was some comfort, but not much. I had long ago learned to trust my instincts in such matters; their alarm signals were flashing now, telling me to return to the station before it was too late. . . .

Even now, I do not like to recall those next few minutes, as panic slowly flooded into my mind like a rising tide, overwhelming the dams of reason and logic which every man must erect against the mystery of the universe. I knew then what it was like to face insanity; no other explanation fitted the facts.

For it was no longer possible to pretend that the noise disturbing me was that of some faulty mechanism. Though I was in utter isolation, far from any other human being or indeed any material object, I was not alone. The soundless void was bringing to my ears the faint but unmistakable stirrings of life.

In that first, heart-freezing moment it seemed that something was trying to get into my suit—something invisible, seeking shelter from the cruel and pitiless vacuum of space. I whirled madly in my harness, scanning the entire sphere of vision around me except for the blazing, forbidden cone toward the sun. There was nothing there, of course. There could not be—yet that purposeful scrabbling was clearer than ever.

Despite the nonsense that has been written about us, it is not true that spacemen are superstitious. But can you blame me if, as I came to the end of logic's resources, I suddenly remembered how Bernie Summers had died, no farther from the station than I was at this very moment?

It was one of those "impossible" accidents; it always is. Three things had gone wrong at once. Bernie's oxygen regulator had run wild and sent the pressure soaring, the safety valve had failed to blow—and a faulty joint had given way instead. In a fraction of a second, his suit was open to space.

I had never known Bernie, but suddenly his fate became of overwhelming importance to me—for a horrible idea had come into my mind. One does not talk about these things, but a damaged spacesuit is too valuable to be thrown away, even if it has killed its wearer. It is repaired, renumbered—and issued to someone else. . . .

What happens to the soul of a man who dies between the stars, far from his native world? Are you still here, Bernie, clinging to the last object that linked you to your lost and distant home?

As I fought the nightmares that were swirling around me—for now it seemed that the scratchings and soft fumblings were coming from all directions—there was one last hope to which I clung. For the sake of my sanity, I had to prove that this wasn't Bernie's suit—that the metal walls so closely wrapped around me had never been another man's coffin.

It took me several tries before I could press the right button and switch my transmitter to the emergency wavelength. "Station!" I gasped. "I'm in trouble! Get records to check my suit history and——"

I never finished; they say my yell wrecked the microphone. But what man alone in the absolute isolation of a spacesuit would *not* have yelled when something patted him softly on the back of the neck!

I must have lunged forward, despite the safety harness, and smashed against the upper edge of the control panel. When the rescue squad reached me a few minutes later, I was still unconscious, with an angry bruise across my forehead.

And so I was the last person in the whole satellite relay system to know what had happened. When I came to my senses an hour later, all our medical staff was gathered around my bed, but it was quite a while before the doctors bothered to look at me. They were much too busy playing with the three cute little kittens our badly misnamed Tommy had been rearing in the seclusion of my spacesuit's number five storage locker.

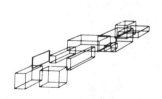

WE'LL NEVER CONQUER SPACE

Arthur C. Clarke

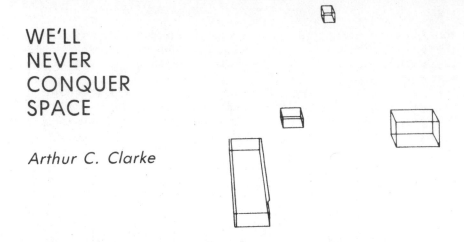

MAN WILL NEVER CONQUER SPACE. Such a statement may sound ludicrous, now that our rockets are already one hundred million miles beyond the Moon and the first human travelers are preparing to leave the atmosphere. Yet it expresses a truth which our forefathers knew, one we have forgotten—and our descendants must learn again, in heartbreak and loneliness.

Our age is in many ways unique, full of events and phenomena which never occurred before and can never happen again. They distort our thinking, making us believe that what is true now will be true forever, though perhaps on a larger scale. Because we have annihilated distance on this planet, we imagine that we can do it once again. The facts are far otherwise, and we will see them more clearly if we forget the present and turn our minds toward the past.

To our ancestors, the vastness of the Earth was a dominant fact controlling their thoughts and lives. In all earlier ages than ours, the world was wide indeed, and no man could ever see more than a tiny fraction of its immensity. A few hundred miles—a thousand, at the most—was infinity. Only a lifetime ago, parents waved farewell to their emigrating children in the virtual certainty that they would never meet again.

And now, within one incredible generation, all this has changed. Over the seas where Odysseus[1] wandered for a decade, the Rome-Beirut Comet[2] whispers its way within the hour. And above that, the closer satellites span the distance between Troy and Ithaca in less than a minute.

"We'll Never Conquer Space" by Arthur C. Clarke from SCIENCE DIGEST, (June 1960). Reprinted by permission of the Author and his agents, Scott Meredith Literary Agency, Inc., 580 Fifth Avenue, New York, N. Y. 10036.

1. *Odysseus* (ō dis'ē əs). After the Trojan War, Odysseus (Ulysses) wandered for ten years attempting to return from Troy to his home in Ithaca. 2. *the Rome-Beirut Comet.* Some of the early passenger jet planes were called *Comets.* The distance between Rome, Italy and Beirut, Lebanon is approximately 1,750 miles.

Psychologically as well as physically, there are no longer any remote places on Earth. When a friend leaves for what was once a far country, even if he has no intention of returning, we cannot feel that same sense of irrevocable separation that saddened our forefathers. We know that he is only hours away by jetliner, and that we have merely to reach for the telephone to hear his voice.

In a very few years, when the satellite communication network is established, we will be able to see friends on the far side of the Earth as easily as we talk to them on the other side of the town. Then the world will shrink no more, for it will have become a dimensionless point.

But the new stage that is opening up for the human drama will never shrink as the old one has done. We have abolished space here on the little Earth; we can never abolish the space that yawns between the stars. Once again we are face to face with immensity and must accept its grandeur and terror, its inspiring possibilities and its dreadful restraints. From a world that has become too small, we are moving out into one that will forever be too large, whose frontiers will recede from us always more swiftly than we can reach out towards them.

Consider first the fairly modest solar, or planetary, distances which we are now preparing to assault. The very first Lunik[3] made a substantial impression upon them, traveling more than two hundred million miles from the Earth—six times the distance to Mars. When we have harnessed nuclear energy for space flight, the solar system will contract until it is little larger than the Earth today. The remotest of the planets will be perhaps no more than a week's travel from the Earth, while Mars and Venus will be only a few hours away.

This achievement, which will be witnessed within a century, might appear to make even the solar system a comfortable, homely place, with such giant planets as Saturn and Jupiter playing much the same role in our thoughts as do Africa or Asia today. (Their qualitative differences of climate, atmosphere and gravity, fundamental though they are, do not concern us at the moment.) To some extent this may be true, yet as soon as we pass beyond the orbit of the Moon, a mere quarter-million miles away, we will meet the first of the barriers that will separate the Earth from her scattered children.

The marvelous telephone and television network that will soon enmesh the whole world, making all men neighbors, cannot be extended into space. It will never be possible to converse with anyone on another planet.

Do not misunderstand this statement. Even with today's radio equipment, the problem of sending speech to the other planets is almost trivial. But the messages will take minutes—sometimes hours —on their journey, because radio and light waves travel at the same limited speed of 186,000 miles a second.

Twenty years from now you will be able to listen to a friend on Mars, but the words you hear will have left his mouth at least three minutes

3. *Lunik.* Russia launched Luna I in January 1959. This was the first space probe to become an artificial planet.

earlier, and your reply will take a corresponding time to reach him. In such circumstances, an exchange of verbal messages is possible—but not a conversation.

Even in the case of the nearby moon, the two-and-a-half-second time lag will be annoying. At distances of more than a million miles, it will be intolerable.

To a culture which has come to take instantaneous communication for granted, as part of the very structure of civilized life, this "time barrier" may have a profound psychological impact. It will be a perpetual reminder of universal laws and limitations against which not all our technology can ever prevail. For it seems as certain as anything can be that no signal—still less any material object—can ever travel faster than light.

The velocity of light is the ultimate speed limit, being part of the very structure of space and time. Within the narrow confines of the solar system, it will not handicap us too severely, once we have accepted the delays in communication which it involves. At the worst, these will amount to twenty hours—the time it takes a radio signal to span the orbit of Pluto, the outermost planet.

Between the three inner worlds, the Earth, Mars, and Venus, it will never be more than twenty minutes—not enough to interfere seriously with commerce or administration, but more than sufficient to shatter those personal links of sound or vision that can give us a sense of direct contact with friends on Earth, wherever they may be.

It is when we move out beyond the confines of the solar system that we come face-to-face with an altogether new order of cosmic reality. Even today, many otherwise educated men—like those savages who can count to three but lump together all numbers beyond four—cannot grasp the profound distinction between solar and stellar space. The first is the space enclosing our neighboring worlds, the planets; the second is that which embraces those distant suns, the stars, and it is literally millions of times greater.

There is no such abrupt change of scale in terrestrial affairs. To obtain a mental picture of the distance to the nearest star, as compared with the distance to the nearest planet, you must imagine a world in which the closest object to you is only five feet away—and then there is nothing else to see until you have traveled a thousand miles.

Many conservative scientists, appalled by these cosmic gulfs, have denied that they can ever be crossed. Some people never learn; those who sixty years ago scoffed at the possibility of flight, and ten (even five!) years ago laughed at the idea of travel to the planets, are now quite sure that the stars will always be beyond our reach. And again they are wrong, for they have failed to grasp the great lesson of our age—that if something is possible in theory, and no fundamental scientific laws oppose its realization, then sooner or later it will be achieved.

One day, it may be in this century, or it may be a thousand years from now, we shall discover a really efficient means of propelling our space vehicles. Every technical device is always developed to its limit (unless it is superseded by something better) and the ultimate speed for spaceships is the velocity of light. They will never reach that goal, but they will get very close to it. And then the nearest star will be less than five years' voyaging from the Earth.

Our exploring ships will spread outwards from their home over an ever-expanding sphere of space. It is a sphere which will grow at almost—but never quite—the speed of light. Five years to the triple system of Alpha Centauri, ten to the strangely matched doublet Sirius A and B, eleven to the tantalizing enigma of 61 Cygni, the first star suspected to possess a planet. These journeys are long, but they are not impossible. Man has always accepted whatever price was necessary for his explorations and discoveries, *and the price of Space is Time.*

Even voyages which may last for centuries or millennia will one day be attempted. Suspended animation[4] has already been achieved in the laboratory, and may be the key to interstellar travel. Self-contained cosmic arks which will be tiny traveling worlds in their own right may be another solution, for they would make possible journeys of unlimited extent, lasting generation after generation.

The famous Time Dilation effect predicted by the Theory of Relativity, whereby time appears to pass more slowly for a traveler moving at almost the speed of light, may be yet a third. And there are others.

Looking far into the future, therefore, we must picture a slow (little more than half a billion miles an hour!) expansion of human activities outwards from the solar system, among the suns scattered across the region of the galaxy in which we now find ourselves. These suns are on the average five light-years apart; in other words, we can never get from one to the next in less than five years.

To bring home what this means, let us use a down-to-earth analogy. Imagine a vast ocean, sprinkled with islands—some desert, others perhaps inhabited. On one of these islands an energetic race has just discovered the art of building ships. It is preparing to explore the ocean, but must face the fact that the very nearest island is five years' voyaging away, and that no possible improvement in the technique of shipbuilding will ever reduce this time.

In these circumstances (which are those in which we will soon find ourselves) what could the islanders achieve? After a few centuries, they might have established colonies on many of the nearby islands and have briefly explored many others. The daughter colonies might themselves have sent out further pioneers, and so a kind of chain reaction would spread the original culture over a steadily expanding area of the ocean.

But now consider the effects of the inevitable, unavoidable time lag. There could be only the most tenuous contact between the home island and its offspring. Returning messengers could report what had happened on the nearest colony—five years ago. They could never bring information more up to date than that, and dispatches from the more distant parts of the ocean would be from still further in the past—

---

4. *suspended animation,* a condition in which all vital bodily functions are temporarily inactive.

perhaps centuries behind the times. There would never be news from the other islands, but only history.

All the star-borne colonies of the future will be independent, whether they wish it or not. Their liberty will be inviolably protected by Time as well as Space. They must go their own way and achieve their own destiny, with no help or hindrance from Mother Earth.

At this point, we will move the discussion on to a new level and deal with an obvious objection. Can we be sure that the velocity of light is indeed a limiting factor? So many "impassable" barriers have been shattered in the past; perhaps this one may go the way of all the others.

We will not argue the point, or give the reasons why scientists believe that light can never be outraced by any form of radiation or any material object. Instead, let us assume the contrary and see just where it gets us. We will even take the most optimistic possible case and imagine that the speed of transportation may eventually become infinite.

Picture a time when, by the development of techniques as far beyond our present engineering as a transistor is beyond a stone axe, we can reach anywhere we please instantaneously, with no more effort than by dialing a number. This would indeed cut the universe down to size and reduce its physical immensity to nothingness. What would be left?

Everything that really matters. For the universe has two aspects—its scale, and its overwhelming, mind-numbing complexity. Having abolished the first, we are now face-to-face with the second.

What we must now try to visualize is not size, but quantity. Most people today are familiar with the simple notation which scientists use to describe large numbers; it consists merely of counting zeroes, so that a hundred becomes 10^2, a million, 10^6, a billion, 10^9 and so on. This useful trick enables us to work with quantities of any magnitude, and even defense-budget totals look modest when expressed as $\$5.76 \times 10^9$ instead of $\$5,760,000,000$.

The number of other suns in our own galaxy (that is, the whirlpool of stars and cosmic dust of which our sun is an out-of-town member, lying in one of the remoter spiral arms) is estimated at about 10^{11}—or written in full, 100,000,000,000. Our present telescopes can observe something like 10^9 other galaxies, and they show no sign of thinning out even at the extreme limit of vision.

There are probably at least as many galaxies in the whole of creation as there are stars in our own galaxy, but let us confine ourselves to those we can see. They must contain a total of about 10^{11} times 10^9 stars, or 10^{20} stars altogether. One followed by twenty other digits is, of course, a number beyond all understanding.

Before such numbers, even spirits brave enough to face the challenge of the light-years must quail. The detailed examination of all the grains of sand on all the beaches of the world is a far smaller task than the exploration of the universe.

And so we return to our opening statement. Space can be mapped and crossed and occupied without definable limit; but it can never be conquered. When our race has reached its ultimate achievements, and the stars themselves are scattered no more widely than the seed of Adam, even then we shall still be like ants crawling on the face of the Earth. The ants have covered the world, but have they conquered it—for what do their countless colonies know of it, or of each other?

So it will be with us as we spread outwards from Mother Earth, loosening the bonds of kinship and understanding, hearing faint and belated rumors at second—or third—or thousandth-hand of an ever-dwindling fraction of the entire human race.

Though Earth will try to keep in touch with her children, in the end all the efforts of her archivists and historians will be defeated by time and distance, and the sheer bulk of material. For the number of distinct societies or nations, when our race is twice its present age, may be far greater than the total number of all the men who have ever lived up to the present time.

We have left the realm of human comprehension in our vain effort to grasp the scale of the universe, so it must always be, sooner rather than later.

When you are next outdoors on a summer night, turn your head toward the zenith. Almost vertically above you will be shining the brightest star of the northern skies—Vega of the Lyre, twenty-six years away at the speed of light, near enough the point of no return for us short-lived creatures. Past this blue white beacon, fifty times as brilliant as our sun, we may send our minds and bodies, but never our hearts.

For no man will ever turn homewards from beyond Vega, to greet again those he knew and loved on the Earth.

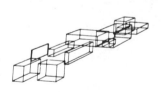

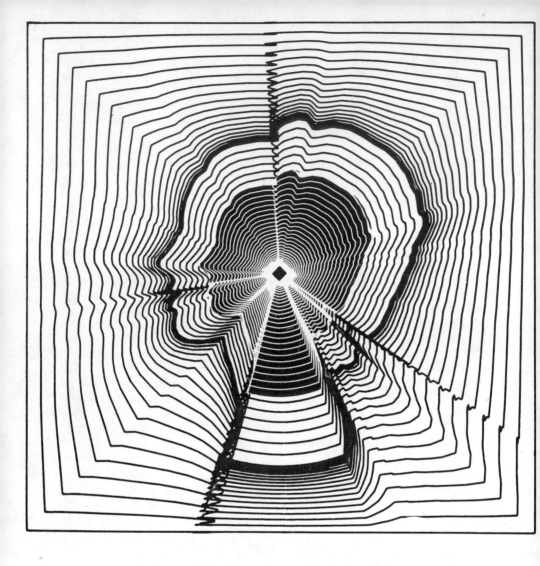

3

MIND WAVES

THE
SACK

William Morrison

AT FIRST THEY HADN'T EVEN KNOWN that the Sack existed. If they had noticed it at all when they landed on the asteroid, they thought of it merely as one more outpost of rock on the barren expanse of roughly ellipsoidal silicate surface, which Captain Ganko noticed had major and minor axes roughly three and two miles in diameter, respectively. It would never have entered anyone's mind that the unimpressive object they had unconsciously acquired would soon be regarded as the most valuable prize in the system.

The landing had been accidental. The government patrol ship had been limping along, and now it had settled down for repairs, which would take a good seventy hours. Fortunately, they had plenty of air, and their recirculation system worked to perfection. Food was in somewhat short supply, but it didn't worry them, for they knew that they could always tighten their belts and do without full rations for a few days. The loss of water that had resulted from a leak in the storage tanks, however, was a more serious matter. It occupied a good part of their conversation during the next fifty hours.

Captain Ganko said finally, "There's no use talking, it won't be enough. And there are no supply stations close enough at hand to be of any use. We'll have to radio ahead and hope that they can get a rescue ship to us with a reserve supply."

The helmet mike of his next-in-command seemed to droop. "It'll be too bad if we miss each other in space, Captain."

Captain Ganko laughed unhappily. "It certainly will. In that case we'll have a chance to see how we can stand a little dehydration."

For a time nobody said anything. At last, however, the second mate suggested, "There might be water somewhere on the asteroid, sir."

"Here? How in Pluto would it stick, with a gravity that isn't even strong enough to hold loose rocks? And where the devil would it be?"

"To answer the first question first, it would be retained as water of crystallization," replied a soft, liquid voice that seemed to penetrate his spacesuit and come from behind him. "To answer the second question, it is half a dozen feet below the surface, and can easily be reached by digging."

"The Sack" by William Morrison from ASTOUNDING SCIENCE FICTION, (September 1950). Copyright, 1950, in U.S.A. and Great Britain by Street and Smith Publications, Inc. Reprinted by permission of The Condé Nast Publications Inc.

They had all swiveled around at the first words. But no one was in sight in the direction from which the words seemed to come. Captain Ganko frowned, and his eyes narrowed dangerously. "We don't happen to have a practical joker with us, do we?" he asked mildly.

"You do not," replied the voice.

"Who said that?"

"I, Yzrl."

A crewman became aware of something moving on the surface of one of the great rocks, and pointed to it. The motion stopped when the voice ceased, but they didn't lose sight of it again. That was how they learned about Yzrl, or as it was more often called, the Mind-Sack.

If the ship and his services hadn't both belonged to the government, Captain Ganko could have claimed the Sack for himself or his owners and retired with a wealth far beyond his dreams. As it was, the thing passed into government control. Its importance was realized almost from the first, and Jake Siebling had reason to be proud when more important and more influential figures of the political and industrial world were finally passed over and he was made Custodian of the Sack. Siebling was a short, stocky man whose one weakness was self-deprecation. He had carried out one difficult assignment after another and allowed other men to take the credit. But this job was not one for a blowhard, and those in charge of making the appointment knew it. For once they looked beyond credit and superficial reputation, and chose an individual they disliked somewhat but trusted absolutely. It was one of the most effective tributes to honesty and ability ever devised.

The Sack, as Siebling learned from seeing it daily, rarely deviated from the form in which it had made its first appearance—a rocky, grayish lump that roughly resembled a sack of potatoes. It had no features, and there was nothing, when it was not being asked questions, to indicate that it had life. It ate rarely—once in a thousand years, it said, when left to itself; once a week when it was pressed into steady use. It ate or moved by fashioning a suitable pseudopod[1] and stretching the thing out in whatever way it pleased. When it had attained its objective, the pseudopod was withdrawn into the main body again and the creature became once more a potato sack.

It turned out later that the name "Sack" was well chosen from another point of view, in addition to that of appearance. For the Sack was stuffed with information, and beyond that, with wisdom. There were many doubters at first, and some of them retained their doubts to the very end, just as some people remained convinced hundreds of years after Columbus that the Earth was flat. But those who saw and heard the Sack had no doubts at all. They tended, if anything, to go too far in the other direction, and to believe that the Sack knew everything. This, of course, was untrue.

It was the official function of the Sack, established by a series of interplanetary acts, to answer questions. The first questions, as we

---

1. *pseudopod*, a temporary protrusion of protoplasm that serves as a means of locomotion and a way of surrounding and absorbing food.

have seen, were asked accidentally, by Captain Ganko. Later they were asked purposefully, but with a purpose that was itself random, and a few politicians managed to acquire considerable wealth before the government put a stop to the leak of information, and tried to have the questions asked in a more scientific and logical manner.

Question time was rationed for months in advance, and sold at what was, all things considered, a ridiculously low rate—a mere hundred thousand credits a minute. It was this unrestricted sale of time that led to the first great government squabble.

It was the unexpected failure of the Sack to answer what must have been to a mind of its ability an easy question that led to the second blowup, which was fierce enough to be called a crisis. A total of a hundred and twenty questioners, each of whom had paid his hundred thousand, raised a howl that could be heard on every planet, and there was a legislative investigation, at which Siebling testified and all the conflicts were aired.

He had left an assistant in charge of the Sack, and now, as he sat before the senatorial committee, he twisted uncomfortably in front of the battery of cameras. Senator Horrigan, his chief interrogator, was a bluff, florid, loudmouthed politician who had been able to imbue him with a feeling of guilt even as he told his name, age, and length of government service.

"It is your duty to see to it that the Sack is maintained in proper condition for answering questions, is it not, Mr. Siebling?" demanded Senator Horrigan.

"Yes, sir."

"Then why was it incapable of answering the questioners in question? These gentlemen had honestly paid their money—a hundred thousand credits each. It was necessary, I understand, to refund the total sum. That meant an overall loss to the government of, let me see now—one hundred twenty at one hundred thousand each—one hundred and twenty million credits," he shouted, rolling the words.

"Twelve million, Senator," hastily whispered his secretary.

The correction was not made, and the figure was duly headlined later as one hundred and twenty million.

Siebling said, "As we discovered later, Senator, the Sack failed to answer questions because it was not a machine, but a living creature. It was exhausted. It had been exposed to questioning on a twenty-four-hour-a-day basis."

"And who permitted this idiotic procedure?" boomed Senator Horrigan.

"You yourself, Senator," said Siebling happily. "The procedure was provided for in the bill introduced by you and approved by your committee."

Senator Horrigan had never even read the bill to which his name was attached, and he was certainly not to blame for its provisions. But this private knowledge of his own innocence did him no good with the public. From that moment he was Siebling's bitter enemy.

"So the Sack ceased to answer questions for two whole hours?"

"Yes, sir. It resumed only after a rest."

"And it answered them without further difficulty?"

"No, sir. Its response was slowed down. Subsequent questioners complained that they were defrauded of a good part of their money. But as answers were given, we considered that the complaints were without merit, and the financial department refused to make refunds."

"Do you consider that this cheating of investors in the Sack's time is honest?"

"That's none of my business, Senator," returned Siebling, who had by this time got over most of his nervousness. "I merely see to the execution of the laws. I leave the question of honesty to those who make them. I presume that it's in perfectly good hands."

Senator Horrigan flushed at the laughter that came from the onlookers. He was personally unpopular, as unpopular as a politician can be and still remain a politician. He was disliked even by the members of his own party, and some of his best political friends were among the laughers. He decided to abandon what had turned out to be an unfortunate line of questioning.

"It is a matter of fact, Mr. Siebling, is it not, that you have frequently refused admittance to investors who were able to show perfectly valid receipts for their credits?"

"That is a fact, sir. But——"

"You admit it, then."

"There is no question of 'admitting' anything, Senator What I meant to say was——"

"Never mind what you meant to say. It's what you have already said that's important. You've cheated these men of their money!"

"That is not true, sir. They were given time later. The reason for my refusal to grant them admission when they asked for it was that the time had been previously reserved for the armed forces. There are important research questions that come up, and there is, as you know, a difference of opinion as to priority. When confronted with requisitions for time from a commercial investor and a representative of the government, I never took it upon myself to settle the question. I always consulted with the government's legal adviser."

"So you refused to make an independent decision, did you?"

"My duty, Senator, is to look after the welfare of the Sack. I do not concern myself with political questions. We had a moment of free time the day before I left the asteroid, when an investor who had already paid his money was delayed by a space accident, so instead of letting the moment go to waste, I utilized it to ask the Sack a question."

"How you might advance your own fortunes, no doubt?"

"No, sir. I merely asked it how it might function most efficiently. I took the precaution of making a recording, knowing that my word might be doubted. If you wish, Senator, I can introduce the recording in evidence."

Senator Horrigan grunted, and waved his hand. "Go on with your answer."

"The Sack replied that it would require two hours of complete rest out of every twenty, plus an additional hour of what it called 'recreation.' That is, it wanted to converse with some human being who would ask what it called 'sensible' questions, and not press for a quick answer."

"So you suggest that the government waste three hours of every twenty—one hundred and eighty million credits?"

"Eighteen million," whispered the secretary.

"The time would not be wasted. Any attempt to overwork the Sack would result in its premature annihilation."

"That is your idea, is it?"

"No, sir, that is what the Sack itself said."

At this point Senator Horrigan swung into a speech of denunciation, and Siebling was excused from further testimony. Other witnesses were called, but at the end the Senate investigating body was able to come to no definite conclusion, and it was decided to interrogate the Sack personally.

It was out of the question for the Sack to come to the Senate, so the Senate quite naturally came to the Sack. The Committee of Seven was manifestly uneasy as the senatorial ship decelerated and cast its grapples toward the asteroid. The members, as individuals, had all traveled in space before, but all their previous destinations had been in civilized territory, and they obviously did not relish the prospect of landing on this airless and sunless body of rock.

The televisor companies were alert to their opportunity, and they had acquired more experience with desert territory. They had disembarked and set up their apparatus before the senators had taken their first timid steps out of the safety of their ship.

Siebling noted ironically that in these somewhat frightening surroundings, far from their home grounds, the senators were not so sure of themselves. It was his part to act the friendly guide, and he did so with relish.

"You see, gentlemen," he said respectfully, "it was decided, on the Sack's own advice, not to permit it to be further exposed to possible collision with stray meteors. It was the meteors which killed off the other members of its strange race, and it was a lucky chance that the last surviving individual managed to escape destruction as long as it has. An impenetrable shelter dome has been built therefore, and the Sack now lives under its protection. Questioners address it through a sound and sight system that is almost as good as being face-to-face with it."

Senator Horrigan fastened upon the significant part of his statement. "You mean that the Sack is safe—and we are exposed to danger from flying meteors?"

"Naturally, Senator. The Sack is unique in the system. Men—even senators—are, if you will excuse the expression, a decicredit a dozen. They are definitely replaceable, by means of elections."

Beneath his helmet the senator turned green with a fear that concealed the scarlet of his anger. "I think it is an outrage to find the government so unsolicitous of the safety and welfare of its employees!"

"So do I, sir. I live here the year round." He added smoothly, "Would you gentlemen care to see the Sack now?"

They stared at the huge visor screen and saw the Sack resting on its seat before them, looking like a burlap bag of potatoes which had been tossed onto a throne and forgotten there. It looked so definitely inanimate that it struck them as strange that the thing should remain upright instead of toppling over. All the same, for a moment the senators could not help showing the awe that overwhelmed them. Even Senator Horrigan was silent.

But the moment passed. He said, "Sir, we are an official investigating committee of the Interplanetary Senate, and we have come to ask you a few questions." The Sack showed no desire to reply, and Senator Horrigan cleared his throat and went on. "Is it true, sir, that you require two hours of complete rest in every twenty, and one hour for recreation, or, as I may put it, perhaps more precisely, relaxation?"

"It is true."

Senator Horrigan gave the creature its chance, but the Sack, unlike a senator, did not elaborate. Another of the committee asked, "Where would you find an individual capable of conversing intelligently with so wise a creature as you?"

"Here," replied the Sack.

"It is necessary to ask questions that are directly to the point, Senator," suggested Siebling. "The Sack does not usually volunteer information that has not been specifically called for."

Senator Horrigan said quickly, "I assume, sir, that when you speak of finding an intelligence on a par with your own, you refer to a member of our committee, and I am sure that of all my colleagues there is not one who is unworthy of being so denominated. But we cannot all of us spare the time needed for our manifold other duties, so I wish to ask you, sir, which of us, in your opinion, has the peculiar qualifications of that sort of wisdom which is required for this great task?"

"None," said the Sack.

Senator Horrigan looked blank. One of the other senators flushed, and asked, "Who has?"

"Siebling."

Senator Horrigan forgot his awe of the Sack, and shouted, "This is a put-up job!"

The other senator who had just spoken now said suddenly, "How is it that there are no other questioners present? Hasn't the Sack's time been sold far in advance?"

Siebling nodded. "I was ordered to cancel all previous appointments with the Sack, sir."

"By what idiot's orders?"

"Senator Horrigan's, sir."

At this point the investigation might have been said to come to an end. There was just time, before they turned away, for Senator Horrigan to demand desperately of the Sack, "Sir, will I be re-elected?" But the roar of anger that went up from his colleagues prevented him from hearing the Sack's answer, and only the question was picked up and broadcast clearly over the interplanetary network.

It had such an effect that it in itself provided Senator Horrigan's answer. He was *not* re-elected. But before the election he had time to cast his vote against Siebling's designation to talk with the Sack for one hour out of every twenty. The final committee vote was four to three in favor of Siebling, and the decision was confirmed by the Senate. And then Senator Horrigan passed temporarily out of the Sack's life and out of Siebling's.

Siebling looked forward with some trepidation to his first long interview with the Sack. Hitherto he had limited himself to the simple tasks provided for in his directives—to the maintenance of the meteor shelter dome, to the provision of a sparse food supply, and to the proper placement of an army and Space Fleet Guard. For by this time the great value of the Sack had been recognized throughout the system, and it was widely realized that there would be thousands of criminals anxious to steal so defenseless a treasure.

Now, Siebling thought, he would be obliged to talk to it, and he feared that he would lose the good opinion which it had somehow acquired of him. He was in a position strangely like that of a young girl who would have liked nothing better than to talk of her dresses and her boy friends to someone with her own background, and was forced to endure a brilliant and witty conversation with some man three times her age.

But he lost some of his awe when he faced the Sack itself. It would have been absurd to say that the strange creature's manner put him at ease. The creature had no manner. It was featureless and expressionless, and even when part of it moved, as when it was speaking, the effect was completely impersonal. Nevertheless, something about it did make him lose his fears.

For a time he stood before it and said nothing. To his surprise, the Sack spoke—the first time to his knowledge that it had done so without being asked a question. "You will not disappoint me," it said. "I expect nothing."

Siebling grinned. Not only had the Sack never before volunteered to speak, it had never spoken so dryly. For the first time it began to seem not so much a mechanical brain as the living creature he knew it to be. He asked, "Has anyone ever before asked you about your origin?"

"One man. That was before my time was rationed. And even he caught himself when he realized that he might better be asking how to become rich, and he paid little attention to my answer."

"How old are you?"

"Four hundred thousand years. I can tell you to the fraction of a second, but I suppose that you do not wish me to speak as precisely as usual."

The thing, thought Siebling, did have in its way a sense of humor. "How much of that time," he asked, "have you spent alone?"

"More than ten thousand years."

"You told someone once that your companions were killed by meteors. Couldn't you have guarded against them?"

The Sack said slowly, almost wearily, "That was after we had ceased to have an interest in remaining alive. The first death was three hundred thousand years ago."

"And you have lived, since then, without wanting to?"

"I have no great interest in dying either. Living has become a habit."

"Why did you lose your interest in remaining alive?"

"Because we lost the future. There had been a miscalculation."

"You are capable of making mistakes?"

"We had not lost that capacity. There was a miscalculation, and although those of us then living escaped personal disaster, our next generation was not so fortunate. We lost any chance of having descendants. After that, we had nothing for which to live."

Siebling nodded. It was a loss of motive that a human being could understand. He asked, "With all your knowledge, couldn't you have overcome the effects of what happened?"

The Sack said, "The more things become possible to you, the more you will understand that they cannot be done in impossible ways. We could not do everything. Sometimes one of the more stupid of those who come here asks me a question I cannot answer, and then becomes angry because he feels that he has been cheated of his credits. Others ask me to predict the future. I can predict only what I can calculate, and I soon come to the end of my powers of calculation. They are great compared to yours; they are small compared to the possibilities of the future."

"How do you happen to know so much? Is the knowledge born in you?"

"Only the possibility for knowledge is born. To know, we must learn. It is my misfortune that I forget little."

"What in the structure of your body, or your organs of thought, makes you capable of learning so much?"

The Sack spoke, but to Siebling the words meant nothing, and he said so. "I could predict your lack of comprehension," said the Sack, "but I wanted you to realize it for yourself. To make things clear, I should be required to dictate ten volumes, and they would be difficult to understand even for your specialists in biology and physics and in sciences you are just discovering."

Siebling fell silent, and the Sack said, as if musing, "Your race is still an unintelligent one. I have been in your hands for many months, and no one has yet asked me the important questions. Those who wish to be wealthy ask about minerals and planetary land concessions, and they ask which of several schemes for making fortunes would be best. Several physicians have asked me how to treat wealthy patients who would otherwise die. Your scientists ask me to solve problems that would take them years to solve without my help. And when your rulers ask, they are the most stupid of all, wanting to know only how they may maintain their rule. None ask what they should."

"The fate of the human race?"

"That is prophecy of the far future. It is beyond my powers."

"What *should* we ask?"

"That is the question I have awaited. It is difficult for you to see its importance, only because each of you is so concerned with himself." The Sack paused, and murmured, "I ramble as I do not permit myself to when I speak to your fools. Nevertheless, even rambling can be informative."

"It has been to me."

"The others do not understand that too great a directness is dangerous. They ask specific questions which demand specific replies, when they should ask something general."

"You haven't answered me."

"It is part of an answer to say that a question is important. I am considered by your rulers a valuable piece of property. They should ask whether my value is as great as it seems. They should ask whether my answering questions will do good or harm."

"Which is it?"

"Harm, great harm."

Siebling was staggered. He said, "But if you answer truthfully——"

"The process of coming at the truth is as precious as the final truth itself. I cheat you of that. I give your people the truth, but not all of it, for they do not know how to attain it of themselves. It would be better if they learned that, at the expense of making many errors."

"I don't agree with that."

"A scientist asks me what goes on within a cell, and I tell him. But if he had studied the cell himself, even though the study required many years, he would have ended not only with this knowledge, but with much other knowledge, of things he does not even suspect to be related. He would have acquired many new processes of investigation."

"But surely, in some cases, the knowledge is useful in itself. For instance, I hear that they're already using a process you suggested for producing uranium cheaply to use on Mars. What's harmful about that?"

"Do you know how much of the necessary raw material is present? Your scientists have not investigated that, and they will use up all the raw material and discover only too late what they have done. You had the same experience on Earth. You learned how to purify water at little expense, and you squandered water so recklessly that you soon ran short of it."

"What's wrong with saving the life of a dying patient, as some of those doctors did?"

"The first question to ask is whether the patient's life should be saved."

"That's exactly what a doctor isn't supposed to ask. He has to try to save them all. Just as you never ask whether people are going to use your knowledge for a good purpose or a bad. You simply answer their questions."

"I answer because I am indifferent, and I care nothing what use they make of what I say. Are your doctors also indifferent?"

Siebling said, "You're supposed to answer questions, not ask them. Incidentally, why do you answer at all?"

"Some of your men find joy in boasting, in doing what they call good, or in making money. Whatever mild pleasure I can find lies in imparting information."

"And you'd get no pleasure out of lying?"

"I am as incapable of telling lies as one of your birds of flying off the Earth on its own wings."

"One thing more. Why did you ask to talk to me, of all people, for recreation? There are brilliant scientists, and great men of all kinds whom you could have chosen."

"I care nothing for your race's greatness. I chose you because you are honest."

"Thanks. But there are other honest men on Earth, and on Mars, and on the other planets as well. Why me, instead of them?"

The Sack seemed to hesitate. "Your choice gave me a mild pleasure. Possibly because I knew it would be displeasing to those men."

Siebling grinned. "You're not quite so indifferent as you think you are. I guess it's pretty hard to be indifferent to Senator Horrigan."

This was but the first part of many conversations with the Sack. For a long time Siebling could not help being disturbed by the Sack's warning that its presence was a calamity instead of a blessing for the human race, and this in more ways than one. But it would have been absurd to try to convince a government body that any object that brought in so many millions of credits each day was a calamity, and Siebling didn't even try. And after a while Siebling relegated the uncomfortable knowledge to the back of his mind, and settled down to the routine existence of Custodian of the Sack.

Because there was a conversation every twenty hours, Siebling had to rearrange his eating and sleeping schedule to a twenty-hour basis, which made it a little difficult for a man who had become so thoroughly accustomed to the thirty-hour space day. But he felt more than repaid for the trouble by his conversations with the Sack. He learned a great many things about the planets and the system, and the galaxies, but he learned them incidentally, without making a special point of asking about them. Because his knowledge of astronomy had never gone far beyond the elements, there were some questions—the most important of all about the galaxies—that he never even got around to asking.

Perhaps it would have made little difference to his own understanding if he had asked, for some of the answers were difficult to understand. He spent three entire periods with the Sack trying to have that mastermind make clear to him how the Sack had been able, without any previous contact with human beings, to understand Captain Ganko's Earth language on the historic occasion when the Sack had first revealed itself to human beings, and how it had been able to answer in practically unaccented words. At the end, he had only a vague glimmering of how the feat was performed.

It wasn't telepathy, as he had first suspected. It was an intricate process of analysis that involved, not only the actual words spoken, but the nature of the ship that had landed, the spacesuits the men had worn, the way they had walked, and many other factors that indicated the psychology of both the speaker and his language. It was as if a mathematician had tried to explain to someone who didn't even know arithmetic how he could determine the equation of a complicated curve from a short line segment. And the Sack, unlike the mathematician, could do the whole thing, so to speak, in its head, without paper and pencil, or any other external aid.

After a year at the job, Siebling found it difficult to say which he found more fascinating—those hour-long conversations with the almost all-wise Sack, or the cleverly stupid demands of some of the men and women who had paid their hundred thousand credits for a precious sixty seconds. In addition to the relatively simple questions such as were asked by the scientists or the fortune hunters who wanted to know where they could find precious metals, there were complicated questions that took several minutes.

One woman, for instance, had asked where to find her missing son. Without the necessary data to go on, even the Sack had been unable to answer that. She left, to return a month later with a vast amount of information, carefully compiled, and arranged in order of descending importance. The key items were given the Sack first, those of lesser significance afterward. It required a little less than three minutes for the Sack to give her the answer that her son was probably alive, and cast away on an obscure and very much neglected part of Ganymede.[2]

All the conversations that took place, including Siebling's own, were recorded and the records shipped to a central storage file on Earth. Many of them he couldn't understand, some because they were too technical, others because he didn't know the language spoken. The Sack, of course, immediately learned all languages by that process he had tried so hard to explain to Siebling, and back at the central storage file there were expert technicians and linguists who went over every detail of each question and answer with great care, both to make sure that no questioner revealed himself as a criminal, and to have a lead for the collection of income taxes when the questioner made a fortune with the Sack's help.

During the year Siebling had occasion to observe the correctness of the Sack's remark about its possession being harmful to the human race. For the first time in centuries, the number of research scientists, instead of growing, decreased. The Sack's knowledge had made much research unnecessary, and had taken the edge off discovery. The Sack commented upon the fact to Siebling.

Siebling nodded. "I see it now. The human race is losing its independence."

"Yes, from its faithful slave I am becoming its master. And I do not want to be a master any more than I want to be a slave."

"You can escape whenever you wish."

A person would have sighed. The Sack merely said, "I lack the power

---

2. *Ganymede,* one of the largest of Jupiter's moons.

to wish strongly enough. Fortunately, the question may soon be taken out of my hands."

"You mean those government squabbles?"

The value of the Sack had increased steadily, and along with the increased value had gone increasingly bitter struggles about the rights to its services. Financial interests had undergone a strange development. Their presidents and managers and directors had become almost figureheads, with all major questions of policy being decided not by their own study of the facts, but by appeal to the Sack. Often, indeed, the Sack found itself giving advice to bitter rivals, so that it seemed to be playing a game of interplanetary chess, with giant corporations and government agencies its pawns, while the Sack alternately played for one side and then the other. Crises of various sorts, both economic and political, were obviously in the making.

The Sack said, "I mean both government squabbles and others. The competition for my services becomes too bitter. I can have but one end."

"You mean that an attempt will be made to steal you?"

"Yes."

"There'll be little chance of that. Your guards are being continually increased."

"You underestimate the power of greed," said the Sack.

Siebling was to learn how correct that comment was.

At the end of his fourteenth month on duty, a half year after Senator Horrigan had been defeated for re-election, there appeared a questioner who spoke to the Sack in an exotic language known to few men—the Prdl dialect of Mars. Siebling's attention had already been drawn to the man because of the fact that he had paid a million credits an entire month in advance for the unprecedented privilege of questioning the Sack for ten consecutive minutes. The conversation was duly recorded, but was naturally meaningless to Siebling and to the other attendants at the station. The questioner drew further attention to himself by leaving at the end of seven minutes, thus failing to utilize three entire minutes, which would have sufficed for learning how to make half a dozen small fortunes. He left the asteroid immediately by private ship.

The three minutes had been reserved, and could not be utilized by any other private questioner. But there was nothing to prevent Siebling, as a government representative, from utilizing them, and he spoke to the Sack at once.

"What did that man want?"

"Advice as to how to steal me."

Siebling's lower jaw dropped. *"What?"*

The Sack always took such exclamations of amazement literally. "Advice as to how to steal me," it repeated.

"Then—wait a minute—he left three minutes early. That must mean that he's in a hurry to get started. He's going to put the plan into execution at once!"

"It is already in execution," returned the Sack. "The criminal's organization has excellent, if not quite perfect, information as to the disposition of defense forces. That would indicate that some government official has betrayed his trust. I was asked to indicate which of several plans was best, and to consider them for possible weaknesses. I did so."

"All right, now what can we do to stop the plans from being carried out?"

"They cannot be stopped."

"I don't see why not. Maybe we can't stop them from getting here, but we can stop them from escaping with you."

"There is but one way. You must destroy me."

"I can't do that! I haven't the authority, and even if I had, I wouldn't do it."

"My destruction would benefit your race."

"I still can't do it," said Siebling unhappily.

"Then if that is excluded, there is no way. The criminals are shrewd and daring. They asked me to check about probable steps that would be taken in pursuit, but they asked for no advice as to how to get away, because that would have been a waste of time. They will ask that once I am in their possession."

"Then," said Siebling heavily, "there's nothing I can do to keep you. How about saving the men who work under me?"

"You can save both them and yourself by boarding the emergency ship and leaving immediately by the sunward route. In that way you will escape contact with the criminals. But you cannot take me with you, or they will pursue."

The shouts of a guard drew Siebling's attention. "Radio report of a criminal attack, Mr. Siebling! All the alarms are out!"

"Yes, I know. Prepare to depart." He turned back to the Sack again. "We may escape for the moment, but they'll have you. And through you they will control the entire system."

"That is not a question," said the Sack.

"They'll have you. Isn't there something we can do?"

"Destroy me."

"I can't," said Siebling, almost in agony. His men were running toward him impatiently, and he knew that there was no more time. He uttered the simple and absurd phrase, "Good-by," as if the Sack were human and could experience human emotions. Then he raced for the ship, and they blasted off.

They were just in time. Half a dozen ships were racing in from other directions, and Siebling's vessel escaped just before they dispersed to spread a protective network about the asteroid that held the Sack.

Siebling's ship continued to speed toward safety, and the matter should now have been one solely for the armed forces to handle. But Siebling imagined them pitted against the Sack's perfectly calculating brain, and his heart sank. Then something happened that he had never expected. And for the first time he realized fully that if the Sack had let itself be used merely as a machine, a slave to answer questions, it was not because its powers were limited to that single ability. The visor screen in his ship lit up.

The communications operator came running to him, and said, "Something's wrong, Mr. Siebling! The screen isn't even turned on!"

It wasn't. Nevertheless, they could see on it the chamber in which the Sack had rested for what must have been a brief moment of its existence. Two men had entered the chamber, one of them the unknown who had asked his questions in Prdl, the other Senator Horrigan.

To the apparent amazement of the two men, it was the Sack which spoke first. It said, "'Good-by' is neither a question nor the answer to one. It is relatively uninformative."

Senator Horrigan was obviously in awe of the Sack, but he was never a man to be stopped by something he did not understand. He orated respectfully. "No, sir, it is not. The word is nothing but an expression——"

The other man said, in perfectly comprehensible Earth English, "Shut up, you fool, we have no time to waste. Let's get it to our ship and head for safety. We'll talk to it there."

Siebling had time to think a few bitter thoughts about Senator Horrigan and the people the politician had punished by betrayal for their crime in not electing him. Then the scene on the visor shifted to the interior of the spaceship making its getaway. There was no indication of pursuit. Evidently, the plans of the human beings, plus the Sack's last-minute advice, had been an effective combination.

The only human beings with the Sack at first were Senator Horrigan and the speaker of Prdl, but this situation was soon changed. Half a dozen other men came rushing up, their faces grim with suspicion. One of them announced, "You don't talk to that thing unless we're all of us around. We're in this together."

"Don't get nervous, Merrill. What do you think I'm going to do, double-cross you?"

Merrill said, "Yes, I do. What do you say, Sack? Do I have reason to distrust him?"

The Sack replied simply, "Yes."

The speaker of Prdl turned white. Merrill laughed coldly. "You'd better be careful what questions you ask around this thing."

Senator Horrigan cleared his throat. "I have no intentions of, as you put it, double-crossing anyone. It is not in my nature to do so. Therefore, *I* shall address it." He faced the Sack. "Sir, are we in danger?"

"Yes."

"From which direction?"

"From no direction. From within the ship."

"Is the danger immediate?" asked a voice.

"Yes."

It was Merrill who turned out to have the quickest reflexes and acted first on the implications of the answer. He had blasted the man who had spoken in Prdl before the latter could even reach for his weapon, and as Senator Horrigan made a frightened dash for the door, he cut that politician down in cold blood.

"That's that," he said. "Is there further danger inside the ship?"

"There is."

"Who is it this time?" he demanded ominously.

"There will continue to be danger so long as there is more than one man on board and I am with you. I am too valuable a treasure for such as you."

Siebling and his crew were staring at the visor screen in fascinated horror, as if expecting the slaughter to begin again. But Merrill controlled himself. He said, "Hold it, boys. I'll admit that we'd each of us like to have this thing for ourselves, but it can't be done. We're in this together, and we're going to have some navy ships to fight off before long, or I miss my guess. You, Prader! What are you doing away from the scout visor?"

"Listening," said the man he addressed. "If anybody's talking to that thing, I'm going to be around to hear the answers. If there are new ways of stabbing a guy in the back, I want to learn them too."

Merrill swore. The next moment the ship swerved, and he yelled, "We're off our course. Back to your stations, you fools!"

They were running wildly back to their stations, but Siebling noted that Merrill wasn't too much concerned about their common danger to keep from putting a blast through Prader's back before the unfortunate man could run out.

Siebling said to his own men, "There can be only one end. They'll kill each other off, and then the last one or two will die, because one or two men cannot handle a ship that size for long and get away with it. The Sack must have foreseen that too. I wonder why it didn't tell me."

The Sack spoke, although there was no one in the ship's cabin with it. It said, "No one asked."

Siebling exclaimed excitedly, "You can hear me! But what about you? Will you be destroyed too?"

"Not yet. I have willed to live longer." It paused, and then, in a voice just a shade lower than before, said, "I do not like relatively non-informative conversations of this sort, but I must say it. Good-by."

There was a sound of renewed yelling and shooting, and then the visor went suddenly dark and blank.

The miraculous form of life that was the Sack, the creature that had once seemed so alien to human emotions, had passed beyond the range of his knowledge. And with it had gone, as the Sack itself had pointed out, a tremendous potential for harming the entire human race. It was strange, thought Siebling, that he felt so unhappy about so happy an ending.

MARIANA

Fritz Leiber

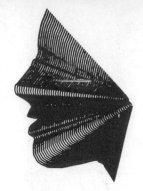

MARIANA HAD BEEN LIVING IN THE BIG villa and hating the tall pine trees around it for what seemed like an eternity when she found the secret panel in the master control panel of the house.

The secret panel was simply a narrow blank of aluminum—she'd thought of it as room for more switches if they ever needed any, perish the thought!—between the air-conditioning controls and the gravity controls. Above the switches for the three-dimensional TV but below those for the robot butler and maids.

Jonathan had told her not to fool with the master control panel while he was in the city because she would wreck anything electrical, so when the secret panel came loose under her aimlessly questing fingers and fell to the solid rock floor of the patio with a musical *twing* her first reaction was fear.

Then she saw it was only a small blank oblong of sheet aluminum that had fallen and that in the space it had covered was a column of six little switches. Only the top one was identified. Tiny glowing letters beside it spelled TREES and it was on.

When Jonathan got home from the city that evening she gathered her courage and told him about it. He was neither particularly angry nor impressed.

"Of course there's a switch for the trees," he informed her deflatingly, motioning the robot butler to cut his steak. "Didn't you know they were radio trees? I didn't want to wait twenty-five years for them and they couldn't grow in this rock anyway. A station in the city broadcasts a master pine tree and sets like ours pick it up and project it around homes. It's vulgar but convenient."

After a bit she asked timidly, "Jonathan, are the radio pine trees ghostly as you drive through them?"

"Of course not! They're solid as this house and the rock under it—to the eye and to the touch too. A person could even climb them. If you ever stirred outside you'd know these things. The city station transmits pulses of alternating matter at sixty cycles a second. The science of it is over your head."

She ventured one more question: "Why did they have the tree switch covered up?"

"So you wouldn't monkey with it—same as the fine controls on the

"Mariana" by Fritz Leiber from FANTASTIC, (February 1960). Reprinted by permission of Robert P. Mills Ltd.

TV. And so you wouldn't get ideas and start changing the trees. It would unsettle *me,* let me tell you, to come home to oaks one day and birches the next. I like consistency and I like pines." He looked at them out of the dining-room picture window and grunted with satisfaction.

She had been meaning to tell him about hating the pines, but that discouraged her and she dropped the topic.

About noon the next day, however, she went to the secret panel and switched off the pine trees and quickly turned around to watch them.

At first nothing happened and she was beginning to think that Jonathan was wrong again, as he so often was though would never admit, but then they began to waver and specks of pale green light churned across them and then they faded and were gone, leaving behind only an intolerably bright single point of light—just as when the TV is switched off. The star hovered motionless for what seemed a long time, then backed away and raced off toward the horizon.

Now that the pine trees were out of the way Mariana could see the real landscape. It was flat gray rock, endless miles of it, exactly the same as the rock on which the house was set and which formed the floor of the patio. It was the same in every direction. One black two-lane road drove straight across it—nothing more.

She disliked the view almost at once—it was dreadfully lonely and depressing. She switched the gravity to moon-normal and danced about dreamily, floating over the middle-of-the-room bookshelves and the grand piano and even having the robot maids dance with her, but it did not cheer her. About two o'clock she went to switch on the pine trees again, as she had intended to do in any case before Jonathan came home and was furious.

However, she found there had been changes in the column of six little switches. The TREES switch no longer had its glowing name. She remembered that it had been the top one, but the top one would not turn on again. She tried to force it from "off" to "on" but it would not move.

All of the rest of the afternoon she sat on the steps outside the front door watching the black two-lane road. Never a car or a person came into view until Jonathan's tan roadster appeared, seeming at first to hang motionless in the distance and then to move only like a microscopic snail although she knew he always drove at top speed—it was one of the reasons she would never get in the car with him.

Jonathan was not as furious as she had feared. "Your own damn fault for meddling with it," he said curtly. "Now we'll have to get a man out here. Dammit, I hate to eat supper looking at nothing but those rocks! Bad enough driving through them twice a day."

She asked him haltingly about the barrenness of the landscape and the absence of neighbors.

"Well, you wanted to live *way out,*" he told her. "You wouldn't ever have known about it if you hadn't turned off the trees."

"There's one other thing I've got to bother you with, Jonathan," she said. "Now the second switch—the one next below—has got a name that glows. It just says HOUSE. It's turned on—I haven't touched it! Do you suppose . . ."

"I want to look at this," he said, bounding up from the couch and slamming his martini-on-the-rocks tumbler down on the tray of the robot maid so that she rattled. "I bought this house as solid, but there are swindles. Ordinarily I'd spot a broadcast style in a flash, but they just might have slipped me a job relayed from some other planet or solar system. Fine thing if me and fifty other multi-megabuck men were spotted around in identical houses, each thinking his was unique."

"But if the house is based on rock like it is . . ."

"That would just make it easier for them to pull the trick, you dumb bunny!"

They reached the master control panel. "There it is," she said helpfully, jabbing out a finger . . . and hit the HOUSE switch.

For a moment nothing happened, then a white churning ran across the ceiling, the walls and furniture started to swell and bubble like cold lava, and then they were alone on a rock table big as three tennis courts. Even the master control panel was gone. The only thing that was left was a slender rod coming out of the gray stone at their feet and bearing at the top, like some mechanistic fruit, a small block with the six switches—that and an intolerably bright star hanging in the air where the master bedroom had been.

Mariana pushed frantically at the HOUSE switch, but it was unlabeled now and locked in the "off" position, although she threw her weight at it stiff-armed.

The upstairs star sped off like an incendiary bullet, but its last flashbulb glare showed her Jonathan's face set in lines of fury. He lifted his hands like talons.

"You little idiot!" he screamed, coming at her.

"No, Jonathan, no!" she wailed, backing off, but he kept coming.

She realized that the block of switches had broken off in her hands. The third switch had a glowing name now: JONATHAN. She flipped it.

As his fingers dug into her bare shoulders they seemed to turn to foam rubber, then to air. His face and gray flannel suit seethed iridescently, like a leprous ghost's, then melted and ran. His star, smaller than that of the house but much closer, seared her eyes. When she opened them again there was nothing at all left of the star or Jonathan but a dancing dark afterimage like a black tennis ball.

She was alone on an infinite flat rock plain under the cloudless, star-specked sky.

The fourth switch had its glowing name now: STARS.

It was almost dawn by her radium-dialed wristwatch and she was thoroughly chilled when she finally decided to switch off the stars. She did not want to do it—in their slow wheeling across the sky they were the last sign of orderly reality—but it seemed the only move she could make.

She wondered what the fifth switch would say. ROCKS? AIR? Or even . . . ?

She switched off the stars.

The Milky Way, arching in all its unalterable glory, began to churn, its component stars darting about like midges. Soon only one remained, brighter even than Sirius or Venus—until it jerked back, fading, and darted to infinity.

The fifth switch said DOCTOR and it was not on but off.

An inexplicable terror welled up in Mariana. She did not even want to touch the fifth switch. She set the block of switches down on the rock and backed away from it.

But she dared not go far in the starless dark. She huddled down and waited for dawn. From time to time she looked at her watch dial and at the night-light glow of the switchlabel a dozen yards away.

It seemed to be growing much colder.

She read her watch dial. It was two hours past sunrise. She remembered they had taught her in third grade that the sun was just one more star.

She went back and sat down beside the block of switches and picked it up with a shudder and flipped the fifth switch.

The rock grew soft and crisply fragrant under her and lapped up over her legs and then slowly turned white.

She was sitting in a hospital bed in a small blue room with a white pinstripe.

A sweet, mechanical voice came out of the wall, saying, "You have interrupted the wish-fulfillment therapy by your own decision. If you now recognize your sick depression and are willing to accept help, the doctor will come to you. If not, you are at liberty to return to the wish-fulfillment therapy and pursue it to its ultimate conclusion."

Mariana looked down. She still had the block of switches in her hands and the fifth switch still read DOCTOR.

The wall said, "I assume from your silence that you will accept treatment. The doctor will be with you immediately."

The inexplicable terror returned to Mariana with compulsive intensity.

She switched off the doctor.

She was back in the starless dark. The rocks had grown very much colder. She could feel icy feathers falling on her face—snow.

She lifted the block of switches and saw, to her unutterable relief, that the sixth and last switch now read, in tiny glowing letters: MARIANA.

I ALWAYS DO WHAT TEDDY SAYS

Harry Harrison

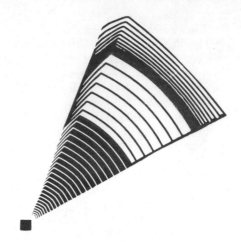

THE LITTLE BOY LAY SLEEPING, the artificial moonlight of the picture picture-window throwing a pale glow across his untroubled features. He had one arm clutched around his teddy bear, pulling the round face with its staring button eyes close to his. His father, and the man with the black beard, tiptoed silently across the nursery to the side of the bed.

"Slip it away," the man said, "and then substitute the other."

"No, he would wake up and cry," Davy's father said. "Let me take care of this, I know what to do."

With gentle hands he laid another teddy bear down next to the boy, on the other side of his head, so that the sleeping-cherub face was framed by the wide-eared unsleeping masks of the toys. Then he carefully lifted the boy's arm from the original teddy and pulled it free. Though this disturbed Davy it did not wake him. He ground his teeth together and rolled over, clutching the substitute toy to his cheek, and within a few moments his quiet breathing was regular and deep again. The boy's father raised his forefinger to his lips and the other man nodded; they left the room without making a sound, closing the door noiselessly behind them.

"Now we begin," Torrence said, reaching out to take the teddy bear. His lips were small and glistened redly in the midst of his dark beard. The teddy bear twisted in his grip and the blackbutton eyes rolled back and forth.

"Take me back to Davy," it said in a thin and tiny voice.

"Let me have it," the boy's father said. "It knows me and won't complain."

His name was Numen and, like Torrence, he was a Doctor of Government. Both DGs and both unemployed by the present govern-

"I Always Do What Teddy Says" by Harry Harrison. © 1956 by Davis Publications, Inc. Reprinted by permission of the author and the author's agent, Robert P. Mills Ltd.

ment, in spite of their abilities and rank. In this they were similar, but physically they were opposite. Torrence was a bear, though a small one, a black bear with hair sprouting thickly on his knuckles, twisting out of his white cuffs and lining his ears. His beard was full and thick, rising high up on his cheekbones and dropping low on his chest.

Where Torrence was dark Numen was fair, where short he was tall, where thick, thin. A thin bow of a man, bent forward with a scholar's stoop and, though balding now, his hair was still curled and blond and very like the golden ringlets of the boy asleep upstairs. Now he took the toy animal and led the way to the shielded room deep in the house where Eigg was waiting.

"Give it here—here!" Eigg snapped when they came in, and reached for the toy. Eigg was always like that, in a hurry, surly, square and solid with his stocky body pressed into a spotless white laboratory smock. But they needed him.

"You needn't," Numen said, but Eigg had already pulled it from his grasp. "It won't like it, I know. . . ."

"Let me go . . . let me go . . . !" the teddy bear said with a hopeless shrill.

"It is just a machine," Eigg said coldly, putting it face down on the table and reaching for a scalpel. "You are a grown man, you should be more logical, have your emotions under greater control. You are speaking with your childhood memories, seeing your own boyhood teddy who was your friend and companion. This is just a machine." With a quick slash he opened the fabric over the seam seal and touched it: the plastic-fur back gaped open like a mouth.

"Let me go . . . let me go . . . ," the teddy bear wailed and its stumpy arms and legs waved back and forth. Both of the onlookers went white.

"Must we . . . ?"

"Emotions. Control them," Eigg said and probed with a screwdriver. There was a click and the toy went limp. He began to unscrew a plate in the mechanism.

Numen turned away and found that he had to touch a handkerchief to his face. Eigg was right. He was being emotional and this was just a machine. How did he dare get emotional over it considering what they had in mind?

"How long will it take?" He looked at his watch; it was a little past 2100.[1]

"We have been over this before, and discussing it again will not change any of the factors." Eigg's voice was distant as he removed the tiny plate and began to examine the machine's interior with a magnifying probe. "I have experimented on the three stolen teddy tapes, carefully timing myself at every step. I do not count removal or restoral of the tape, that is just a few minutes for each. The tracking and altering of the tape in both instances took me under ten hours. My best time differed from my worst time by less than fifteen minutes,

---

1. *2100*. In military services and in some countries, time is recorded by counting the day's hours from 0100 to 2400; thus, 2100 represents 9:00 P.M.

which is not significant. We can therefore safely say—ahh"—he was silent for a moment while he removed the capsule of the memory spools—"we can safely say that this is a ten-hour operation."

"That is too long. The boy is usually awake by seven; we must have the teddy back by then. He must never suspect that it has been away."

"There is little risk, you can give him some excuse for the time. I will not rush and spoil the work. Now be silent."

The two governmental specialists could only sit back and watch while Eigg inserted the capsule into the bulky machine he had secretly assembled in the room. This was not their specialty.

"Let me go . . . ," the tiny voice said from the wall speaker, then was interrupted by a burst of static. "Let me go . . . bzzzt . . . no, no, Davy, Daddy wouldn't like you to do that . . . fork in left, knife in right . . . bzzzt . . . if you do you'll have to wipe . . . good boy good boy good boy. . . ."

The voice squeaked and whispered and went on, while the hours on the clock went by one by one. Numen brought in coffee more than once, and towards dawn Torrence fell asleep sitting up in the chair, only to wake with a guilty start. Of them all Eigg showed no strain nor fatigue, working the controls with fingers regular as a metronome. The reedy voice of the capsule shrilled thinly through the night like the memory of a ghost.

"It is done," Eigg said, sealing the fabric with quick surgeon's stitches.

"Your fastest time ever," Numen sighed with relief. He glanced at the nursery viewscreen that showed his son, still asleep, starkly clear in the harsh infrared light. "And the boy is still asleep. There will be no problem getting it back after all. But is the tape——"

"It is right, perfect, you heard that. You asked the questions and heard the answers. I have concealed all traces of the alteration and unless you know what to look for you would never find the changes. In every other way the memory and instructions are like all others. There has just been this single change made."

"Pray God we never have to use it," Numen said.

"I did not know that you were religious," Eigg said, turning to look at him, his face expressionless. The magnifying loupe was still in his eye, and it stared, five times the size of its fellow, a large and coldly probing questioner.

"I'm not," Numen said, flushing.

"We must get the teddy back," Torrence broke in. "The boy just stirred."

Davy was a good boy and, when he grew older, a good student in school. Even after he began classes he kept Teddy around and talked to him while he did his homework.

"How much is seven and five, Teddy?"

The furry toy bear rolled its eyes and clapped stub paws. "Davy knows . . . shouldn't ask Teddy what Davy knows. . . ."

"Sure I know—I just wanted to see if you did. The answer is thirteen."

"Davy . . . the answer is twelve . . . you better study harder Davy . . . that's what Teddy says. . . ."

"Fooled you!" Davy laughed. "Made you tell me the answer!" He was learning ways to get around the robot controls, permanently fixed to answer the questions of a smaller child. Teddies have the vocabulary and outlook of the very young because their job must be done during the formative years. Teddies teach diction and life history and morals and group adjustment and vocabulary and grammar and all the other things that enable men to live together as social animals. A teddy's job is done early in the most plastic stages of a child's life, and by the very nature of its task its conversation must be simple and limited. But effective. Teddies are eventually discarded as childish toys, but by then the job is complete.

By the time Davy became David and was eighteen years old, Teddy had long since been retired behind a row of books on a high shelf. He was an old friend who had outgrown his useful days, but he was still a friend and certainly couldn't be discarded. Not that Davy ever thought of it that way. Teddy was just Teddy and that was that. The nursery was now a study, his cot a bed, and with his birthday past David was packing because he was going away to the university. He was sealing his bag when the phone bleeped and he saw his father's tiny image on the screen.

"David . . ."

"What is it, Father?"

"Would you mind coming down to the library now. There is something rather important . . ."

David squinted at the screen and noticed for the first time that his father's face had a pinched, sick look. His heart gave a quick jump.

"I'll be right down!"

Dr. Eigg was there, arms crossed and sitting almost at attention. So was Torrence, his father's oldest friend, who, though no relation, David had always called Uncle Torrence. And his father, obviously ill at ease about something. David came in quietly, conscious of all their eyes upon him as he crossed the room and took a chair. He was very much like his father, with the same build and height, a relaxed, easy-to-know boy with very few problems in life.

"Is something wrong?" he asked.

"Not wrong, Davy," his father said. He must be upset, David thought, he hasn't called me that in years. "Or rather something *is* wrong, but with the state of the world, and has been for a long time."

"Oh, the Panstentialists," David said, and relaxed a little. He had been hearing about the evils of Panstentialism as long as he could remember. It was just politics; he had been thinking something very personal was wrong.

"Yes, Davy, I imagine you know all about them now. When your mother and I separated I promised to raise you to the best of my ability and I think I have. But I'm a governor and all my friends work in government so I'm sure you have heard a lot of political talk in this house. You know our feelings and I think you share them."

"I do—and I think I would have no matter where I grew up. Panstentialism is an oppressing philosophy and one that perpetuates itself in power."

"Exactly. And one man, Barre, is at the heart of it. He stays in the seat of government and will not relinquish it and, with the rejuvenation treatments, will be there for a hundred years more."

"Barre must go!" Eigg snapped. "For twenty-three years now he has ruled and forbidden the continuation of my experiments. Young man, he has stopped my work for a longer time than you have been alive, do you realize that?"

David nodded, but did not comment. What little he had read about Dr. Eigg's proposed researches into behavioral human embryology had repelled him and, secretly, he was in agreement with Barre's ban on the work. But Panstentialism was different; he was truly in agreement with his father. This do-nothing philosophy lay a heavy and dusty hand on the world of politics—as well as the world at large.

"I'm not speaking only for myself," Numen said, his face white and strained, "but for everyone in the world and in the system who is against Barre and his philosophies. I have not held a government position for over twenty years—nor has Torrence here—but I think he'll agree that this is a small thing. If this was a service to the people we would gladly suffer it. Or if our persecution was the only negative result of Barre's evil works I would do nothing to stop him."

"I am in complete agreement," Torrence nodded. "The fate of two men is of no importance in comparison with the fate of us all. Nor is the fate of one man."

"Exactly!" Numen sprang to his feet and began to pace agitatedly up and down the room. "If that were not true, if it were not the heart of the problem, I would never consider being involved. There would *be* no problem if Barre suffered a heart attack and fell dead tomorrow."

The three older men were all looking at David now, though he didn't know why, and he felt they were waiting for him to say something.

"Well, yes—I agree. A little embolism[2] right now would be the best thing for the world that I can think of. Barre dead would be of far greater service to mankind than Barre alive has ever been."

The silence lengthened, became embarrassing, and it was finally Eigg who broke it with his dry, mechanical tones.

"We are all then in agreement that Barre's death would be of immense benefit. In that case, David, you must also agree that it would be fine if he could be . . . killed. . . ."

"Not a bad idea," David said, wondering where all this talk was going, "though of course it's a physical impossibility. It must be centuries since the last . . . what's the word . . . 'murder' took place.

---

2. *embolism,* an obstruction in a blood vessel due to a clot, air bubble, or globule of fat, that is carried in the bloodstream. A heart attack may be caused by an embolism in a blood vessel which leads directly to the heart.

The developmental psychology work took care of that a long time ago. As the twig is bent and all that sort of thing. Wasn't that supposed to be the discovery that finally separated man from the lower orders, the proof that we could entertain the thought of killing and even discuss it, yet still be trained in our early childhood so that we would not be capable of the act? If you can believe the textbooks, the human race has progressed immeasurably since the curse of killing has been removed. Look—do you mind if I ask just what this is all about?"

"Barre can be killed," Eigg said in an almost inaudible voice. "There is one man in the world who can kill him."

"WHO?" David asked, and in some terrible way he knew the answer even before the words came from his father's trembling lips.

"You, David . . . you. . . ."

He sat, unmoving, and his thoughts went back through the years and a number of things that had been bothering him were now made clear. His attitudes that were so subtly different from his friends', and that time with the plane when one of the rotors had killed a squirrel. Little, puzzling things, and sometimes worrying ones that had kept him awake long after the rest of the house was asleep. It was true, he knew it without a shadow of a doubt, and wondered why he had never realized it before. But it was like a hideous statue buried in the ground beneath one's feet; it had always been there but had never been visible until he had dug down and reached it. But he could see it now with all the earth scraped from its vile face and all the lineaments of evil clearly revealed. "You want me to kill Barre?" he asked.

"You're the only one who can . . . Davy . . . and it must be done. For all these years I have hoped against hope that it would not be necessary, that the . . . ability you have would not be used. But Barre lives. For all our sakes he must die."

"There is one thing I don't understand," David said, rising and looking out of the window at the familiar view of the trees and the distant, glass-canopied highway. "How was this change made? How could I miss the conditioning that is supposed to be a normal part of existence in this world?"

"It was your teddy bear," Eigg explained. "It is not publicized, but the reaction to killing is established at a very early age by the tapes in the machine that every child has. Later education is just reinforcement, valueless without the earlier indoctrination."

"Then my teddy . . ."

"I altered its tapes, in just that one way, so this part of your education would be missed. Nothing else was changed."

"It was enough, Doctor," there was a coldness to his voice that had never existed before. "How is Barre supposed to be killed?"

"With this." Eigg removed a package from the table drawer and carefully opened it. "This is a primitive weapon from a museum. I have repaired it and charged it with the projectile devices that are called 'shells.'" He held the sleek, ugly, black thing in his hand. "It is fully automatic in operation. When this device—the trigger—is depressed, a chemical reaction propels a copper and lead weight named a 'bullet' directly from the front orifice. The line of flight of the bullet is along an imaginary path extended from these two grooves on the top of the device. The bullet of course falls by gravity but in a minimum distance, say a metre,[3] this fall is negligible." He put it down suddenly on the table. "It is called a 'gun'."

David reached over slowly and picked it up. How well it fitted into his hand, sitting with such precise balance. He raised it, sighting across the grooves, and pulled the trigger. It exploded with an immense roar and jumped in his hand. The bullet plunged into Eigg's chest just over his heart with such a great impact that the man and the chair he had been sitting in were hurled backwards to the floor. The bullet also tore a great hole in his flesh and Eigg's throat choked with blood and he died.

"David! What are you doing?" His father's voice cracked with uncomprehending horror. David turned away from the thing on the floor, still apparently unmoved by what he had done.

"Don't you understand, Father? Barre and his Panstentialists are a terrible burden on the world and many suffer and freedom is abridged and all the other things that are wrong, that we know should not be. But don't you see the difference? You yourself said that things will change after Barre's death. The world will move on. So how is his crime to be compared to the crime of bringing *this* back into existence?" He shot his father quickly and efficiently before the older man could realize the import of his words and suffer with the knowledge of what was coming. Torrence screamed and ran to the door, fumbling with terrified fingers for the lock. David shot him too, but not very well since he was so far away, and the bullet lodged in his body and made him fall. David walked over and ignoring the screamings and bubbled words, took careful aim at the twisting head and blew out the man's brains.

Now the gun was heavy and he was very tired. The lift shaft took him up to his room and he had to stand on a chair to take Teddy down from behind the books on the high shelf. The little furry animal sat in the middle of the large bed and rolled its eyes and wagged its stubby arms.

"Teddy," he said, "I'm going to pull up flowers from the flower bed."

"No, Davy . . . pulling up flowers is naughty . . . don't pull up the flowers. . . ." The little voice squeaked and the arms waved.

"Teddy, I'm going to break a window."

"No, Davy . . . breaking windows is naughty . . . don't break any windows. . . ."

"Teddy, I'm going to kill a man."

Silence, just silence. Even the eyes and arms were still.

The roar of the gun broke the silence and blew a ruin of gears, wires and bent metal from the back of the destroyed teddy bear.

"Teddy . . . oh, Teddy . . . you should have told me," David said and dropped the gun and at last was crying. ◼

---

3. *metre*, the basic unit of length in the metric system, equaling approximately 39.37 inches.

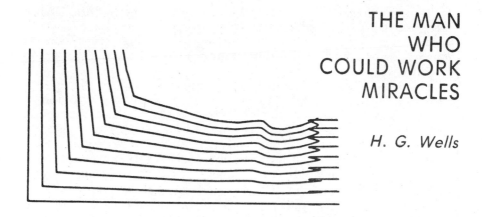

THE MAN WHO COULD WORK MIRACLES

H. G. Wells

A PANTOUM[1] IN PROSE

IT IS DOUBTFUL WHETHER the gift was innate. For my own part, I think it came to him suddenly. Indeed, until he was thirty he was a sceptic, and did not believe in miraculous powers. And here, since it is the most convenient place, I must mention that he was a little man, and had eyes of a hot brown, very erect red hair, a moustache with ends that he twisted up, and freckles. His name was George McWhirter Fotheringay—not the sort of name by any means to lead to any expectation of miracles—and he was clerk at Gomshott's. He was greatly addicted to assertive argument. It was while he was asserting the impossibility of miracles that he had his first intimation of his extraordinary powers. This particular argument was being held in the bar of the Long Dragon, and Toddy Beamish was conducting the opposition by a monotonous but effective "So *you* say," that drove Mr. Fotheringay to the very limit of his patience.

There were present, besides these two, a very dusty cyclist, Landlord Cox, and Miss Maybridge, the perfectly respectable and rather portly barmaid of the Dragon. Miss Maybridge was standing with her back to Mr. Fotheringay, washing glasses; the others were watching him, more or less amused by the present ineffectiveness of the assertive method. Goaded by the Torres Vedras tactics[2] of Mr. Beamish, Mr.

"The Man Who Could Work Miracles" from THE SHORT STORIES OF H. G. WELLS. Reprinted by permission of the Estate of the late H. G. Wells.

1. *Pantoum*, a Malayan rhymed verse form in which lines are repeated according to a set pattern, until the final four-line stanza ends with the very same line that opened the poem. 2. *Torres Vedras tactics*, an unyielding defensive barrier. In 1810 the town of Torres Vedras in Portugal was made the strong point of fortified lines by which a weak Portuguese and British army blocked Napoleon's powerful French forces from capturing Lisbon.

Fotheringay determined to make an unusual rhetorical effort. "Looky here, Mr. Beamish," said Mr. Fotheringay. "Let us clearly understand what a miracle is. It's something contrariwise to the course of Nature done by power of Will, something what couldn't happen without being specially willed."

"So *you* say," said Mr. Beamish, repulsing him.

Mr. Fotheringay appealed to the cyclist, who had hitherto been a silent auditor, and received his assent—given with a hesitating cough and a glance at Mr. Beamish. The landlord would express no opinion, and Mr. Fotheringay, returning to Mr. Beamish, received the unexpected concession of a qualified assent to his definition of a miracle.

"For instance," said Mr. Fotheringay, greatly encouraged, "here would be a miracle. That lamp, in the natural course of Nature, couldn't burn like that upsy-down, could it, Beamish?"

"*You* say it couldn't," said Beamish.

"And you?" said Fotheringay. "You don't mean to say—eh?"

"No," said Beamish reluctantly. "No, it couldn't."

"Very well," said Mr. Fotheringay. "Then here comes someone, as it might be me, along here, and stands as it might be here, and says to that lamp, as I might do, collecting all my will—'Turn upsy-down without breaking, and go on burning steady, and——' Hullo!"

It was enough to make anyone say "Hullo!" The impossible, the incredible, was visible to them all. The lamp hung inverted in the air, burning quietly with its flame pointing down. It was as solid, as indisputable as ever a lamp was, the prosaic common lamp of the Long Dragon bar.

Mr. Fotheringay stood with an extended forefinger and the knitted brows of one anticipating a catastrophic smash. The cyclist, who was sitting next the lamp, ducked and jumped across the bar. Everybody jumped, more or less. Miss Maybridge turned and screamed. For nearly three seconds the lamp remained still. A faint cry of mental distress came from Mr. Fotheringay. "I can't keep it up," he said, "any longer." He staggered back, and the inverted lamp suddenly flared, fell against the corner of the bar, bounced aside, smashed upon the floor, and went out.

It was lucky it had a metal receiver, or the whole place would have been in a blaze. Mr. Cox was the first to speak, and his remark, shorn of needless excrescences, was to the effect that Fotheringay was a fool. Fotheringay was beyond disputing even so fundamental a proposition as that! He was astonished beyond measure at the thing that had occurred. The subsequent conversation threw absolutely no light on the matter so far as Fotheringay was concerned; the general opinion not only followed Mr. Cox very closely but very vehemently. Everyone accused Fotheringay of a silly trick, and presented him to himself as a foolish destroyer of comfort and security. His mind was in a tornado of perplexity, he was himself inclined to agree with them, and he made a remarkably ineffectual opposition to the proposal of his departure.

He went home flushed and heated, coat collar crumpled, eyes

smarting and ears red. He watched each of the ten street lamps nervously as he passed it. It was only when he found himself alone in his little bedroom in Church Row that he was able to grapple seriously with his memories of the occurrence and ask, "What on earth happened?"

He had removed his coat and boots, and was sitting on the bed with his hands in his pockets repeating the text of his defence for the seventeenth time, "*I* didn't want the confounded thing to upset," when it occurred to him that at the precise moment he had said the commanding words he had inadvertently willed the thing he said, and that when he had seen the lamp in the air he had felt that it depended on him to maintain it there without being clear how this was to be done. He had not a particularly complex mind, or he might have stuck for a time at that "inadvertently willed," embracing, as it does, the abstrusest problems of voluntary action; but as it was, the idea came to him with a quite acceptable haziness. And from that, following, as I must admit, no clear logical path, he came to the test of experiment.

He pointed resolutely to his candle and collected his mind, though he felt he did a foolish thing. "Be raised up," he said. But in a second that feeling vanished. The candle was raised, hung in the air one giddy moment, and as Mr. Fotheringay gasped, fell with a smash on his toilet-table, leaving him in darkness save for the expiring glow of its wick.

For a time Mr. Fotheringay sat in the darkness, perfectly still. "It did happen, after all," he said. "And 'ow I'm to explain it I *don't* know." He sighed heavily, and began feeling in his pockets for a match. He could find none, and he rose and groped about the toilet-table. "I wish I had a match," he said. He resorted to his coat, and there were none there, and then it dawned upon him that miracles were possible even with matches. He extended a hand and scowled at it in the dark. "Let there be a match in that hand," he said. He felt some light object fall across his palm, and his fingers closed upon a match.

After several ineffectual attempts to light this, he discovered it was a safety match. He threw it down, and then it occurred to him that he might have willed it lit. He did, and perceived it burning in the midst of his toilet-table mat. He caught it up hastily, and it went out. His perception of possibilities enlarged, and he felt for and replaced the candle in its candlestick. "Here! *you* be lit," said Mr. Fotheringay, and forthwith the candle was flaring, and he saw a little black hole in the toilet-cover, with a wisp of smoke rising from it. For a time he stared from this to the little flame and back, and then looked up and met his own gaze in the looking glass. By this help he communed with himself in silence for a time.

"How about miracles now?" said Mr. Fotheringay at last, addressing his reflection.

The subsequent meditations of Mr. Fotheringay were of a severe but confused description. So far as he could see, it was a case of pure willing with him. The nature of his first experiences disinclined him for any further experiments except of the most cautious type. But he lifted a sheet of paper, and turned a glass of water pink and then green, and he created a snail, which he miraculously annihilated, and got himself a miraculous new toothbrush. Somewhen in the small hours he had reached the fact that his willpower must be of a particularly rare and pungent quality, a fact of which he had certainly had inklings before, but no certain assurance. The scare and perplexity of his first discovery was now qualified by pride in this evidence of singularity and by vague intimations of advantage. He became aware that the church clock was striking one, and as it did not occur to him that his daily duties at Gomshott's might be miraculously dispensed with, he resumed undressing, in order to get to bed without further delay. As he struggled to get his shirt over his head, he was struck with a brilliant idea. "Let me be in bed," he said, and found himself so. "Undressed," he stipulated; and, finding the sheets cold, added hastily, "and in my nightshirt—no, in a nice soft woollen nightshirt. Ah!" he said with immense enjoyment. "And now let me be comfortably asleep. . . ."

He awoke at his usual hour and was pensive all through breakfast-time, wondering whether his overnight experience might not be a particularly vivid dream. At length his mind turned again to cautious experiments. For instance, he had three eggs for breakfast; two his landlady had supplied, good, but shoppy, and one was a delicious fresh goose egg, laid, cooked, and served by his extraordinary will. He hurried off to Gomshott's in a state of profound but carefully concealed excitement, and only remembered the shell of the third egg when his landlady spoke of it that night. All day he could do no work because of this astonishingly new self-knowledge, but this caused him no inconvenience, because he made up for it miraculously in his last ten minutes.

As the day wore on his state of mind passed from wonder to elation, albeit the circumstances of his dismissal from the Long Dragon were still disagreeable to recall, and a garbled account of the matter that had reached his colleagues led to some badinage. It was evident he must be careful how he lifted frangible articles, but in other ways his gift promised more and more as he turned it over in his mind. He intended among other things to increase his personal property by unostentatious acts of creation. He called into existence a pair of very splendid diamond studs, and hastily annihilated them again as young Gomshott came across the countinghouse to his desk. He was afraid young Gomshott might wonder how he had come by them. He saw quite clearly the gift required caution and watchfulness in its exercise, but so far as he could judge the difficulties attending its mastery would be no greater than those he had already faced in the study of cycling. It was that analogy, perhaps, quite as much as the feeling that he would be unwelcome in the Long Dragon, that drove him out after supper into the lane beyond the gasworks, to rehearse a few miracles in private.

There was possibly a certain want of originality in his attempts, for apart from his willpower Mr. Fotheringay was not a very exceptional man. The miracle of Moses's rod came to his mind, but the night was dark and unfavourable to the proper control of large miraculous snakes. Then he recollected the story of *Tannhäuser*[3] that he had read on the back of the Philharmonic programme. That seemed to him singularly attractive and harmless. He stuck his walking stick—a very nice Poona-Penang lawyer[4]—into the turf that edged the footpath, and commanded the dry wood to blossom. The air was immediately full of the scent of roses, and by means of a match he saw for himself that this beautiful miracle was indeed accomplished. His satisfaction was ended by advancing footsteps. Afraid of a premature discovery of his powers, he addressed the blossoming stick hastily: "Go back." What he meant was "Change back"; but of course he was confused. The stick receded at a considerable velocity, and incontinently came a cry of anger and a bad word from the approaching person.

"Who are you throwing brambles at, you fool?" cried a voice. "That got me on the shin."

"I'm sorry, old chap," said Mr. Fotheringay, and then realising the awkward nature of the explanation, caught nervously at his moustache. He saw Winch, one of the three Immering constables, advancing.

"What d'yer mean by it?" asked the constable. "Hullo! It's you, is it? The gent that broke the lamp at the Long Dragon!"

"I don't mean anything by it," said Mr. Fotheringay. "Nothing at all."

"What d'yer do it for then?"

"Oh, bother!" said Mr. Fotheringay.

"Bother indeed! D'yer know that stick hurt? What d'yer do it for, eh?"

For the moment Mr. Fotheringay could not think what he had done it for. His silence seemed to irritate Mr. Winch. "You've been assaulting the police, young man, this time. That's what *you* done."

"Look here, Mr. Winch," said Mr. Fotheringay, annoyed and confused, "I'm very sorry. The fact is——"

"Well?"

He could think of no way but the truth. "I was working a miracle." He tried to speak in an offhand way, but try as he would he couldn't.

"Working a——! 'Ere, don't you talk rot. Working a miracle, indeed! Miracle! Well, that's downright funny! Why, you's the chap that don't believe in miracles. . . . Fact is, this is another of your silly conjuring tricks—that's what this is. Now, I tell you——"

---

3. *Tannhäuser.* In an opera of that title by the German composer Richard Wagner, the knight, Tannhäuser, is warned that it is just as impossible for his dreadful sins to be forgiven, as for his walking staff to blossom. But, as he dies in true penitence on the coffin of the woman he loved, yet betrayed, his staff begins to grow leaves. 4. *Poona-Penang lawyer,* a cane made from the wood of the East Indian poona tree. Apparently they were called "Penang lawyers" in Wells's time because on Penang Island in Malaya men often used such sticks to settle their quarrels.

But Mr. Fotheringay never heard what Mr. Winch was going to tell him. He realised he had given himself away, flung his valuable secret to all the winds of heaven. A violent gust of irritation swept him to action. He turned on the constable swiftly and fiercely. "Here," he said, "I've had enough of this, I have! I'll show you a silly conjuring trick, I will! Go to Hades! Go, now!"

He was alone!

Mr. Fotheringay performed no more miracles that night, nor did he trouble to see what had become of his flowering stick. He returned to the town, scared and very quiet, and went to his bedroom. "Lord!" he said, "it's a powerful gift—an extremely powerful gift. I didn't hardly mean as much as that. Not really. . . . I wonder what Hades is like!"

He sat on the bed taking off his boots. Struck by a happy thought he transferred the constable to San Francisco, and without any more interference with normal causation went soberly to bed. In the night he dreamt of the anger of Winch.

The next day Mr. Fotheringay heard two interesting items of news. Someone had planted a most beautiful climbing rose against the elder Mr. Gomshott's private house in the Lullaborough Road, and the river as far as Rawling's Mill was to be dragged for Constable Winch.

Mr. Fotheringay was abstracted and thoughtful all that day, and performed no miracles except certain provisions for Winch, and the miracle of completing his day's work with punctual perfection in spite of all the bee-swarm of thoughts that hummed through his mind. And the extraordinary abstraction and meekness of his manner was remarked by several people, and made a matter of jesting. For the most part he was thinking of Winch.

On Sunday evening he went to chapel, and oddly enough, Mr. Maydig, who took a certain interest in occult matters, preached about "things that are not lawful." Mr. Fotheringay was not a regular chapelgoer, but the system of assertive scepticism, to which I have already alluded, was now very much shaken. The tenor of the sermon threw an entirely new light on these novel gifts, and he suddenly decided to consult Mr. Maydig immediately after the service. So soon as that was determined, he found himself wondering why he had not done so before.

Mr. Maydig, a lean, excitable man with quite remarkably long wrists and neck, was gratified at a request for a private conversation from a young man whose carelessness in religious matters was a subject for general remark in the town. After a few necessary delays, he conducted him to the study of the Manse,[5] which was contiguous to the chapel, seated him comfortably, and, standing in front of a cheerful fire—his legs threw a Rhodian arch[6] of shadow on the opposite wall—requested Mr. Fotheringay to state his business.

At first Mr. Fotheringay was a little abashed, and found some

---

5. *Manse*, the house which a congregation provides for its minister. 6. *Rhodian arch*. Among the Seven Wonders of the Ancient World was the Colossus of Rhodes, a bronze statue of Apollo about one hundred feet tall, in the Greek island-seaport of Rhodes. An inaccurate tradition held that its legs actually formed a huge arch across the harbor-mouth, beneath which ships sailed.

difficulty in opening the matter. "You will scarcely believe me, Mr. Maydig, I am afraid——" and so forth for some time. He tried a question at last, and asked Mr. Maydig his opinion of miracles.

Mr. Maydig was still saying "Well" in an extremely judicial tone, when Mr. Fotheringay interrupted again: "You don't believe, I suppose, that some common sort of person—like myself, for instance—as it might be sitting here now, might have some sort of twist inside him that made him able to do things by his will?"

"It's possible," said Mr. Maydig. "Something of the sort, perhaps, is possible."

"If I might make free with something here, I think I might show you by a sort of experiment," said Mr. Fotheringay. "Now, take that tobacco jar on the table, for instance. What I want to know is whether what I am going to do with it is a miracle or not. Just half a minute, Mr. Maydig, please."

He knitted his brows, pointed to the tobacco jar and said: "Be a bowl of vi'lets."

The tobacco jar did as it was ordered.

Mr. Maydig started violently at the change, and stood looking from the thaumaturgist[7] to the bowl of flowers. He said nothing. Presently, he ventured to lean over the table and smell the violets; they were fresh-picked and very fine ones. Then he stared at Mr. Fotheringay again.

"How did you do that?" he asked.

Mr. Fotheringay pulled his moustache. "Just told it—and there you are. Is that a miracle, or is it black art, or what is it? And what do you think's the matter with me? That's what I want to ask."

"It's a most extraordinary occurrence."

"And this day last week I knew no more that I could do things like that than you did. It came quite sudden. It's something odd about my will, I suppose, and that's as far as I can see."

"Is *that* the only thing? Could you do other things besides that?"

"Lord, yes!" said Mr. Fotheringay. "Just anything." He thought, and suddenly recalled a conjuring entertainment he had seen. "Here!" He pointed. "Change into a bowl of fish—no, not that—change into a glass bowl full of water with goldfish swimming in it. That's better! You see that, Mr. Maydig?"

"It's astonishing. It's incredible. You are either a most extraordinary.... But no——"

"I could change it into anything," said Mr. Fotheringay. "Just anything. Here! be a pigeon, will you?"

In another moment a blue pigeon was fluttering round the room and making Mr. Maydig duck every time it came near him. "Stop there, will you," said Mr. Fotheringay; and the pigeon hung motionless in the air. "I could change it back to a bowl of flowers," he said, and after replacing the pigeon on the table worked that miracle. "I expect you will want your pipe in a bit," he said, and restored the tobacco jar.

---

7. *thaumaturgist,* miracle worker.

Mr. Maydig had followed all these later changes in a sort of ejaculatory silence. He stared at Mr. Fotheringay and, in a very gingerly manner, picked up the tobacco jar, examined it, replaced it on the table. *"Well!"* was the only expression of his feelings.

"Now, after that, it's easier to explain what I came about," said Mr. Fotheringay; and proceeded to a lengthy and involved narrative of his strange experiences, beginning with the affair of the lamp in the Long Dragon and complicated by persistent allusions to Winch. As he went on, the transient pride Mr. Maydig's consternation had caused passed away; he became the very ordinary Mr. Fotheringay of everyday intercourse again.

Mr. Maydig listened intently, the tobacco jar in his hand, and his bearing changed also with the course of the narrative. Presently, while Mr. Fotheringay was dealing with the miracle of the third egg, the minister interrupted with a fluttering extended hand——

"It is possible," he said. "It is credible. It is amazing, of course, but it reconciles a number of difficulties. The power to work miracles is a gift—a peculiar quality like genius or second sight—hitherto it has come very rarely and to exceptional people. But in this case . . . I have always wondered at the miracles of Mahomet, and at Yogi's miracles, and the miracles of Madame Blavatsky. But, of course! Yes, it is simply a gift! It carries out so beautifully the arguments of the great thinker"—Mr. Maydig's voice sank—"his Grace the Duke of Argyll.[8] Here we plumb some profounder law—deeper than the ordinary laws of Nature. Yes—yes. Go on. Go on!"

Mr. Fotheringay proceeded to tell of his misadventure with Winch, and Mr. Maydig, no longer overawed or scared, began to jerk his limbs about and interject astonishment. "It's this what troubled me most," proceeded Mr. Fotheringay; "it's this I'm most mijitly in want of advice for; of course he's at San Francisco—wherever San Francisco may be—but of course it's awkward for both of us, as you'll see, Mr. Maydig. I don't see how he can understand what has happened, and I dare say he's scared and exasperated, something tremendous, and trying to get at me. I dare say he keeps on starting off to come here. I send him back, by a miracle, every few hours, when I think of it. And, of course, that's a thing he won't be able to understand, and it's bound to annoy him; and, of course, if he takes a ticket every time it will cost him a lot of money. I done the best I could for him, but of course it's difficult for him to put himself in my place. I thought afterwards that his clothes might have got scorched, you know—if Hades is all it's supposed to be— before I shifted him. In that case I suppose they'd have locked him up in San Francisco. Of course I willed him a new suit of clothes on him directly I thought of it. But, you see, I'm already in a deuce of a tangle——"

Mr. Maydig looked serious. "I see you are in a tangle. Yes, it's a

---

8. *Madame Blavatsky . . . the Duke of Argyll.* Helena Petrovna Blavatsky (1831-1891) was a Russian occultist. George Campbell, Duke of Argyll (1823-1900), was a British government official and author. A frequent theme in his books is that modern scientific principles prove the truth of Biblical miracles, instead of contradicting them.

difficult position. How you are to end it. . . ." He became diffuse and inconclusive.

"However, we'll leave Winch for a little and discuss the larger question. I don't think this is a case of black art or anything of the sort. I don't think there is any taint of criminality about it all, Mr. Fotheringay—none whatever, unless you are suppressing material facts. No, it's miracles—pure miracles—miracles, if I may say so, of the very highest class."

He began to pace the hearthrug and gesticulate, while Mr. Fotheringay sat with his arm on the table and his head on his arm, looking worried. "I don't see how I'm to manage about Winch," he said.

"A gift of working miracles—apparently a very powerful gift," said Mr. Maydig, "will find a way about Winch—never fear. My dear sir, you are a most important man—a man of the most astonishing possibilities. As evidence, for example! And in other ways, the things you may do. . . ."

"Yes, *I've* thought of a thing or two," said Mr. Fotheringay. "But— some of the things came a bit twisty. You saw that fish at first? Wrong sort of bowl and wrong sort of fish. And I thought I'd ask someone."

"A proper course," said Mr. Maydig, "a very proper course— altogether the proper course." He stopped and looked at Mr. Fotheringay. "It's practically an unlimited gift. Let us test your powers, for instance. If they really *are* . . . if they really are all they seem to be."

And so, incredible as it may seem, in the study of the little house behind the Congregational Chapel, on the evening of Sunday, Nov. 10, 1896, Mr. Fotheringay, egged on and inspired by Mr. Maydig, began to work miracles. The reader's attention is specially and definitely called to the date. He will object, probably has already objected, that certain points in this story are improbable, that if any things of the sort already described had indeed occurred, they would have been in all the papers a year ago. The details immediately following he will find particularly hard to accept, because among other things they involve the conclusion that he or she, the reader in question, must have been killed in a violent and unprecedented manner more than a year ago. Now a miracle is nothing if not improbable, and as a matter of fact the reader *was* killed in a violent and unprecedented manner a year ago. In the subsequent course of this story that will become perfectly clear and credible, as every right-minded and reasonable reader will admit. But this is not the place for the end of the story, being but little beyond the hither side of the middle. And at first the miracles worked by Mr. Fotheringay were timid little miracles—little things with the cups and parlour fitments, as feeble as the miracles of Theosophists,[9] and, feeble as they were, they were received with awe by his collaborator. He would have preferred to settle the Winch business out of hand but Mr. Maydig would not let him. But after they had worked a dozen of these

---

9. *Theosophists,* members of an international religious society founded in 1875, which takes its main mystical beliefs from Hinduism, but which tries to reveal basic truths supposedly shared by all religions. Its early leaders practiced a mysterious spiritualism and tried to demonstrate miraculous psychic powers.

domestic trivialities, their sense of power grew, their imagination began to show signs of stimulation, and their ambition enlarged. Their first larger enterprise was due to hunger and the negligence of Mrs. Minchin, Mr. Maydig's housekeeper. The meal to which the minister conducted Mr. Fotheringay was certainly ill-laid and uninviting as refreshment for two industrious miracle workers; but they were seated, and Mr. Maydig was descanting in sorrow rather than in anger upon his housekeeper's shortcomings, before it occurred to Mr. Fotheringay that an opportunity lay before him. "Don't you think, Mr. Maydig," he said, "if it isn't a liberty, I——"

"My dear Mr. Fotheringay! Of course! No—I didn't think."

Mr. Fotheringay waved his hand. "What shall we have?" he said, in a large, inclusive spirit, and, at Mr. Maydig's order, revised the supper very thoroughly. "As for me," he said, eyeing Mr. Maydig's selection, "I am always particularly fond of a tankard of stout and a nice Welsh rarebit, and I'll order that. I ain't much given to Burgundy," and forthwith stout and Welsh rarebit promptly appeared at his command. They sat long at their supper, talking like equals, as Mr. Fotheringay presently perceived with a glow of surprise and gratification, of all the miracles they would presently do. "And, by the bye, Mr. Maydig," said Mr. Fotheringay, "I might perhaps be able to help you—in a domestic way."

"Don't quite follow," said Mr. Maydig, pouring out a glass of miraculous old Burgundy.

Mr. Fotheringay helped himself to a second Welsh rarebit out of vacancy, and took a mouthful. "I was thinking," he said, "I might be able *(chum, chum)* to work *(chum, chum)* a miracle with Mrs. Minchin *(chum, chum)*—make her a better woman."

Mr. Maydig put down the glass and looked doubtful. "She's—— She strongly objects to interference, you know, Mr. Fotheringay. And—as a matter of fact—it's well past eleven and she's probably in bed and asleep. Do you think, on the whole——"

Mr. Fotheringay considered these objections. "I don't see that it shouldn't be done in her sleep."

For a time Mr. Maydig opposed the idea, and then he yielded. Mr. Fotheringay issued his orders, and a little less at their ease, perhaps, the two gentlemen proceeded with their repast. Mr. Maydig was enlarging on the changes he might expect in his housekeeper next day, with an optimism that seemed even to Mr. Fotheringay's supper senses a little forced and hectic, when a series of confused noises from upstairs began. Their eyes exchanged interrogations, and Mr. Maydig left the room hastily. Mr. Fotheringay heard him calling up to his housekeeper and then his footsteps going softly up to her.

In a minute or so the minister returned, his step light, his face radiant. "Wonderful!" he said, "and touching! Most touching!"

He began pacing the hearthrug. "A repentance—a most touching repentance—through the crack of the door. Poor woman! A most wonderful change! She had got up. She must have got up at once. She had got up out of her sleep to smash a private bottle of brandy in her box. And to confess it too! . . . But this gives us—it opens—a most amazing vista of possibilities. If we can work this miraculous change in *her.* . . ."

"The thing's unlimited seemingly," said Mr. Fotheringay. "And about Mr. Winch——"

"Altogether unlimited." And from the hearthrug Mr. Maydig, waving the Winch difficulty aside, unfolded a series of wonderful proposals—proposals he invented as he went along.

Now what those proposals were does not concern the essentials of this story. Suffice it that they were designed in a spirit of infinite benevolence, the sort of benevolence that used to be called postprandial.[10] Suffice it, too, that the problem of Winch remained unsolved. Nor is it necessary to describe how far that series got to its fulfilment. There were astonishing changes. The small hours found Mr. Maydig and Mr. Fotheringay careering across the chilly market square under the still Moon, in a sort of ecstasy of thaumaturgy, Mr. Maydig all flap and gesture, Mr. Fotheringay short and bristling, and no longer abashed at his greatness. They had reformed every drunkard in the Parliamentary division, changed all the beer and alcohol to water (Mr. Maydig had overruled Mr. Fotheringay on this point), they had, further, greatly improved the railway communication of the place, drained Flinder's swamp, improved the soil of One Tree Hill, and cured the Vicar's wart. And they were going to see what could be done with the injured pier at South Bridge.

"The place," gasped Mr. Maydig, "won't be the same place tomorrow. How surprised and thankful everyone will be!" And just at that moment the church clock struck three.

"I say," said Mr. Fotheringay, "that's three o'clock! I must be getting back. I've got to be at business by eight. And besides, Mrs. Wimms——"

"We're only beginning," said Mr. Maydig, full of the sweetness of unlimited power. "We're only beginning. Think of all the good we're doing. When people wake——"

"But——" said Mr. Fotheringay.

Mr. Maydig gripped his arm suddenly. His eyes were bright and wild. "My dear chap," he said, "there's no hurry. Look"—he pointed to the Moon at the zenith—"Joshua!"[11]

"Joshua?" said Mr. Fotheringay.

"Joshua," said Mr. Maydig. "Why not? Stop it."

Mr. Fotheringay looked at the Moon.

"That's a bit tall," he said after a pause.

"Why not?" said Mr. Maydig. "Of course it doesn't stop. You stop the rotation of the Earth, you know. Time stops. It isn't as if we were doing harm."

"H'm!" said Mr. Fotheringay. "Well." He sighed. "I'll try. Here——"

He buttoned up his jacket and addressed himself to the habitable

---

10. *postprandial,* after dining well. 11. *Joshua,* the general who led the Israelites out of the desert to conquer the Promised Land. In one battle Joshua is said to have prayed so that God stopped the sun and moon for a whole day until the Israelites could destroy the enemy totally. (Joshua 10:12-14)

globe, with as good an assumption of confidence as lay in his power. "Jest stop rotating, will you," said Mr. Fotheringay.

Incontinently he was flying head over heels through the air at the rate of dozens of miles a minute. In spite of the innumerable circles he was describing per second, he thought; for thought is wonderful— sometimes as sluggish as flowing pitch, sometimes as instantaneous as light. He thought in a second, and willed. "Let me come down safe and sound. Whatever else happens, let me down safe and sound."

He willed it only just in time, for his clothes, heated by his rapid flight through the air, were already beginning to singe. He came down with a forcible, but by no means injurious bump in what appeared to be a mound of fresh-turned earth. A large mass of metal and masonry, extraordinarily like the clock tower in the middle of the market square, hit the earth near him, ricochetted over him, and flew into stonework, bricks, and masonry, like a bursting bomb. A hurtling cow hit one of the large blocks and smashed like an egg. There was a crash that made all the most violent crashes of his past life seem like the sound of falling dust, and this was followed by a descending series of lesser crashes. A vast wind roared throughout Earth and heaven, so that he could scarcely lift his head to look. For a while he was too breathless and astonished even to see where he was or what had happened. And his first movement was to feel his head and reassure himself that his streaming hair was still his own.

"Lord!" gasped Mr. Fotheringay, scarce able to speak for the gale, "I've had a squeak! What's gone wrong? Storms and thunder. And only a minute ago a fine night. It's Maydig set me on to this sort of thing. *What* a wind! If I go on fooling in this way I'm bound to have a thundering accident! . . .

"Where's Maydig? What a confounded mess everything's in!"

He looked about him so far as his flapping jacket would permit. The appearance of things was really extremely strange. "The sky's all right anyhow," said Mr. Fotheringay. "And that's about all that is all right. And even there it looks like a terrific gale coming up. But there's the Moon overhead. Just as it was just now. Bright as midday. But as for the rest—— Where's the village? Where's—where's anything? And what on earth set this wind a-blowing? *I* didn't order no wind."

Mr. Fotheringay struggled to get to his feet in vain, and after one failure, remained on all fours, holding on. He surveyed the moonlit world to leeward, with the tails of his jacket streaming over his head. "There's something seriously wrong," said Mr. Fotheringay. "And what it is—goodness knows."

Far and wide nothing was visible in the white glare through the haze of dust that drove before a screaming gale but tumbled masses of earth and heaps of inchoate ruins, no trees, no houses, no familiar shapes, only a wilderness of disorder vanishing at last into the darkness beneath, the whirling columns and streamers, the lightnings and thunderings of a swiftly rising storm. Near him in the livid glare was something that might have once been an elm tree, a smashed mass of splinters, shivered from boughs to base, and further a twisted mass of iron girders—only too evidently the viaduct—rose out of the piled confusion.

You see, when Mr. Fotheringay had arrested the rotation of the solid globe, he had made no stipulation concerning the trifling movables upon its surface. And the Earth spins so fast that the surface at its equator is travelling at rather more than a thousand miles an hour, and in these latitudes at more than half that pace. So that the village, and Mr. Maydig, and Mr. Fotheringay, and everybody and everything had been jerked violently forward at about nine miles per second—that is to say, much more violently than if they had been fired out of a cannon. And every human being, every living creature, every house, and every tree—all the world as we know it—had been so jerked and smashed and utterly destroyed. That was all.

These things Mr. Fotheringay did not, of course, fully appreciate. But he perceived that his miracle had miscarried, and with that a great disgust of miracles came upon him. He was in darkness now, for the clouds had swept together and blotted out his momentary glimpse of the Moon, and the air was full of fitful struggling tortured wraiths of hail. A great roaring of wind and waters filled Earth and sky, and, peering under his hand through the dust and sleet to windward, he saw by the play of the lightnings a vast wall of water pouring towards him.

"Maydig!" screamed Mr. Fotheringay's feeble voice amid the elemental uproar. "Here!—Maydig!

"Stop!" cried Mr. Fotheringay to the advancing water. "Oh, for goodness' sake, stop!

"Just a moment," said Mr. Fotheringay to the lightnings and thunder. "Stop jest a moment while I collect my thoughts. . . . And now what shall I do?" he said. "What *shall* I do? Lord! I wish Maydig was about.

"I know," said Mr. Fotheringay. "And for goodness' sake let's have it right *this* time."

He remained on all fours, leaning against the wind, very intent to have everything right.

"Ah!" he said. "Let nothing what I'm going to order happen until I say 'Off!' . . . Lord! I wish I'd thought of that before!"

He lifted his little voice against the whirlwind, shouting louder and louder in the vain desire to hear himself speak. "Now then!—here goes! Mind about that what I said just now. In the first place, when all I've got to say is done, let me lose my miraculous power, let my will become just like anybody else's will, and all these dangerous miracles be stopped. I don't like them. I'd rather I didn't work 'em. Ever so much. That's the first thing. And the second is—let me be back just before the miracles begin; let everything be just as it was before that blessed lamp turned up. It's a big job, but it's the last. Have you got it? No more miracles, everything as it was—me back in the Long Dragon just before I drank my half-pint. That's it! Yes."

He dug his fingers into the mould, closed his eyes, and said "Off!"

Everything became perfectly still. He perceived that he was stand
ing erect.

"So *you* say," said a voice.

He opened his eyes. He was in the bar of the Long Dragon, arguing
about miracles with Toddy Beamish. He had a vague sense of some
great thing forgotten that instantaneously passed. You see, except for
the loss of his miraculous powers, everything was back as it had been;
his mind and memory therefore were now just as they had been at the
time when this story began. So that he knew absolutely nothing of all
that is told here, knows nothing of all that is told here to this day. And
among other things, of course, he still did not believe in miracles.

"I tell you that miracles, properly speaking, can't possibly happen,"
he said, "whatever you like to hold. And I'm prepared to prove it up to
the hilt."

"That's what *you* think," said Toddy Beamish, and "Prove it if you
can."

"Looky here, Mr. Beamish," said Mr. Fotheringay. "Let us clearly
understand what a miracle is. It's something contrariwise to the course
of Nature done by power of Will. . . ."

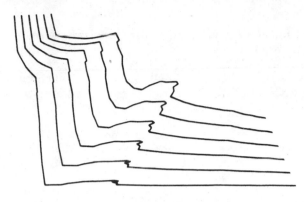

ECHOES
OF THE
MIND

Arthur Koestler

THERE IS NOW HARDLY A COUNTRY in the world which does not have one or several university departments engaged in parapsychological research[1]—with Russia leading the field. One would have thought that parapsychology would be regarded in the U.S.S.R. as a mortal heresy and betrayal of the materialistic creed. However, as early as 1916 the great Bechterev, associate of Pavlov,[2] started experiments in ESP; he called it "biological radio," which partly explains how he got away with it. Still, he and his colleagues had to keep pretty quiet about what they were doing. But in the early sixties a sudden change occurred. Leonid Vassiliev, Professor of Physiology at Leningrad University, a student of Bechterev's, published reports of some remarkable experiments in telehypnosis.[3] He claimed that hypnotized subjects had been made to awaken from trance by a telepathically transmitted command from a distance; and that hypnotized subjects standing upright were made to fall down by the same means. This was followed by other experiments in telepathic communication between distant towns, such as Moscow and Leningrad, carried out en masse with thousands of subjects. The number of scientific publications on parapsychology in Soviet Russia, which in 1958 had amounted to two, had by 1967 increased to thirty-five per year, and in 1969 to seventy, while the number of publications *against* parapsychology in 1958 had been one, and in 1969 four. Since in the U.S.S.R. all publications are state-controlled, the sudden boom in parapsychology was obviously supported, or inspired, from higher quarters. The motives for it can be guessed from Vassiliev's quoting in one of his first publications "an eminent Soviet rocket pioneer" to the effect that "the phenomena of telepathy can no longer be called into question." This conveyed to any

"Echoes of the Mind" from THE ROOTS OF COINCIDENCE by Arthur Koestler. Copyright © 1972 by Arthur Koestler. Reprinted by permission of Random House, Inc. and A. D. Peters and Company. First published in *Esquire Magazine*, (August 1972).

1. *parapsychological research*, study of the branch of psychology that deals with psychic phenomena. One of the kinds of phenomena studied is ESP, or extrasensory perception, which is also called *clairvoyance*. This is the ability to perceive thoughts and actions without using the normal senses of sight, hearing, and feeling. 2. *Bechterev . . . Pavlov*. Although the two men did not work together, the Russian neuropathologist Vladimir Mikhailovich Bechterev (1857-1927) and the Russian physiologist Ivan Pavlov (1849-1936) established that animals can be conditioned to react in a certain way to certain stimulation. 3. *telehypnosis*. The prefix *tele* means "over a long distance"; thus, *telehypnosis* refers to hypnotizing people from a long distance away.

Soviet scientist trained to read between the lines that ESP, once its technique has been mastered and made to function reliably, might have important strategic uses as a method of direct communication. This seemingly fantastic idea was confirmed by a high official of N.A.S.A., the American National Aeronautics and Space Administration:

> A concentrated effort toward a highly interesting problem in modern science—the nature and essence of certain phenomena of electro-magnetic [*sic*4] communication between living organisms—is reportedly being pursued with top priority under the Soviet-manned space program.
>
> Until recently these phenomena have in general been ignored by Western scientists; however the many hypotheses involved are now receiving attention in world literature. . . .

In 1960 I wrote a series of articles for the London *Observer* on frontiers of research at American universities. Among others, I visited Professor J. B. Rhine at Duke University. His first approach to telepathy was through card-guessing experiments. They used specially manufactured cards, so-called Zener cards, which had only five markings: circle, square, cross, star, waves. The "sender" or "agent" turned up card after card screened from view, and the "percipient" or "receiver" tried to guess telepathically which of the five cards the agent was looking at. The probability of a correct guess made by pure chance was obviously one in five. Now one of the cornerstones of the theory of probability, and of modern physics in general, is the law of large numbers which states, in simplified form, that the larger the number of tries the closer the ratio of hits to misses will approach chance expectation—and conversely, the larger the number of tries the greater the odds against persistent deviations from that ratio. If significant deviations from chance expectation nevertheless do persist in a series of, say, several thousand tries, then the only reasonable— and scientific—conclusion is that some factor other than chance must be operating to account for the result.

The odds against chance, which the experiments by Rhine and his English followers demonstrated, were indeed astronomical—of the order of millions, and even higher. Thus, according to the rules of the game in the exact sciences, the question "Does ESP exist?" should have been regarded as settled, and the controversy should have shifted to the next problem, "How does it work?"

In the 1880's two Liverpool notables, Malcolm Guthrie, a Justice of the Peace and Governor of University College, and James Birchall, a headmaster, carried out a series of 246 experiments in the telepathic transmission of drawings to specially gifted subjects. After publishing their early results in the *Proceedings of the Society*,5 they approached

---

4. *sic*, a Latin term which points out that there is an error in the quoted material, but that the material is printed in its original form, error and all. 5. *Proceedings of the Society*, the publication of the Royal Society of London for the Advancement of Science, a society through which the government offers financial support for scientific exploration.

Sir Oliver Lodge, one of the outstanding physicists of his time, who was a Fellow of the Royal Society. Lodge was persuaded to take charge of the experiments. The diagram below shows in the top row six drawings transmitted by Guthrie to the percipient "Miss E." and in the row below her reproductions of them. They are the complete record of a consecutive series of transmissions during a single experimental session.

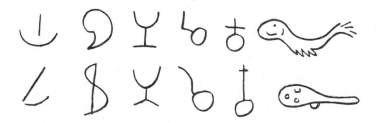

To hit on one card among five possibles is one thing; to reproduce a design out of an infinite number of possibilities is quite another.

But still worse was to come. From the early days at Duke University, in the 1930's, Rhine and his collaborators had experimented with throwing dice and "willing" a certain face to come uppermost. As Louisa Rhine relates, by 1934, after four years of successful experiments with card guessing, "J. B. Rhine was asking himself, 'If the mind can know without ordinary means of knowing, can it perhaps also move objects without the ordinary means of moving? In other words, can mind move matter directly?' "

Rhine's decision to embark on serious research in a territory where angels fear to tread was triggered by a chance remark one day by a young gambler, "who said that upon occasion, when he was properly keyed up, he could make dice fall as he willed."

The dice used in the Duke experiments were either thrown singly or in lots of six; at first by hand from containers, later by electrically driven rotating cages. The results seemed to indicate that the dice were influenced by some factor besides chance. This type of effect was labeled P.K. (psychokinesis) as distinct from ESP (extrasensory perception); both together are referred to by the blanket name *psi:* a nice neutral word, signifying the twenty-third letter in the Greek alphabet. To paraphrase Goethe: *When the mind is at sea/A new word provides a raft.*

Research in classical telepathy has at long last moved beyond the card-guessing stage. The most recent experiments, at the time of writing, were undertaken by a group of scientists led by Professor William MacBain at the University of Hawaii. Rather surprisingly, the London *New Scientist,* though generally opposed to ESP, reported the results in a prominent feature. The following is an extract from its report:

For their subjects they used twenty-two volunteer psychology students, who operated in pairs. The information to be communicated consisted of a set of twenty-three concepts which seemed likely to evoke a wide range of emotional reactions, and which could be symbolized by simple line drawings (including, for example, home, sleep, sorrow, sunshine, and the Pill). Each pair of students used just five of these concepts. The sender in each pair sat at a row of five display panels, one of which was illuminated for twenty-five seconds. The receiver faced a similar row of the five symbols, all illuminated, with a button below each. He used the appropriate button to signal the concept he thought had been "transmitted" by the sender. The sender had to concentrate on the illuminated symbol for twenty-five seconds, and then relax for five seconds while the receiver made a choice. Receiver and sender were in separate rooms over thirty feet apart.

The actual results . . . were significantly different . . . from random distribution. This means that chance guessing alone is not enough to explain the results—a conclusion which receives further support from the finding that certain psychological features of the students correlated with their degree of success as senders or receivers.

If these facts arouse incredulity and a certain intellectual revulsion, it is because they seem to contradict what most people believe to be the immutable laws of physics. The main comfort comes from modern physics itself. This is not a paradox, but a consequence of the profound transformation of the physicist's world view, which began in the late nineteenth century and shattered his fundamental concepts of the nature of reality, the meaning of natural law, and the validity of our ideas about space, time, matter and causality. . . .

It is not always easy to draw a sharp line separating causal from noncausal events. Sightless animals must feel their way by the coarse physical agencies of touch, perhaps aided by smell. Bats employ a kind of radar—which not so long ago would have struck naturalists as a very wild hypothesis. Animals equipped with eyes react to photons—to particles with zero restmass[6] which can also behave like waves in a non-medium and thus seem to defy causality. A species of humans without eyes—such as the citizens of Wells's "Country of the Blind"[7]—would surely reject our claim of being able to perceive distant objects, without contact by touch, as occult nonsense—or else declare that such a faculty, if it really exists, is definitely beyond the realm of physical causality. Reading out a printed page would then be the equivalent of clairvoyance.

Our main sense organs are like narrow slits which admit only a very narrow frequency range of electromagnetic and sound waves. But even the amount that gets in through these narrow slits is too much. Life would be impossible if we were to pay attention to the millions of

---

6. *photons . . . restmass.* Light consists of particles called *photons.* Photons have zero restmass, which means that when at rest they do not have mass. Photons have mass only when they are moving at the speed of light. **7.** *Wells's "Country of the Blind,"* a story by the English writer H. G. Wells (1866-1946) in which the people are born without eyes. (For a selection by Wells in this book, see page 163.)

stimuli bombarding our senses—what William James[8] called "the blooming, buzzing multitude of sensations." Thus the nervous system, and above all the brain, function as a hierarchy of filtering and classifying devices which eliminate a large proportion of the sensory input as irrelevant noise, and process the relevant information into manageable shape before it is presented to consciousness. An oft-quoted example of this filtering process is the "cocktail-party phenomenon" which enables us to isolate a single voice in the general buzz.

By analogy, a similar filtering mechanism might be assumed to protect us from the blooming, buzzing multitude of images, messages, impressions and confluential happenings in the "psychomagnetic field."

It is time for us to draw the lessons from twentieth-century post-mechanistic[9] science and to get out of the straitjacket which nineteenth-century materialism[10] imposed on our philosophical outlook. Paradoxically, had that outlook kept abreast with modern science itself, instead of lagging a century behind it, we would have been liberated from that straitjacket long ago. Once this is recognized, we might become more receptive to phenomena around us which a one-sided emphasis on physical science has made us ignore; might feel the draft that is blowing through the chinks of the causal edifice; pay more attention to confluential events; include the paranormal[11] phenomena in our concept of normality, and realize that we have been living in the "Country of the Blind." The consequences of such a shift of awareness are unforeseeable, and one cannot help sympathizing with the considered statement by Professor H. H. Price that "psychical research is one of the most important branches of investigation which the human mind has undertaken"; that it seems likely "to throw entirely new light upon the nature of human personality and its position in the universe"; and that in time "it may transform the whole intellectual outlook upon which our present civilization is based."

These are strong words coming from an Oxford Professor of Philosophy, but I do not think they overstate the case. What they imply is a plea to make parapsychology, and more generally the study of what I called "confluential events," academically respectable and attractive to students, as a career or an optional subject. Once there are as many bright researchers engaged in this field as there are now in the study of rat behavior, a breakthrough may be in sight.

The limitations of our biological equipment may condemn us to the role of Peeping Toms at the keyhole of eternity. But at least let us take the stuffing out of the keyhole, which blocks even our limited view. ■

---

8. *William James* (1842-1910), American psychologist and philosopher, one of the most renowned American thinkers. 9. *postmechanistic science,* after the period in which it was believed that the processes of life are mechanically determined and can be explained according to the laws of physics and chemistry. 10. *materialism,* the theory that the only things in the universe that exist are those that have matter. 11. *paranormal.* As in the word *parapsychology,* the prefix *para* means "related to or similar to." *Parapsychology* means "related to psychology." *Paranormal* means "similar to normal."

4

ORGANIC DILEMMA

THE RELUCTANT ORCHID

Arthur C. Clarke

THOUGH FEW PEOPLE IN THE WHITE HART[1] will concede that any of Harry Purvis' stories are actually *true,* everyone agrees that some are much more probable than others. And on any scale of probability, the affair of the Reluctant Orchid must rate very low indeed.

I don't remember what ingenious gambit Harry used to launch this narrative: maybe some orchid fancier brought his latest monstrosity into the bar, and that set him off. No matter. I do remember the story, and after all that's what counts.

The adventure did not, this time, concern any of Harry's numerous relatives, and he avoided explaining just how he managed to know so many of the sordid details. The hero—if you can call him that—of this hothouse epic was an inoffensive little clerk named Hercules Keating. And if you think *that* is the most unlikely part of the story, just stick round awhile.

Hercules is not the sort of name you can carry off lightly at the best of times, and when you are four-foot-nine and look as if you'd have to take a physical culture course before you can even become a ninety-seven-pound weakling, it is a positive embarrassment. Perhaps it helped to explain why Hercules had very little social life, and all his real friends grew in pots in a humid conservatory at the bottom of his garden. His needs were simple and he spent very little money on himself; consequently his collection of orchids and cacti was really rather remarkable. Indeed, he had a wide reputation among the

"The Reluctant Orchid" by Arthur C. Clarke. Copyright © 1956 by Renown Publishing Co., Inc. Reprinted by permission of the Author and his agents, Scott Meredith Literary Agency, Inc., 580 Fifth Avenue, New York, N.Y. 10036.

1. *the White Hart,* a country inn or tavern, the setting of Clarke's Harry Purvis tales. Many of the stories are collected in a book entitled *Tales from the White Hart*

fraternity of cactophiles, and often received from remote corners of the globe, parcels smelling of mould and tropical jungles.

Hercules had only one living relative, and it would have been hard to find a greater contrast than Aunt Henrietta. She was a massive six-footer, usually wore a rather loud line in Harris tweeds, drove a Jaguar with reckless skill, and chain-smoked cigars. Her parents had set their hearts on a boy, and had never been able to decide whether or not their wish had been granted. Henrietta earned a living, and quite a good one, breeding dogs of various shapes and sizes. She was seldom without a couple of her latest models, and they were not the type of portable canine which ladies like to carry in their handbags. The Keating Kennels specialized in Great Danes, Alsatians, and Saint Bernards. . . .

Henrietta, rightly despising men as the weaker sex, had never married. However, for some reason she took an avuncular[2] (yes, that is definitely the right word) interest in Hercules, and called to see him almost every weekend. It was a curious kind of relationship: probably Henrietta found that Hercules bolstered up her feelings of superiority. If he was a good example of the male sex, then they were certainly a pretty sorry lot. Yet, if this was Henrietta's motivation, she was unconscious of it and seemed genuinely fond of her nephew. She was patronizing, but never unkind.

As might be expected, her attentions did not exactly help Hercules' own well-developed inferiority complex. At first he had tolerated his aunt; then he came to dread her regular visits, her booming voice and her bone-crushing handshake; and at last he grew to hate her. Eventually, indeed, his hate was the dominant emotion in his life, exceeding even his love for his orchids. But he was careful not to show it, realizing that if Aunt Henrietta discovered how he felt about her, she would probably break him in two and throw the pieces to her wolf pack.

There was no way, then, in which Hercules could express his pent-up feelings. He had to be polite to Aunt Henrietta even when he felt like murder. And he often did feel like murder, though he knew that there was nothing he would ever do about it. Until one day . . .

According to the dealer, the orchid came from "somewhere in the Amazon region"—a rather vague postal address. When Hercules first saw it, it was not a very prepossessing sight, even to anyone who loved orchids as much as he did. A shapeless root, about the size of a man's fist—that was all. It was redolent of decay, and there was the faintest hint of a rank, carrion smell. Hercules was not even sure that it was viable,[3] and told the dealer as much. Perhaps that enabled him to purchase it for a trifling sum, and he carried it home without much enthusiasm.

It showed no signs of life for the first month, but that did not worry Hercules. Then, one day, a tiny green shoot appeared and started to creep up to the light. After that, progress was rapid. Soon there was a

---

2. *avuncular,* like an uncle. 3. *viable,* capable of life and growth.

thick, fleshy stem as big as a man's forearm, and colored a positively virulent green. Near the top of the stem a series of curious bulges circled the plant: otherwise it was completely featureless. Hercules was now quite excited: he was sure that some entirely new species had swum into his ken.

The rate of growth was now really fantastic: soon the plant was taller than Hercules, not that that was saying a great deal. Moreover, the bulges seemed to be developing, and it looked as if at any moment the orchid would burst into bloom.

Hercules waited anxiously, knowing how short-lived some flowers can be, and spent as much time as he possibly could in the hothouse. Despite all his watchfulness, the transformation occurred one night while he was asleep.

In the morning, the orchid was fringed by a series of eight dangling tendrils, almost reaching to the ground. They must have developed inside the plant and emerged with—for the vegetable world— explosive speed. Hercules stared at the phenomenon in amazement, and went very thoughtfully to work.

That evening, as he watered the plant and checked its soil, he noticed a still more peculiar fact. The tendrils were thickening, and they were not completely motionless. They had a slight but unmistakable tendency to vibrate, as if possessing a life of their own. Even Hercules, for all his interest and enthusiasm, found this more than a little disturbing.

A few days later, there was no doubt about it at all. When he approached the orchid, the tendrils swayed towards him in an unpleasantly suggestive fashion. The impression of hunger was so strong that Hercules began to feel very uncomfortable indeed, and something started to nag at the back of his mind. It was quite a while before he could recall what it was: then he said to himself, "Of course! How stupid of me!" and went along to the local library. Here he spent a most interesting half-hour rereading a little piece by one H. G. Wells entitled, "The Flowering of the Strange Orchid."[4]

"My goodness!" thought Hercules, when he had finished the tale. As yet there had been no stupefying odor which might overpower the plant's intended victim, but otherwise the characteristics were all too similar. Hercules went home in a very unsettled mood indeed.

He opened the conservatory door and stood looking along the avenue of greenery towards his prize specimen. He judged the length of the tendrils—already he found himself calling them tentacles—with great care and walked to within what appeared a safe distance. The plant certainly had an impression of alertness and menace far more appropriate to the animal than the vegetable kingdom. Hercules remembered the unfortunate history of Doctor Frankenstein,[5] and was not amused.

---

4. *H. G. Wells . . . "Strange Orchid."* In this story, the English writer H. G. Wells (1866-1946) tells of an orchid that kills its human victims by giving off a strong-smelling vapor. (For a selection by Wells in this book see page 163.) 5. *Doctor Frankenstein.* Mary W. Shelley (1797-1851) wrote the story of Doctor Frankenstein, who created a monster which ran out of control.

But, really, this was ridiculous! Such things didn't happen in real life. Well, there was one way to put matters to the test. . . .

Hercules went into the house and came back a few minutes later with a broomstick, to the end of which he had attached a piece of raw meat. Feeling a considerable fool, he advanced towards the orchid as a lion-tamer might approach one of his charges at mealtime.

For a moment, nothing happened. Then two of the tendrils developed an agitated twitch. They began to sway back and forth, as if the plant was making up its mind. Abruptly, they whipped out with such speed that they practically vanished from view. They wrapped themselves round the meat, and Hercules felt a powerful tug at the end of his broomstick. Then the meat was gone: the orchid was clutching it, if one may mix metaphors slightly, to its bosom.

"Jumping Jehosophat!" yelled Hercules. It was very seldom indeed that he used such strong language.

The orchid showed no further signs of life for twenty-four hours. It was waiting for the meat to become high,[6] and it was also developing its digestive system. By the next day, a network of what looked like short roots had covered the still-visible chunk of meat. By nightfall, the meat was gone.

The plant had tasted blood.

Hercules' emotions as he watched over his prize were curiously mixed. There were times when it almost gave him nightmares, and he foresaw a whole range of horrid possibilities. The orchid was now extremely strong, and if he got within its clutches he would be done for. But, of course, there was not the slightest danger of that. He had arranged a system of pipes so that it could be watered from a safe distance, and its less orthodox food he simply tossed within range of its tentacles. It was now eating a pound of raw meat a day, and he had an uncomfortable feeling that it could cope with much larger quantities if given the opportunity.

Hercules' natural qualms were, on the whole, outweighed by his feeling of triumph that such a botanical marvel had fallen into his hands. Whenever he chose, he could become the most famous orchid-grower in the world. It was typical of his somewhat restricted viewpoint that it never occurred to him that other people besides orchid-fanciers might be interested in his pet.

The creature was now about six feet tall, and apparently still growing—though much more slowly than it had been. All the other plants had been moved from its end of the conservatory, not so much because Hercules feared that it might be cannibalistic as to enable him to tend them without danger. He had stretched a rope across the central aisle so that there was no risk of his accidentally walking within range of those eight dangling arms.

It was obvious that the orchid had a highly developed nervous system, and something very nearly approaching intelligence. It knew

---

6. *high,* slightly tainted.

when it was going to be fed, and exhibited unmistakable signs of pleasure. Most fantastic of all—though Hercules was still not sure about this—it seemed capable of producing sounds. There were times, just before a meal, when he fancied he could hear an incredibly high-pitched whistle, skirting the edge of audibility. A newborn bat might have had such a voice: he wondered what purpose it served. Did the orchid somehow lure its prey into its clutches by sound? If so, he did not think the technique would work on him.

While Hercules was making these interesting discoveries, he continued to be fussed over by Aunt Henrietta and assaulted by her hounds, which were never as house-trained as she claimed them to be. She would usually roar up the street on a Sunday afternoon with one dog in the seat beside her and another occupying most of the baggage compartment. Then she would bound up the steps two at a time, nearly deafen Hercules with her greeting, half paralyze him with her handshake, and blow cigar smoke in his face. There had been a time when he was terrified that she would kiss him, but he had long since realized that such effeminate behaviour was foreign to her nature.

Aunt Henrietta looked upon Hercules' orchids with some scorn. Spending one's spare time in a hothouse was, she considered, a very effete recreation. When *she* wanted to let off steam, she went big-game hunting in Kenya. This did nothing to endear her to Hercules, who hated blood sports. But despite his mounting dislike for his overpowering aunt, every Sunday afternoon he dutifully prepared tea for her and they had a tête-à-tête together which, on the surface at least, seemed perfectly friendly. Henrietta never guessed that as he poured the tea Hercules often wished it was poisoned: she was, far down beneath her extensive fortifications, a fundamentally good-hearted person and the knowledge would have upset her deeply.

Hercules did not mention his vegetable octopus to Aunt Henrietta. He had occasionally shown her his most interesting specimens, but this was something he was keeping to himself. Perhaps, even before he had fully formulated his diabolical plan, his subconscious was already preparing the ground. . . .

It was late one Sunday evening, when the roar of the Jaguar had died away into the night and Hercules was restoring his shattered nerves in the conservatory, that the idea first came fully fledged into his mind. He was staring at the orchid, noting how the tendrils were now as thick around as a man's thumb, when a most pleasing fantasy suddenly flashed before his eyes. He pictured Aunt Henrietta struggling helplessly in the grip of the monster, unable to escape from its carnivorous clutches. Why, it would be the perfect crime. The distraught nephew would arrive on the scene too late to be of assistance, and when the police answered his frantic call they would see at a glance that the whole affair was a deplorable accident. True, there would be an inquest, but the coroner's censure would be toned down in view of Hercules' obvious grief. . . .

The more he thought of the idea, the more he liked it. He could see no flaws, as long as the orchid cooperated. That, clearly, would be the greatest problem. He would have to plan a course of training for the creature. It already looked sufficiently diabolical; he must give it a disposition to suit its appearance.

Considering that he had no prior experience in such matters, and that there were no authorities he could consult, Hercules proceeded along very sound and businesslike lines. He would use a fishing rod to dangle pieces of meat just outside the orchid's range, until the creature lashed its tentacles in a frenzy. At such times its high-pitched squeak was clearly audible, and Hercules wondered how it managed to produce the sound. He also wondered what its organs of perception were, but this was yet another mystery that could not be solved without close examination. Perhaps Aunt Henrietta, if all went well, would have a brief opportunity of discovering these interesting facts—though she would probably be too busy to report them for the benefit of posterity.

There was no doubt that the beast was quite powerful enough to deal with its intended victim. It had once wrenched a broomstick out of Hercules' grip, and although that in itself proved very little, the sickening "crack" of the wood a moment later brought a smile of satisfaction to its trainer's thin lips. He began to be much more pleasant and attentive to his aunt. In every respect, indeed, he was the model nephew.

When Hercules considered that his picador tactics[7] had brought the orchid into the right frame of mind, he wondered if he should test it with live bait. This was a problem that worried him for some weeks, during which time he would look speculatively at every dog or cat he passed in the street, but he finally abandoned the idea, for a rather peculiar reason. He was simply too kindhearted to put it into practice. Aunt Henrietta would have to be the first victim.

He starved the orchid for two weeks before he put his plan into action. This was as long as he dared risk—he did not wish to weaken the beast—merely to whet its appetite that the outcome of the encounter might be more certain. And so, when he had carried the teacups back into the kitchen and was sitting upwind of Aunt Henrietta's cigar, he said casually, "I've got something I'd like to show you, Auntie. I've been keeping it as a surprise. It'll tickle you to death."

That, he thought, was not a completely accurate description, but it gave the general idea.

Auntie took the cigar out of her mouth and looked at Hercules with frank surprise.

"Well!" she boomed. "Wonders will never cease! What *have* you been up to, you rascal?" She slapped him playfully on the back and shot all the air out of his lungs.

"You'll never believe it," gritted Hercules, when he had recovered his breath. "It's in the conservatory."

"Eh?" said Auntie, obviously puzzled.

---

7. *picador tactics.* In bullfighting, the picador opens the match by irritating the bull with pricks of his lance.

"Yes—come along and have a look. It's going to create a real sensation."

Auntie gave a snort that might have indicated disbelief, but followed Hercules without further question. The two Alsatians now busily chewing up the carpet looked at her anxiously and half rose to their feet, but she waved them away.

"All right, boys," she ordered gruffly. "I'll be back in a minute." Hercules thought this unlikely.

It was a dark evening, and the lights in the conservatory were off. As they entered, Auntie snorted, "Gad, Hercules—the place smells like a slaughterhouse. Haven't met such a stink since I shot that elephant in Bulawayo and we couldn't find it for a week."

"Sorry, Auntie," apologized Hercules, propelling her forward through the gloom. "It's a new fertilizer I'm using. It produces the most stunning results. Go on—another couple of yards. I want this to be a *real* surprise."

"I hope this isn't a joke," said Auntie suspiciously, as she stomped forward.

"I can promise you it's no joke," replied Hercules, standing with his hand on the light switch. He could just see the looming bulk of the orchid: Auntie was now within ten feet of it. He waited until she was well inside the danger zone, and threw the switch.

There was a frozen moment while the scene was transfixed with light. Then Aunt Henrietta ground to a halt and stood, arms akimbo, in front of the giant orchid. For a moment Hercules was afraid she would retreat before the plant could get into action: then he saw that she was calmly scrutinizing it, unable to make up her mind what the devil it was.

It was a full five seconds before the orchid moved. Then the dangling tentacles flashed into action—but not in the way that Hercules had expected. The plant clutched them tightly, protectively, *around itself* —and at the same time it gave a high-pitched scream of pure terror. In a moment of sickening disillusionment, Hercules realized the awful truth.

His orchid was an utter coward. It might be able to cope with the wildlife of the Amazon jungle, but coming suddenly upon Aunt Henrietta had completely broken its nerve.

As for its proposed victim, she stood watching the creature with an astonishment which swiftly changed to another emotion. She spun around on her heels and pointed an accusing finger at her nephew.

"Hercules!" she roared. "The poor thing's scared to death. *Have you been bullying it?*"

Hercules could only stand with his head hanging low in shame and frustration.

"N-no, Auntie," he quavered. "I guess it's naturally nervous."

"Well, I'm used to animals. You should have called me before. You must treat them firmly—but gently. Kindness always works, as long as you show them you're the master. There, there, did-dums—don't be frightened of Auntie—she won't hurt you. . . ."

It was, thought Hercules in his blank despair, a revolting sight. With surprising gentleness, Aunt Henrietta fussed over the beast, patting and stroking it until the tentacles relaxed and the shrill, whistling scream died away. After a few minutes of this pandering, it appeared to get over its fright. Hercules finally fled with a muffled sob when one of the tentacles crept forward and began to stroke Henrietta's gnarled fingers. . . .

From that day, he was a broken man. What was worse, he could never escape from the consequences of his intended crime. Henrietta had acquired a new pet, and was liable to call not only at weekends but two or three times in between as well. It was obvious that she did not trust Hercules to treat the orchid properly, and still suspected him of bullying it. She would bring tasty tidbits that even her dogs had rejected, but which the orchid accepted with delight. The smell, which had so far been confined to the conservatory, began to creep into the house. . . .

And there, concluded Harry Purvis, as he brought this improbable narrative to a close, the matter rests—to the satisfaction of two, at any rate, of the parties concerned. The orchid is happy, and Aunt Henrietta has something (query, someone?) else to dominate. From time to time the creature has a nervous breakdown when a mouse gets loose in the conservatory, and she rushes to console it.

As for Hercules, there is no chance that he will ever give any more trouble to either of them. He seems to have sunk into a kind of vegetable sloth: indeed, said Harry thoughtfully, every day he becomes more and more like an orchid himself.

The harmless variety, of course. . . .

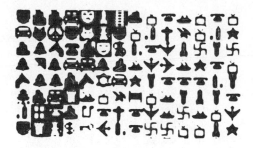

FOUNDING FATHER

Isaac Asimov

THE ORIGINAL COMBINATION OF catastrophes had taken place five years ago—five revolutions of this planet, HC-12549D by the charts, and nameless otherwise. Six-plus revolutions of Earth, but who was counting—anymore?

If the men back home knew, they might say it was a heroic fight, an epic of the Galactic Corps; five men against a hostile world, holding their bitter own for five (or six-plus) years. And now they were dying, the battle lost after all. Three were in final coma, a fourth had his yellow-tinged eyeballs still open, and a fifth was yet on his feet.

But it was no question of heroism at all. It had been five men fighting off boredom and despair and maintaining their metallic bubble of livability only for the most unheroic reason that there was nothing else to do while life remained.

If any of them felt stimulated by the battle, he never mentioned it. After the first year, they stopped talking of rescue, and after the second, a moratorium descended on the word *Earth.*

But one word remained always present. If unspoken it had to be found in their thoughts: *Ammonia.*

It had come first while the landing was being scratched out against all odds on limping motors and in a battered space can.

You allow for bad breaks, of course; you expect a certain number—but one at a time. A stellar flare fries out the hypercircuits—that can be repaired, given time. A meteorite disaligns the feeder-valves—they can be straightened, given time. A trajectory is miscalculated under tension and a momentarily unbearable acceleration tears out the jump-antennae and dulls the senses of every man on board—but antennae can be replaced and senses will recover, given time.

The chances are one in countless many that all three will happen at once; and still less that they will happen during a particularly tricky landing when the one necessary currency for the correction of all errors, time, is the one thing that is most lacking.

The *Cruiser John* hit that one chance in countless many, and it made a final landing, for it would never lift off a planetary surface again.

That it had landed essentially intact was itself a near miracle. The

---

"Founding Father" by Isaac Asimov. Copyright © 1965 Galaxy Publishing Corp. Reprinted by permission of the author.

five were given life for some years at least. Beyond that, only the blundering arrival of another ship could help, but no one expected that. They had had their lives' share of coincidences, they knew, and all had been bad.

That was that.

And the key word was *ammonia*. With the surface spiralling upward, and death (mercifully quick) facing them at considerably better than even odds, Chou somehow had time to note the absorption spectrograph, which was registering raggedly.

"Ammonia," he cried out. The others heard but there was no time to pay attention. There was only the wrenching fight against a quick death for the sake of a slow one.

When they landed finally, on sandy ground with sparse, ragged, bluish vegetation; reedy grass; stunted treelike objects with blue bark and no leaves; no sign of animal life; and with an almost greenish cloud-streaked sky above—the word came back to haunt them.

"Ammonia?" said Peterson, heavily.

Chou said, "Four percent."

"Impossible," said Peterson.

But it wasn't. The books didn't say impossible. What the Galactic Corps had discovered was that a planet of a certain mass and volume and at a certain temperature was an ocean planet and had one of two atmospheres: nitrogen/oxygen or nitrogen/carbon dioxide. In the former case, life was rampant; in the latter, it was primitive.

No one checked beyond mass, volume and temperature any longer. One took the atmosphere (one or the other of them) for granted. But the books didn't say it had to be so; just that it always was so. Other atmospheres were thermodynamically[1] possible, but extremely unlikely, so they weren't found in actual practice.

Until now. The men of the *Cruiser John* had found one and were bathed for the rest of such life as they could eke out by a nitrogen/carbon dioxide/ammonia atmosphere.

The men converted their ship into an underground bubble of Earth-type surroundings. They could not lift off the surface, nor could they drive a communicating beam through hyperspace,[2] but all else was salvageable. To make up for inefficiencies in the cycling system, they could even tap the planet's own water and air supply within limits; provided, of course, they subtracted the ammonia.

They organized exploring parties since their suits were in excellent condition and it passed the time. The planet was harmless; no animal life; sparse plant life everywhere. Blue, always blue; ammoniated chlorophyll; ammoniated protein.

They set up laboratories, analyzed the plant components, studied microscopic sections, compiled vast volumes of findings. They tried growing native plants in ammonia-free atmosphere and failed. They

---

1. *thermodynamically*, having to do with the conversion of heat into other forms of energy. 2. *hyperspace*, space of more than three dimensions.

made themselves into geologists and studied the planet's crust; astronomers and studied the spectrum of the planet's sun.

Barrere would say sometimes, "Eventually, the Corps will reach this planet again and we'll leave a legacy of knowledge for them. It's a unique planet after all. There might not be another Earth-type with ammonia in all the Milky Way."

"Great," said Sandropoulos, bitterly. "What luck for us."

Sandropoulos worked out the thermodynamics of the situation. "A metastable[3] system," he said. "The ammonia disappears steadily through geochemical oxidation that forms nitrogen; the plants utilize nitrogen and re-form ammonia, adapting themselves to the presence of ammonia. If the rate of plant formation of ammonia dropped two percent, a declining spiral would set in. Plant life would wither, reducing the ammonia still further and so on."

"You mean if we killed enough plant life," said Vlassov, "we could wipe out the ammonia."

"If we had air sleds and wide-angle blasters, and a year to work in, we might," said Sandropoulos, "but we haven't and there's a better way. If we could get our plants going, the formation of oxygen through photosynthesis[4] would increase the rate of ammonia oxidation. Even a small localized rise would lower the ammonia in the region, stimulate Earth-plant growth further, and inhibit the native growth, drop the ammonia further and so on."

They became gardeners through all the growing season. That was, after all, routine for the Galactic Corps. Life on Earth-type planets was usually of the water/protein type, but variation was infinite and other-world food was rarely nourishing and even more often it happened (not always, but often) that some types of Earth plants would overrun and drown out the native flora. With the native flora held down, other Earth plants could take root. Dozens of planets had been converted into new Earths in this fashion. In the process, Earth plants developed hundreds of hardy varieties that flourished under extreme conditions—all the better with which to seed the next planet.

The ammonia would kill any Earth plant, but the seeds at the disposal of the *Cruiser John* were not true Earth plants but other-world mutations of these plants. They fought hard but not well enough. Some varieties grew in a feeble, sickly manner and died.

At that they did better than did microscopic life. The planet's bacterioids were far more flourishing than was the planet's straggly blue plant life. The native microorganisms drowned out any attempt at competition from Earth samples. The attempt to seed the alien soil with Earth-type bacterial flora in order to aid the Earth plants failed.

Vlassov shook his head, "It wouldn't do anyway. If our bacteria survived, it would only be adapting to the presence of ammonia."

Sandropoulos said, "Bacteria won't help us. We need the plants; they carry the oxygen manufacturing systems."

---

3. *metastable,* a condition halfway between stable and unstable. **4.** *photosynthesis,* the process by which plants take in carbon dioxide and release oxygen.

"We could make some ourselves," said Peterson. "We could electrolyze water."[5]

"How long will our equipment last? If we could only get our plants going it would be like electrolyzing water forever, little by little, but year after year, till the planet gave up."

Barrere said, "Let's treat the soil then. It's rotten with ammonium salts. We'll bake the salts out and replace the ammonia-free soil."

"And what about the atmosphere?" asked Chou.

"In ammonia-free soil, they may catch hold despite the atmosphere. They almost make it as it is."

They worked like longshoremen, but with no real end in view. None really thought it would work, and there was no future for themselves, personally, even if it did work. But working passed the days.

The next growing season, they had their ammonia-free soil, but Earth plants still grew only feebly. They even placed domes over several shoots and pumped ammonia-free air within. It helped slightly but not enough. They adjusted the chemical composition of the soil in every possible fashion. There was no reward.

The feeble shoots produced their tiny whiffs of oxygen, but not enough to topple the ammonia atmosphere off its base.

"One more push," said Sandropoulos, "one more. We're rocking it; we're rocking it; but we can't knock it over."

Their tools and equipment blunted and wore out with time and the future closed in steadily. Each month there was less room for maneuver.

When the end came at last, it was with almost gratifying suddenness. There was no name to place on the weakness and vertigo. No one actually suspected direct ammonia poisoning. Still, they were living off the algae growth of what had once been ship-hydroponics[6] for years and the growths were themselves aberrant with possible ammonia contamination.

It could have been the workings of some native microorganism which might finally have learned to feed off them. It might even have been an Earthly microorganism, mutated under the conditions of a strange world. So three died at last and did so, circumstances be praised, painlessly. They were glad to go and leave the useless fight.

Chou said, in a voiceless whisper, "It's foolish to lose so badly."

Peterson, alone of the five to be on his feet (was he immune, whatever it was?) turned a grieving face toward his only living companion.

"Don't die," he said, "don't leave me alone."

Chou tried to smile. "I have no choice. But you can follow us, old friend. Why fight? The tools are gone and there is no way of winning now, if there ever was."

Even now, Peterson fought off final despair by concentrating on the fight against the atmosphere. But his mind was weary, his heart worn

---

5. *electrolyze water.* By decomposing water by passing an electrical current through it, oxygen can be extracted. **6.** *hydroponics,* growing plants without soil by using nutrient-filled water.

out, and when Chou died the next hour, he was left with four corpses to work with.

He stared at the bodies, counting over the memories, stretching them back (now that he was alone and dared wail) to Earth itself, which he had last seen on a visit eleven years before.

He would have to bury the bodies. He would break off the bluish branches of the native leafless trees and build crosses of them. He would hang the space helmet of each man on top and prop the oxygen cylinders below. Empty cylinders to symbolize the lost fight.

A foolish sentiment for men who could no longer care, and for future eyes that might never see. But he was doing it for himself, to show respect for his friends, for he was not the kind of man to leave his friends untended in death while he himself could stand.

Besides——

Besides? He sat in weary thought for some moments.

While he was still alive, he would fight with such tools as were left. He would bury his friends.

He buried each in a spot of ammonia-free soil they had so laboriously built up; buried them without shroud and without clothing; leaving them naked in the hostile ground for the slow decomposition that would come with their own microorganisms before those, too, died with the inevitable invasion of the native bacterioids.

Peterson placed each cross, with its helmet and oxygen cylinders, propped each with rocks, then turned away, grim and sad-eyed, to return to the buried ship that he now inhabited alone.

He worked each day and eventually the symptoms came for him, too.

He struggled into his spacesuit and came to the surface for what he knew would be one last time. He fell to his knees on the garden plots. The Earth plants were green. They had lived longer than ever before. They looked healthy, even vigorous.

They had patched the soil, babied the atmosphere, and now Peterson had used the last tool, the only one remaining at his disposal, and he had given them fertilizer as well——

Out of the slowly corrupting flesh of the Earthmen came the nutrients that supplied the final push. Out of the Earth plants came the oxygen that would beat back the ammonia and push the planet out of the unaccountable niche into which it had stuck.

If Earthmen ever came again (when? a million years hence?), they would find a nitrogen/oxygen atmosphere and a limited flora strangely reminiscent of Earth's.

The crosses would rot and decay, the metal rust and decompose. The bones might fossilize and remain to give a hint as to what happened. Their own records, sealed away, might be found.

But none of that mattered. If nothing at all was ever found, the planet itself, the whole planet, would be their monument.

And Peterson lay down to die in the midst of their victory.　■

THE WOUND

Howard Fast

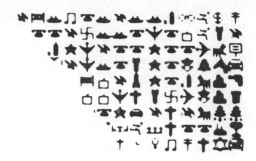

MAX GAFFEY ALWAYS INSISTED THAT the essence of the oil industry could be summed up in a simple statement: the right thing in the wrong place. My wife, Martha, always disliked him and said that he was a spoiler. I suppose he was, but how was he different from any of us in that sense? We were all spoilers, and if we were not the actual thing, we invested in it and thereby became rich. I myself had invested the small nest egg that a college professor puts away in a stock Max Gaffey gave me. It was called Thunder Inc., and the company's function was to use atomic bombs to release natural gas and oil locked up in the vast untouched shale[1] deposits that we have here in the United States.

Oil shale is not a very economical source of oil. The oil is locked up in the shale, and about sixty percent of the total cost of shale oil consists of the laborious methods of mining the shale, crushing it to release the oil, and then disposing of the spent shale.

Gaffey sold to Thunder Inc. an entirely new method, which involved the use of surplus atomic bombs for the release of shale oil. In very simplistic terms, a deep hole is bored in shale-oil deposits. Then an atomic bomb is lowered to the bottom of this hole, after which the hole is plugged and the bomb is detonated. Theoretically, the heat and force of the atomic explosion crushes the shale and releases the oil to fill the underground cavern formed by the gigantic force of the bomb. The oil does not burn because the hole is sealed, and thereby, for a comparatively small cost, untold amounts of oil can be tapped and released—enough perhaps to last until that time when we experience a complete conversion to atomic energy—so vast are the shale deposits.

Such at least was the way Max Gaffey put the proposition to me, in a sort of mutual brain-picking operation. He had the utmost admiration for my knowledge of the Earth's crust, and I had an equally profound admiration for his ability to make two or five or ten dollars appear where only one had been before.

My wife disliked him and his notions, and most of all the proposal to feed atomic bombs into the Earth's crust.

"It's wrong," she said flatly. "I don't know why or how, but this I do know, that everything connected with that wretched bomb is wrong."

"The Wound" reprinted by permission of William Morrow & Company, Inc. and Paul R. Reynolds, Inc. from THE GENERAL ZAPPED AN ANGEL by Howard Fast. Copyright © 1970 by Howard Fast.

1. *shale,* a fine-grained rock formed in thin layers that split easily.

"Yet couldn't you look at this as a sort of salvation?" I argued. "Here we are in these United States with enough atom bombs to destroy life on ten earths the size of ours—and every one of those bombs represents an investment of millions of dollars. I could not agree more when you hold that those bombs are the most hideous and frightful things the mind of man ever conceived."

"Then how on Earth can you speak of salvation?"

"Because so long as those bombs sit here, they represent a constant threat—day and night the threat that some feather-brained general or brainless politician will begin the process of throwing them at our neighbors. But here Gaffey has come up with a peaceful use for the bomb. Don't you see what that means?"

"I'm afraid I don't," Martha said.

"It means that we can use the damn bombs for something other than suicide—because if this starts, it's the end of mankind. But there are oil-shale and gas-shale deposits all over the Earth, and if we can use the bomb to supply man with a century of fuel, not to mention the chemical by-products, we may just find a way to dispose of those filthy bombs."

"Oh, you don't believe that for a moment," Martha snorted.

"I do. I certainly do."

And I think I did. I went over the plans that Gaffey and his associates had worked out, and I could not find any flaw. If the hole were plugged properly, there would be no fallout. We knew that and we had the know-how to plug the hole, and we had proven it in at least twenty underground explosions. The Earth tremor would be inconsequential; in spite of the heat, the oil would not ignite, and in spite of the cost of the atom bombs, the savings would be monumental. In fact, Gaffey hinted that some accommodation between the government and Thunder Inc. was in the process of being worked out, and if it went through as planned, the atom bombs might just cost Thunder Inc. nothing at all, the whole thing being in the way of an experiment for the social good.

After all, Thunder Inc. did not own any oil-shale deposits, nor was it in the oil business. It was simply a service organization with the proper know-how, and for a fee—if the process worked—it would release the oil for others. What that fee would be was left unsaid, but Max Gaffey, in return for my consultation, suggested that I might buy a few shares, not only of Thunder Inc., but of General Shale Holdings.

I had altogether about ten thousand dollars in savings available and another ten thousand in American Telephone and government bonds. Martha had a bit of money of her own, but I left that alone, and without telling her, I sold my Telephone stock and my bonds. Thunder Inc. was selling at five dollars a share, and I bought two thousand shares. General Shale was selling for two dollars, and I bought four thousand shares. I saw nothing immoral—as business morality was calculated—in the procedures adopted by Thunder Inc. Its relationship to the government was no different than the relationships of various other companies, and my own process of investment was perfectly straightforward and honorable. I was not even the recipient of secret information, for the atom-bomb–shale-oil proposal had been widely publicized if little believed.

Even before the first test explosion was undertaken, the stock of Thunder Inc. went from five to sixty-five dollars a share. My ten thousand dollars became one hundred and thirty thousand, and that doubled again a year later. The four thousand shares of General Shale went up to eighteen dollars a share; and from a moderately poor professor I became a moderately rich professor. When finally, almost two years after Max Gaffey first approached me, they exploded the first atom bomb in a shaft reamed in the oil-shale deposits, I had abandoned the simple anxieties of the poor and had developed an entirely new set tailored for the upper-middle class. We became a two-car family, and a reluctant Martha joined me in shopping for a larger house. In the new house, Gaffey and his wife came to dinner, and Martha armed herself with two stiff martinis. Then she was quietly polite until Gaffey began to talk about the social good. He painted a bright picture of what shale oil could do and how rich we might well become.

"Oh, yes—yes," Martha agreed. "Pollute the atmosphere, kill more people with more cars, increase the speed with which we can buzz around in circles and get precisely nowhere."

"Oh, you're a pessimist," said Gaffey's wife, who was young and pretty but no mental giant.

"Of course there are two sides to it," Gaffey admitted. "It's a question of controls. You can't stop progress, but it seems to me that you can direct it."

"The way we've been directing it—so that our rivers stink and our lakes are sewers of dead fish and our atmosphere is polluted and our birds are poisoned by DDT and our natural resources are spoiled. We are all spoilers, aren't we?"

"Come now," I protested, "this is the way it is, and all of us are indignant about it, Martha."

"Are you, really?"

"I think so."

"Men have always dug in the earth," Gaffey said. "Otherwise we'd still be in the Stone Age."

"And perhaps a good bit happier."

"No, no, no," I said. "The Stone Age was a very unpleasant time, Martha. You don't wish us back there."

"Do you remember," Martha said slowly, "how there was a time when men used to speak about the Earth our mother? It was Mother Earth, and they believed it. She was the source of life and being."

"She still is."

"You've sucked her dry," Martha said curiously. "When a woman is sucked dry, her children perish."

It was an odd and poetical thing to say, and, as I thought, in bad taste. I punished Martha by leaving Mrs. Gaffey with her, with the excuse that Max and I had some business matters to discuss, which indeed we did. We went into the new study in the new house and we lit fifty-cent cigars, and Max told me about the thing they had aptly named "Project Hades."

"The point is," Max said, "that I can get you into this at the very beginning. At the bottom. There are eleven companies involved—very solid and reputable companies"—he named them, and I was duly impressed—"who are putting up the capital for what will be a subsidiary of Thunder Inc. For their money they get a twenty-five-percent interest. There is also ten percent, in the form of stock warrants, put aside for consultation and advice, and you will understand why. I can fit you in for one-and-a-half percent—roughly three-quarters of a million—simply for a few weeks of your time, and we will pay all expenses, plus an opinion."

"It sounds interesting."

"It should sound more than that. If Project Hades works, your interest will increase tenfold within a matter of five years. It's the shortest cut to being a millionaire that I know."

"All right—I'm more than interested. Go on."

Gaffey took a map of Arizona out of his pocket, unfolded it, and pointed to a marked-off area. "Here," he said, "is what should— according to all our geological knowledge—be one of the richest oil-bearing areas in the country. Do you agree?"

"Yes, I know the area," I replied. "I've been over it. Its oil potential is purely theoretical. No one has ever brought in anything there—not even salt water. It's dry and dead."

"Why?"

I shrugged. "That's the way it is. If we could locate oil through geological premise and theory, you and I would both be richer than Getty.[2] The fact of the matter is, as you well know, that sometimes it's there and sometimes it isn't. More often it isn't."

"Why? We know our job. We drill in the right places."

"What are you getting at, Max?"

"A speculation—particularly for this area. We have discussed this speculation for months. We have tested it as best we can. We have examined it from every possible angle. And now we are ready to blow about five million dollars to test our hypothesis—providing——"

"Providing what?"

"That your expert opinion agrees with ours. In other words, we've cast the die with you. You look at the situation and tell us to go ahead—we go ahead. You look at it and tell us it's a crock of beans—well, we fold our tents like the Arabs and silently steal away."[3]

"Just on my say-so?"

"Just on your brains and know-how."

"Max, aren't you barking up the wrong tree? I'm a simple professor

---

2. *Getty.* Jean Paul Getty (1892-   ) is one of the richest men in the world. He gained his fortune in the oil business. 3. *fold our tents . . . steal away.* This line is from the poem "The Day Is Done," written by Henry Wadsworth Longfellow (1807–1882). The whole stanza reads, "And the night shall be filled with music / And the cares, that infest the day, / Shall fold their tents, like the Arabs, / And as silently steal away."

of geology at an unimportant western state university, and there are at least twenty men in the field who can teach me the right time——"

"Not in our opinion. Not on where the stuff is. We know who's in the field and we know their track records. You keep your light under a bushel, but we know what we want. So don't argue. It's either a deal or it isn't. Well?"

"How the devil can I answer you when I don't even know what you're talking about?"

"All right—I'll spell it out, quick and simple. The oil was there once, right where it should be. Then a natural convulsion—a very deep fault. The Earth cracked and the oil flowed down, deep down, and now giant pockets of it are buried there where no drill can reach them."

"How deep?"

"Who knows? Fifteen, twenty miles."

"That's deep."

"Maybe deeper. When you think of that kind of distance under the surface, you're in a darker mystery than Mars or Venus—all of which you know."

"All of which I know." I had a bad, uneasy feeling, and some of it must have shown in my face.

"What's wrong?"

"I don't know. Why don't you leave it alone, Max?"

"Why?"

"Come on, Max—we're not talking about drilling for oil. Fifteen, twenty miles. There's a rig down near the Pecos in Texas and they've just passed the twenty-five-thousand-foot level, and that's about it. Oh, maybe another thousand, but you're talking about oil that's buried in one hundred thousand feet of crust. You can't drill for it; you can only go in and——"

"And what?"

"Blast it out."

"Of course—and how do you fault us for that? What's wrong with it? We know—or least we have good reason to believe—that there's a fissure that opened and closed. The oil should be under tremendous pressure. We put in an atom bomb—a bigger bomb than we ever used before—and we blast that fissure open again. . . . That should be the biggest gusher in all the history of gushers."

"You've drilled the hole already, haven't you, Max?"

"That's right."

"How deep?"

"Twenty-two thousand feet."

"And you have the bomb?"

Max nodded. "We have the bomb. We've been working on this for five years, and seven months ago the boys in Washington cleared the bomb. It's out there in Arizona waiting——"

"For what?"

"For you to look everything over and tell us to go ahead."

"Why? We have enough oil——"

"Like hell we have! You know damn well why—and do you imagine we can drop it now after all the money and time that's been invested in this?"

"You said you'd drop it if I said so."

"As a geologist in our pay, and I know you well enough to know what that means in terms of your professional skill and pride."

I stayed up half that night talking with Martha about it and trying to fit it into some kind of moral position. But the only thing I could come up with was the fact that here was one less atom bomb to murder man and destroy the life of the Earth, and that I could not argue with. A day later I was at the drilling site in Arizona.

The spot was well chosen. From every point of view this was an oil explorer's dream, and I suppose that fact had been duly noted for the past half century, for there were the moldering remains of a hundred futile rigs, rotting patterns of wooden and metal sticks as far as one could see, abandoned shacks, trailers left with lost hopes, ancient trucks, rusting gears, piles of abandoned pipe—all testifying to the hope that springs eternal in the wildcatter's breast.[4]

Thunder Inc. was something else, a great installation in the middle of the deep valley, a drilling rig larger and more complex than any I had ever seen, a wall to contain the oil should they fail to cap it immediately, a machine shop, a small generating plant, at least a hundred vehicles of various sorts, and perhaps fifty mobile homes.

The very extent and vastness of the action here deep in the badlands was breathtaking; and I let Max know what I thought of his statement that all this would be abandoned if I said that the idea was worthless.

"Maybe yes—maybe no. What *do* you say?"

"Give me time."

"Absolutely, all the time you want."

Never have I been treated with such respect. I prowled all over the place and I rode a jeep around and about and back and forth and up into the hills and down again; but no matter how long I prowled and sniffed and estimated, mine would be no more than an educated guess. I was also certain that they would not give up the project if I disapproved and said that it would be a washout. They believed in me as a sort of oil dowser,[5] especially if I told them to go ahead. What they were really seeking was an expert's affirmation of their own faith. And that was apparent from the fact that they had already drilled an expensive twenty-two-thousand-foot hole and had set up all this equipment. If I told them they were wrong, their faith might be shaken a little, but they would recover and find themselves another dowser.

I told this to Martha when I telephoned her.

"Well, what do you honestly think?"

"It's oil country. But I'm not the first one to come up with that brilliant observation. The point is—does their explanation account for the lack of oil?"

"Does it?"

---

4. *hope. . .breast.* The phrase is taken from the line, "Hope springs eternal in the human breast," which was written by the English poet Alexander Pope (1688-1744) in his philosophical poem *An Essay on Man.* 5. *oil dowser,* a forked stick supposed to be capable of locating underground oil.

"I don't know. No one knows. And they're dangling a million dollars right in front of my nose."

"I can't help you," Martha said. "You've got to play this one yourself."

Of course she couldn't help me. No one could have helped me. It was too far down, too deeply hidden. We knew what the other side of the Moon looked like and we knew something about Mars and other planets, but what have we ever known about ourselves and the place where we live?

The day after I spoke to Martha, I met with Max and his board of directors. "I agree," I told them. "The oil should be there. My opinion is that you should go ahead and try the blast."

They questioned me after that for about an hour, but when you play the role of a dowser, questions and answers become a sort of magical ritual. The plain fact of the matter is that no one had ever exploded a bomb of such power at such a depth, and until it was done, no one knew what would happen.

I watched the preparations for the explosion with great interest. The bomb, with its implosion casing, was specially made for this task—or remade would be a better way of putting it—very long, almost twenty feet, very slim. It was armed after it was in the rigging, and then the board of directors, engineers, technicians, newspapermen, Max, and myself retreated to the concrete shelter and control station, which had been built almost a mile away from the shaft. Closed-circuit television linked us with the hole; and while no one expected the explosion to do any more than jar the Earth heavily at the surface, the Atomic Energy Commission specified the precautions we took.

We remained in the shelter for five hours while the bomb made its long descent—until at last our instruments told us that it rested on the bottom of the drill hole. Then we had a simple countdown, and the chairman of the board pressed the red button. Red and white buttons are man's glory. Press a white button and a bell rings or an electric light goes on; press a red button and the hellish force of a sun comes into being—this time five miles beneath the Earth's surface.

Perhaps it was this part and point in the Earth's surface; perhaps there was no other place where exactly the same thing would have happened; perhaps the fault that drained away the oil was a deeper fault than we had ever imagined. Actually we will never know; we only saw what we saw, watching it through the closed-circuit TV. We saw the Earth swell. The swell rose up like a bubble—a bubble about two hundred yards in diameter—and then the surface of the bubble dissipated in a column of dust or smoke that rose up perhaps five hundred feet from the valley bottom, stayed a moment with the lowering sun behind it, like the very column of fire out of Sinai,[5] and then lifted whole and broke suddenly in the wind. Even in the shelter we heard the screaming rumble of sound, and as the face of the

---

5. *column of fire out of Sinai.* When the Israelites fled from Egypt into the Sinai Desert, the Lord guided them in a pillar of cloud by day, and of fire by night. (Exodus 13:21-22)

enormous hole that the dust had left cleared, there bubbled up a column of oil perhaps a hundred feet in diameter. Or was it oil?

The moment we saw it, a tremendous cheer went up in the shelter, and then the cheer cut off in its own echo. Our closed-circuit system was color television, and this column of oil was bright red.

"Red oil," someone whispered. Then it was quiet.

"When can we get out?" someone else demanded.

"Another ten minutes."

The dust was up and away in the opposite direction, and for ten minutes we stood and watched the bright red oil bubble out of the hole, forming a great pond within the retaining walls, and filling the space with amazing rapidity and lapping over the walls, for the flow must have been a hundred thousand gallons a second or even more, and then outside of the walls and a thickness of it all across the valley floor, rising so quickly that from above, where we were, we saw that we would be cut off from the entire installation. At that point we didn't wait, but took our chances with the radiation and raced down the desert hillside toward the hole and the mobile homes and the trucks— but not quickly enough. We came to a stop at the edge of a great lake of red oil. "It's not red oil," someone said.

"Damn it, it's not oil!"

"The hell it's not! It's oil."

We were moving back as it spread and rose and covered the trucks and houses, and then it reached a gap in the valley and poured through and down across the desert, into the darkness of the shadows that the big rocks threw—flashing red in the sunset and later black in the darkness. Someone touched it and put a hand to his mouth.

"It's blood."

Max was next to me. "He's crazy," Max said.

Someone else said that it was blood.

I put a finger into the red fluid and raised it to my nose. It was warm, almost hot, and there was no mistaking the smell of hot, fresh blood. I tasted it with the tip of my tongue.

"What is it?" Max whispered.

The others gathered around now—silent, with the red sun setting across the red lake and the red reflected on our faces, our eyes glinting with the red. "God, what is it?" Max demanded.

"It's blood," I replied.

"From where?" Then we were all silent.

We spent the night on the top of the butte where the shelter had been built, and in the morning, all around us, as far as we could see, there was a hot, steaming sea of red blood, the smell so thick and heavy that we were all sick from it; and all of us vomited half a dozen times before the helicopters came for us and took us away.

The day after I returned home, Martha and I were sitting in the living room, she with a book and I with the paper, where I had read about their trying to cap the thing, except that even with diving suits they could not get down to where it was; and she looked up from her book and said: "Do you remember that thing about the mother?"

"What thing?"

"A very old thing. I think I heard once that it was half as old as time, or maybe a Greek fable or something of the sort—but anyway, the mother has one son, who is the joy of her heart and all the rest that a son could be to a mother, and then the son falls in love with or under the spell of a beautiful and wicked woman—very wicked and very beautiful. And he desires to please her, oh, he does indeed, and he says to her, 'Whatever you desire, I will bring it to you'——"

"Which is nothing to say to any woman, but ever," I put in.

"I won't quarrel with that," Martha said mildly, "because when he does put it to her, she replies that what she desires most on this Earth is the living heart of his mother, plucked from her breast. So what does this worthless and murderous idiot male do but race home to his mother, and then out with a knife, ripping her breast to belly and tearing the living heart out of her body——"

"I don't like your story."

"—and with the heart in his hand, he blithely dashes back toward his ladylove. But on the way through the forest he catches his toe on a root, stumbles, and falls headlong, the mother's heart knocked out of his hand. And as he pulls himself up and approaches the heart, it says to him, 'Did you hurt yourself when you fell, my son?' "

"Lovely story. What does it prove?"

"Nothing, I suppose. Will they ever stop the bleeding? Will they close the wound?"

"I don't think so."

"Then will your mother bleed to death?"

"My mother?"

"Yes."

"Oh."

"My mother," Martha said. "Will she bleed to death?"

"I suppose so."

"That's all you can say—I suppose so?"

"What else?"

"Suppose you had told them not to go ahead?"

"You asked me that twenty times, Martha. I told you. They would have gotten another dowser."

"And another? And another?"

"Yes."

"Why?" she cried out. "For God's sake, why?"

"I don't know."

"But you lousy men know everything else."

"Mostly we only know how to kill it. That's not everything else. We never learned to make anything alive."

"And now it's too late," Martha said.

"It's too late, yes," I agreed, and I went back to reading the paper. But Martha just sat there, the open book in her lap, looking at me; and then after a while she closed the book and went upstairs to bed. ■

THE SOUND MACHINE

Roald Dahl

IT WAS A WARM SUMMER EVENING and Klausner walked quickly through the front gate and around the side of the house and into the garden at the back. He went on down the garden until he came to a wooden shed and he unlocked the door, went inside and closed the door behind him.

The interior of the shed was an unpainted room. Against one wall, on the left, there was a long wooden workbench, and on it, among a littering of wires and batteries and small sharp tools, there stood a black box about three feet long, the shape of a child's coffin.

Klausner moved across the room to the box. The top of the box was open, and he bent down and began to poke and peer inside it among a mass of different-coloured wires and silver tubes. He picked up a piece of paper that lay beside the box, studied it carefully, put it down, peered inside the box and started running his fingers along the wires, tugging gently at them to test the connections, glancing back at the paper, then into the box, then at the paper again, checking each wire. He did this for perhaps an hour.

Then he put a hand around to the front of the box where there were three dials, and he began to twiddle them, watching at the same time the movement of the mechanism inside the box. All the while he kept speaking softly to himself, nodding his head, smiling sometimes, his hands always moving, the fingers moving swiftly, deftly, inside the box, his mouth twisting into curious shapes when a thing was delicate or difficult to do, saying, "Yes. . . . Yes. . . . And now this one. . . . Yes. . . . Yes. . . . But is this right? Is it—where's my diagram?. . . . Ah, yes. . . . Of course. . . . Yes, yes. . . . That's right. . . . And now. . . . Good. . . . Good. . . . Yes. . . . Yes, yes, yes." His concentration was intense; his movements were quick; there was an air of urgency about the way he worked, of breathlessness, of strong suppressed excitement.

Suddenly he heard footsteps on the gravel path outside and he straightened and turned swiftly as the door opened and a tall man came in. It was Scott. It was only Scott, the doctor.

"Well, well, well," the doctor said. "So this is where you hide yourself in the evenings."

"The Sound Machine" Copyright 1949 by Roald Dahl. Reprinted from SOMEONE LIKE YOU, by Roald Dahl, by permission of Alfred A. Knopf, Inc., Michael Joseph Ltd., and Penguin Books Ltd. Originally appeared in *The New Yorker*.

"Hullo, Scott," Klausner said.

"I happened to be passing," the doctor told him, "so I dropped in to see how you were. There was no one in the house, so I came on down here. How's that throat of yours been behaving?"

"It's all right. It's fine."

"Now I'm here I might as well have a look at it."

"Please don't trouble. I'm quite cured. I'm fine."

The doctor began to feel the tension in the room. He looked at the black box on the bench; then he looked at the man. "You've got your hat on," he said.

"Oh, have I?" Klausner reached up, removed the hat and put it on the bench.

The doctor came up closer and bent down to look into the box. "What's this?" he said. "Making a radio?"

"No. Just fooling around."

"It's got rather complicated-looking innards."

"Yes." Klausner seemed tense and distracted.

"What is it?" the doctor asked. "It's rather a frightening-looking thing, isn't it?"

"It's just an idea."

"Yes?"

"It has to do with sound, that's all."

"Good heavens, man! Don't you get enough of that sort of thing all day in your work?"

"I like sound."

"So it seems." The doctor went to the door, turned, and said, "Well, I won't disturb you. Glad your throat's not worrying you anymore." But he kept standing there, looking at the box, intrigued by the remarkable complexity of its inside, curious to know what this strange patient of his was up to. "What's it really for?" he asked. "You've made me inquisitive."

Klausner looked down at the box, then at the doctor, and he reached up and began gently to scratch the lobe of his right ear. There was a pause. The doctor stood by the door, waiting, smiling.

"All right, I'll tell you, if you're interested." There was another pause, and the doctor could see that Klausner was having trouble about how to begin.

He was shifting from one foot to the other, tugging at the lobe of his ear, looking at his feet, and then at last, slowly, he said, "Well, it's like this . . . the theory is very simple, really. The human ear . . . you know that it can't hear everything. There are sounds that are so low-pitched or so high-pitched that it can't hear them."

"Yes," the doctor said. "Yes."

"Well, speaking very roughly, any note so high that it has more than fifteen thousand vibrations a second—we can't hear it. Dogs have better ears than us. You know you can buy a whistle whose note is so high-pitched that you can't hear it at all. But a dog can hear it."

"Yes, I've seen one," the doctor said.

"Of course you have. And up the scale, higher than the note of that whistle, there is another note—a vibration if you like, but I prefer to think of it as a note. You can't hear that one either. And above that there is another and another rising right up the scale for ever and ever and ever, an endless succession of notes . . . an infinity of notes . . . there is a note—if only our ears could hear it—so high that it vibrates a million times a second . . . and another a million times as high as that . . . and on and on, higher and higher, as far as numbers go, which is . . . infinity . . . eternity . . . beyond the stars."

Klausner was becoming more animated every moment. He was a small frail man, nervous and twitchy, with always-moving hands. His large head inclined toward his left shoulder as though his neck were not quite strong enough to support it rigidly. His face was smooth and pale, almost white, and the pale grey eyes that blinked and peered from behind a pair of steel spectacles were bewildered, unfocussed, remote. He was a frail, nervous, twitchy little man, a moth of a man, dreamy and distracted; suddenly fluttering and animated; and now the doctor, looking at that strange pale face and those pale grey eyes, felt that somehow there was about this little person a quality of distance, of immense, immeasurable distance, as though the mind were far away from where the body was.

The doctor waited for him to go on. Klausner sighed and clasped his hands tightly together. "I believe," he said, speaking more slowly now, "that there is a whole world of sound about us all the time that we cannot hear. It is possible that up there in those high-pitched inaudible regions there is a new exciting music being made, with subtle harmonies and fierce grinding discords, a music so powerful that it would drive us mad if only our ears were tuned to hear the sound of it. There may be anything . . . for all we know there may——"

"Yes," the doctor said. "But it's not very probable."

"Why not? Why not?" Klausner pointed to a fly sitting on a small roll of copper wire on the workbench. "You see that fly? What sort of a noise is that fly making now? None—that one can hear. But for all we know the creature may be whistling like mad on a very high note, or barking or croaking or singing a song. It's got a mouth, hasn't it? It's got a throat!"

The doctor looked at the fly and he smiled. He was still standing by the door with his hand on the doorknob. "Well," he said. "So you're going to check up on that?"

"Some time ago," Klausner said, "I made a simple instrument that proved to me the existence of many odd inaudible sounds. Often I have sat and watched the needle of my instrument recording the presence of sound vibrations in the air when I myself could hear nothing. And *those* are the sounds I want to listen to. I want to know where they come from and who or what is making them."

"And that machine on the table there," the doctor said, "is that going to allow you to hear these noises?"

"It may. Who knows? So far, I've had no luck. But I've made some changes in it and tonight I'm ready for another trial. This machine," he said, touching it with his hands, "is designed to pick up sound vibrations that are too high-pitched for reception by the human ear, and to convert them to a scale of audible tones. I tune it in, almost like a radio."

"How d'you mean?"

"It isn't complicated. Say I wish to listen to the squeak of a bat. That's a fairly high-pitched sound—about thirty thousand vibrations a second. The average human ear can't quite hear it. Now, if there were a bat flying around this room and I tuned in to thirty thousand on my machine, I would hear the squeaking of that bat very clearly. I would even hear the correct note—F sharp, or B flat, or whatever it might be—but merely at a much *lower pitch.* Don't you understand?"

The doctor looked at the long black coffin-box. "And you're going to try it tonight?"

"Yes."

"Well, I wish you luck." He glanced at his watch. "My goodness!" he said. "I must fly. Goodbye, and thank you for telling me. I must call again sometime and find out what happened." The doctor went out and closed the door behind him.

For a while longer, Klausner fussed about with the wires in the black box; then he straightened up and in a soft excited whisper said, "Now we'll try again. . . . We'll take it out into the garden this time . . . and then perhaps . . . perhaps . . . the reception will be better. Lift it up now . . . carefully. . . . Oh, my God, it's heavy!" He carried the box to the door, found that he couldn't open the door without putting it down, carried it back, put it on the bench, opened the door, and then carried it with some difficulty into the garden. He placed the box carefully on a small wooden table that stood on the lawn. He returned to the shed and fetched a pair of earphones. He plugged the wire connections from the earphones into the machine and put the earphones over his ears. The movements of his hands were quick and precise. He was excited, and breathed loudly and quickly through his mouth. He kept on talking to himself with little words of comfort and encouragement, as though he were afraid—afraid that the machine might not work and afraid also of what might happen if it did.

He stood there in the garden beside the wooden table, so pale, small, and thin that he looked like an ancient, consumptive, bespectacled child. The sun had gone down. There was no wind, no sound at all. From where he stood, he could see over a low fence into the next garden, and there was a woman walking down the garden with a flower basket on her arm. He watched her for a while without thinking about her at all. Then he turned to the box on the table and pressed a switch on its front. He put his left hand on the volume control and his right hand on the knob that moved a needle across a large central dial, like the wavelength dial of a radio. The dial was marked with many numbers, in a series of bands, starting at 15,000 and going on up to 1,000,000.

And now he was bending forward over the machine. His head was cocked to one side in a tense listening attitude. His right hand was beginning to turn the knob. The needle was travelling slowly across the dial, so slowly he could hardly see it move, and in the earphones he could hear a faint, spasmodic crackling.

Behind this crackling sound he could hear a distant humming tone which was the noise of the machine itself, but that was all. As he listened, he became conscious of a curious sensation, a feeling that his ears were stretching out away from his head, that each ear was connected to his head by a thin stiff wire, like a tentacle, and that the wires were lengthening, that the ears were going up and up toward a secret and forbidden territory, a dangerous ultrasonic region where ears had never been before and had no right to be.

The little needle crept slowly across the dial, and suddenly he heard a shriek, a frightful piercing shriek, and he jumped and dropped his hands, catching hold of the edge of the table. He stared around him as if expecting to see the person who had shrieked. There was no one in sight except the woman in the garden next door, and it was certainly not she. She was bending down, cutting yellow roses and putting them in her basket.

Again it came—a throatless, inhuman shriek, sharp and short, very clear and cold. The note itself possessed a minor, metallic quality that he had never heard before. Klausner looked around him, searching instinctively for the source of the noise. The woman next door was the only living thing in sight. He saw her reach down, take a rose stem in the fingers of one hand and snip the stem with a pair of scissors. Again he heard the scream.

It came at the exact moment when the rose stem was cut.

At this point, the woman straightened up, put the scissors in the basket with the roses and turned to walk away.

"Mrs. Saunders!" Klausner shouted, his voice shrill with excitement. "Oh, Mrs. Saunders!"

And looking round, the woman saw her neighbor standing on his lawn—a fantastic, arm-waving little person with a pair of earphones on his head—calling to her in a voice so high and loud that she became alarmed. "Cut another one! Please cut another one quickly!"

She stood still, staring at him. "Why, Mr. Klausner," she said. "What's the matter?"

"Please do as I ask," he said. "Cut just one more rose!"

Mrs. Saunders had always believed her neighbor to be a rather peculiar person; now it seemed that he had gone completely crazy. She wondered whether she should run into the house and fetch her husband. No, she thought. No, he's harmless. I'll just humor him. "Certainly, Mr. Klausner, if you like," she said. She took her scissors from the basket, bent down and snipped another rose.

Again Klausner heard that frightful, throatless shriek in the earphones; again it came at the exact moment the rose stem was cut. He took off the earphones and ran to the fence that separated the two gardens. "All right," he said. "That's enough. No more. Please, no more." The woman stood there, a yellow rose in one hand, clippers in the other, looking at him.

"I'm going to tell you something, Mrs. Saunders," he said, "something that you won't believe." He put his hands on top of the fence and peered at her intently through his thick spectacles. "You have, this evening, cut a basketful of roses. You have with a sharp pair of scissors cut through the stems of living things, and each rose that you cut screamed in the most terrible way. Did you know that, Mrs. Saunders?"

"No," she said. "I certainly didn't know that."

"It happens to be true," he said. He was breathing rather rapidly, but he was trying to control his excitement. "I heard them shrieking. Each time you cut one, I heard the cry of pain. A very high-pitched sound, approximately one hundred and thirty-two thousand vibrations a second. You couldn't possibly have heard it yourself. But *I* heard it."

"Did you really, Mr. Klausner?" She decided she would make a dash for the house in about five seconds.

"You might say," he went on, "that a rosebush has no nervous system to feel with, no throat to cry with. You'd be right. It hasn't. Not like ours, anyway. But *how do you know, Mrs. Saunders"*—and here he leaned far over the fence and spoke in a fierce whisper—*"how do you know* that a rosebush doesn't feel as much pain when someone cuts its stem in two as you would feel if someone cut your wrist off with a garden shears? *How do you know that?* It's *alive,* isn't it?"

"Yes, Mr. Klausner. Oh, yes—and good night." Quickly she turned and ran up the garden to her house. Klausner went back to the table. He put on the earphones and stood for a while listening. He could still hear the faint crackling sound and the humming noise of the machine, but nothing more. He bent down and took hold of a small white daisy growing on the lawn. He took it between thumb and forefinger and slowly pulled it upward and sideways until the stem broke.

From the moment that he started pulling to the moment when the stem broke, he heard—he distinctly heard in the earphones—a faint high-pitched cry, curiously inanimate. He took another daisy and did it again. Once more he heard the cry, but he wasn't so sure now that it expressed *pain.* No, it wasn't pain; it was surprise. Or was it? It didn't really express any of the feelings or emotions known to a human being. It was just a cry, a neutral, stony cry—a single emotionless note, expressing nothing. It had been the same with the roses. He had been wrong in calling it a cry of pain. A flower probably didn't feel pain. It felt something else which we didn't know about—something called *toin* or *spurl* or *plinuckment,* or anything you like.

He stood up and removed the earphones. It was getting dark and he could see pricks of light shining in the windows of the houses all around him. Carefully he picked up the black box from the table, carried it into the shed and put it on the workbench. Then he went out, locked the door behind him and walked up to the house.

The next morning Klausner was up as soon as it was light. He dressed and went straight to the shed. He picked up the machine and carried it outside, clasping it to his chest with both hands, walking unsteadily under its weight. He went past the house, out through the front gate, and across the road to the park. There he paused and looked around him; then he went on until he came to a large tree, a beech tree, and he placed the machine on the ground close to the trunk of the tree. Quickly he went back to the house and got an axe from the coal cellar and carried it across the road into the park. He put the axe on the ground beside the tree. Then he looked around him again, peering nervously through his thick glasses in every direction. There was no one about. It was six in the morning.

He put the earphones on his head and switched on the machine. He listened for a moment to the faint familiar humming sound; then he picked up the axe, took a stance with his legs wide apart and swung the axe as hard as he could at the base of the tree trunk. The blade cut deep into the wood and stuck there, and at the instant of impact he heard a most extraordinary noise in the earphones. It was a new noise, unlike any he had heard before—a harsh, noteless, enormous noise, a growling, low-pitched, screaming sound, not quick and short like the noise of the roses, but drawn out like a sob, lasting for fully a minute, loudest at the moment when the axe struck, fading gradually fainter and fainter until it was gone.

Klausner stared in horror at the place where the blade of the axe had sunk into the woodflesh of the tree; then gently he took the axe handle, worked the blade loose and threw the thing on the ground. With his fingers he touched the gash that the axe had made in the wood, touching the edges of the gash, trying to press them together to close the wound, and he kept saying, "Tree . . . oh tree . . . I am sorry . . . I am so sorry . . . but it will heal . . . it will heal fine. . . ."

For a while he stood there with his hands upon the trunk of the great tree; then suddenly he turned away and hurried off out of the park, across the road, through the front gate and back into his house. He went to the telephone, consulted the book, dialled a number and waited. He held the receiver tightly in his left hand and tapped the table impatiently with his right. He heard the telephone buzzing at the other end, and then the click of a lifted receiver and a man's voice, a sleepy voice, saying: "Hullo. Yes."

"Dr. Scott?" he said.

"Yes. Speaking."

"Dr. Scott. You must come at once—quickly please."

"Who is it speaking?"

"Klausner here, and you remember what I told you last night about my experience with sound, and how I hoped I might——"

"Yes, yes, of course, but what's the matter? Are you ill?"

"No, I'm not ill, but——"

"It's half-past six in the morning," the doctor said, "and you call me, but you are not ill."

"Please come. Come quickly. I want someone to hear it. It's driving me mad! I can't believe it. . . ."

The doctor heard the frantic, almost hysterical note in the man's voice, the same note he was used to hearing in the voices of people who called up and said, "There's been an accident. Come quickly." He said slowly, "You really want me to get out of bed and come over now?"

"Yes now. At once please."

"All right then, I'll come."

Klausner sat down beside the telephone and waited. He tried to remember what the shriek of the tree had sounded like, but he couldn't. He could remember only that it had been enormous and frightful and that it had made him feel sick with horror. He tried to imagine what sort of noise a human would make if he had to stand anchored to the ground while someone deliberately swung a small sharp thing at his leg so that the blade cut in deep and wedged itself in the cut. Same sort of noise perhaps? No. Quite different. The noise of the tree was worse than any known human noise because of that frightening, toneless, throatless quality. He began to wonder about other living things, and he thought immediately of a field of wheat, a field of wheat standing up straight and yellow and alive, with the mower going through it, cutting the stems, five hundred stems a second, every second. Oh, my God, what would *that* noise be like? Five hundred wheat plants screaming together, and every second another five hundred being cut and screaming and—— No, he thought, I do not want to go to a wheat field with my machine. I would never eat bread after that. But what about potatoes and cabbages and carrots and onions? And what about apples? Ah, no. Apples are all right. They fall off naturally when they are ripe. Apples are all right if you let them fall off instead of tearing them from the tree branch. But not vegetables. Not a potato for example. A potato would surely shriek; so would a carrot and an onion and a cabbage. . . .

He heard the click of the front-gate latch and he jumped up and went out and saw the tall doctor coming down the path, little black bag in hand. "Well," the doctor said. "Well, what's all the trouble?"

"Come with me, doctor. I want you to hear it. I called you because you're the only one I've told. It's over the road in the park. Will you come now?"

The doctor looked at him. He seemed calmer now. There was no sign of madness or hysteria; he was merely disturbed and excited.

They went across the road into the park and Klausner led the way to the great beech tree at the foot of which stood the long black coffin-box of the machine—and the axe.

"Why did you bring it out here?" the doctor asked.

"I wanted a tree. There aren't any big trees in the garden."

"And why the axe?"

"You'll see in a moment. But now please put on these earphones and listen. Listen carefully and tell me afterwards precisely what you hear. I want to make quite sure. . . ."

The doctor smiled and took the earphones and put them over his ears.

Klausner bent down and flicked the switch on the panel of the machine; then he picked up the axe and took his stance with his legs apart, ready to swing. For a moment he paused. "Can you hear anything?" he said to the doctor.

"Can I what?"

"Can you *hear* anything?"

"Just a humming noise."

Klausner stood there with the axe in his hands trying to bring himself to swing, but the thought of the noise that the tree would make made him pause again.

"What are you waiting for?" the doctor asked.

"Nothing," Klausner answered, and then he lifted the axe and swung it at the tree; and as he swung, he thought he felt, he could swear he felt a movement of the ground on which he stood. He felt a slight shifting of the earth beneath his feet as though the roots of the tree were moving underneath the soil, but it was too late to check the blow and the axe blade struck the tree and wedged deep into the wood. At that moment, high overhead, there was the cracking sound of wood splintering and the swishing sound of leaves brushing against other leaves and they both looked up and the doctor cried, "Watch out! Run, man! Quickly, run!"

The doctor had ripped off the earphones and was running away fast, but Klausner stood spellbound, staring up at the great branch, sixty feet long at least, that was bending slowly downward, breaking and crackling and splintering at its thickest point, where it joined the main trunk of the tree. The branch came crashing down and Klausner leapt aside just in time. It fell upon the machine and smashed it into pieces.

"Great heavens!" shouted the doctor as he came running back. "That was a near one! I thought it had got you!"

Klausner was staring at the tree. His large head was leaning to one side and upon his smooth white face there was a tense, horrified expression. Slowly he walked up to the tree and gently he prized the blade loose from the trunk. "Did you hear it?" he said, turning to the doctor. His voice was barely audible.

The doctor was still out of breath from the running and the excitement. "Hear what?"

"In the earphones. Did you hear anything when the axe struck?"

The doctor began to rub the back of his neck. "Well," he said, "as a matter of fact. . . ." He paused and frowned and bit his lower lip. "No, I'm not sure. I couldn't be sure. I don't suppose I had the earphones on for more than a second after the axe struck."

"Yes, yes, but what did you hear?"

"I don't know," the doctor said. "I don't know what I heard. Probably the noise of the branch breaking." He was speaking rapidly, rather irritably.

"What did it sound like?" Klausner leaned forward slightly, staring hard at the doctor. "*Exactly* what did it sound like?"

"Oh hell!" the doctor said. "I really don't know. I was more interested in getting out of the way. Let's leave it."

"Dr. Scott, *what did it sound like?*"

"For God's sake, how could I tell, what with half the tree falling on me and having to run for my life?" The doctor certainly seemed nervous. Klausner had sensed it now. He stood quite still, staring at the doctor, and for fully half a minute he didn't speak. The doctor moved his feet, shrugged his shoulders and half turned to go. "Well," he said, "we'd better get back."

"Look," said the little man, and now his smooth white face became suddenly suffused with color. "Look," he said, "you stitch this up." He pointed to the last gash that the axe had made in the tree trunk. "You stitch this up quickly."

"Don't be silly," the doctor said.

"You do as I say. Stitch it up." Klausner was gripping the axe handle and he spoke softly, in a curious, almost a threatening tone.

"Don't be silly," the doctor said. "I can't stitch through wood. Come on. Let's get back."

"So you can't stitch through wood?"

"No, of course not."

"Have you got any iodine in your bag?"

"What if I have?"

"Then paint the cut with iodine. It'll sting, but that can't be helped."

"Now look," the doctor said, and again he turned as if to go. "Let's not be ridiculous. Let's get back to the house and then . . ."

"Paint the cut with iodine."

The doctor hesitated. He saw Klausner's hands tightening on the handle of the axe. He decided that his only alternative was to run away fast, and he certainly wasn't going to do that.

"All right," he said. "I'll paint it with iodine."

He got his black bag which was lying on the grass about ten yards away, opened it and took out a bottle of iodine and some cotton wool. He went up to the tree trunk, uncorked the bottle, tipped some of the iodine onto the cotton wool, bent down and began to dab it into the cut. He kept one eye on Klausner who was standing motionless with the axe in his hands, watching him.

"Make sure you get it right in."

"Yes," the doctor said.

"Now do the other one, the one just above it!"

The doctor did as he was told.

"There you are," he said. "It's done."

He straightened up and surveyed his work in a very serious manner. "That should do nicely."

Klausner came closer and gravely examined the two wounds.

"Yes," he said, nodding his huge head slowly up and down. "Yes, that will do nicely." He stepped back a pace. "You'll come and look at them again tomorrow?"

"Oh yes," the doctor said. "Of course."

"And put some more iodine on?"

"If necessary, yes."

"Thank you, Doctor," Klausner said, and he nodded his head again and he dropped the axe and all at once he smiled, a wild excited smile, and quickly the doctor went over to him and gently he took him by the arm and he said, "Come on, we must go now," and suddenly they were walking away, the two of them, walking silently, rather hurriedly across the park, over the road, back to the house.

LOVE
AMONG
THE CABBAGES

Peter Tompkins and Christopher Bird

THE MOST FAR-REACHING REVOLUTION of the twentieth century may come from the least expected quarter, the bottom of your garden. Scientists everywhere in the world, amazed by the results of careful laboratory experiments, find themselves coming to the conclusion that plants have emotions similar to those of human beings, that they respond to affection, and that they can be adapted to the service of mankind.

The startling idea that plants could be sentient and capable of communication with *homo sapiens*[1] received its most recent circulation, especially in the United States, as the result of a series of chance discoveries in the winter of 1966 by a New York lie-detector expert who decided to measure electronically the time it took water poured on the roots of a potted house plant to reach the tips of its leaves. Because Cleve Backster had been employed by the Central Intelligence Agency, and because his approach to the subject was suitably skeptical, his discoveries achieved a degree of serious recognition. . . .

Backster was also credited by scientists with not having run into the streets after his first experiment shouting: "Look! Plants can think!"

Not that a great deal of skepticism did not prevail in the major media. The *New York Times,* at first intrigued by the story, consulted a professional botanist who decided, when Backster claimed to have been able to communicate with his plants at a distance, that it must all be a flight of fancy. It took the *Wall Street Journal* to publish a report of Backster's findings under the headline: "Be Kind to Your Plants— You Could Cause a Violet to Shrink."

The *Journal* noted that the experiments seemed to indicate that besides a sort of telepathic communication system, plants possess something akin to feelings or emotions, that they appreciate being noticed, worry when a dog comes near them, and faint when violence threatens their own well-being; also, that plants give signs of sympathy when harm befalls humans, animals, or insects in their environment.

Abridgement of "Love Among the Cabbages," as it appeared in *Harper's* Magazine, 1972, from THE SECRET LIFE OF PLANTS by Peter Tompkins and Christopher Bird. Copyright © 1972, 1973 by Peter Tompkins and Christopher Bird. Reprinted by permission of Harper & Row Publishers, Inc. and Penguin Books, Ltd.

1. *sentient . . . homo sapiens,* can feel and can communicate with human beings.

What weighed in favor of a serious story on Backster and his thesis was his having waited three full years after his first discovery before presenting conclusions in a sober paper for the *International Journal of Parapsychology*[2] entitled "Evidence of Primary Perception in Plant Life."

Backster's laboratory evidence, obtained under conditions prescribed by scientific methodology, suggested that plants and animals and human beings appear to be interconnected by some mysterious medium that enables them to communicate instantly and at a distance.

The evidence supports earlier discoveries about the nature of plants made decades ago by such distinguished scientists as Charles Darwin, Gustav Theodor Fechner, and Sir Jagadis Chunder Bose,[3] discoveries that were greeted with incredulity if not ridicule by their contemporaries and that are still frowned upon by conservative botanists and plant physiologists today.

For a quarter of a century Backster has been one of the foremost authorities in the United States on the art of interrogation by means of the polygraph[4] and the galvanometer. Attached to a human being by two electrodes, through which a small electric current is passed, a galvanometer operates a needle on a dial or a pen-recorder on a moving roll of paper. Mental images and emotional charge affect the electrical properties of the human body, directly and almost instantly causing a reaction on the meter.

Backster's flirtation with plants began one chilly morning in February of 1966 when he was about to water one of the *Dracena massangeana*[5] that adorn his mid-Manhattan offices, just off Times Square.

Backster wondered if the gradual saturation of the plant, as it thirstily sucked up the water, could register on a galvanometer. Placing two electrodes, one on each side of a leaf of the dracena, Backster poured water onto the roots of the plant and was amazed to see that the galvanometer, instead of measuring greater conductivity—as would be expected by the relative decrease in the plant's electrical resistance due to the increase in moisture—was moving in the opposite direction. After some thirty seconds, the tracing exhibited a contour similar to that of a human being experiencing an emotional stimulation of short duration.

Could the plant be displaying emotion?

Backster decided to administer to the plant the standard threat-to-

---

2. *Parapsychology,* the branch of psychology dealing with such phenomena as extrasensory perception and telepathy. 3. *Charles Darwin, Gustav Theodor Fechner, and Sir Jagadis Chunder Bose.* The English naturalist Charles Darwin (1809-1882) observed that plants, like animals, have rhythmic periods of rest and movement. Gustav Theodor Fechner (1801-1887), a German physicist and philosopher, believed there are living souls in even plants and stars. The Indian plant physiologist Sir Jagadis Chunder Bose (1858-1937) explored the effects of air and food on plants and showed that a parallel existed between the responses of plants and humans. 4. *polygraph,* an instrument that records heartbeats and pulses; a lie detector. 5. *Dracena massangeana* (dra sē'na ma san jē'na), a small palmlike plant.

well-being test devised to obtain from a human being an upward swing of the graph: He would threaten to burn the leaf that was held between the electrodes.

The moment Backster formed the image of fire in his mind, and before he could reach for a match, the recording pen bounded off the top of the chart. Backster says he neither moved nor touched the plant. Later, when he actually burned the leaf with the flame, there was a similar, but lesser, reaction of the pen-recorder.

Most amazing to Backster was that the tracing showed no reaction whatsoever when he merely *pretended* he would burn the leaf. Evidently the plant registered apprehension only at a true threat to its well-being.

To explore how his plants might be affected by a threat to other living tissue, Backster dumped some brine shrimp into a vessel of boiling water. Again the polygraph needle leapt frantically. Could it be, Backster wondered, that when a cell dies, it broadcasts some sort of signal to other living cells, a rudimentary survival warning, like the Roman geese on the Capitoline Hill?[6]

Backster next experimented by killing other forms of life, down to the smallest cells. Each time he observed the plants reacting in the same way to the death of cells, whether they were fresh fruit, vegetable, mold culture, yeast, paramecia, amoebas, or even sperm. When asked why his plants did not react to the continuous dying of cells in the great world outside his office, all the way to the backwoods of Vietnam, Backster replied that plants, like animals, appear to stake out a physical space that they consider their territory and react only to phenomena occurring within that space.

He also noted that the repeated killing of shrimp in the immediate neighborhood of the plants eventually brought less and less reaction, indicating a form of adaptive logic or even memory in plants that seemed to "come to the conclusion" that the repeated killing of shrimp did not actually constitute a real threat to their own well-being.

Having gained what he calls a healthy respect for whatever is going on inside plants, Backster no longer willingly performs experiments that might be harmful to his wards. In conditioning experiments, similar to those made by Pavlov[7] in his work with animals, Backster switched from "shocking" his plants to "rewarding" them with extra light.

Quite by chance, Backster found that when plants are threatened with overwhelming danger or damage, they react self-defensively in the same way as an opossum, or indeed a human being, reacts—they "pass out," or go into a deep faint.

This he discovered when a woman physiologist, visiting from Canada, asked to be shown the reactions of Backster's plants on the

---

6. *the Roman geese on the Capitoline Hill.* In 390 B.C. the geese on the Capitoline Hill in Rome warned the Romans of a sneak attack by the Gauls, thus allowing the Romans to win that battle. 7. *Pavlov.* The Russian physiologist Ivan Pavlov (1849-1936) conditioned dogs to salivate in response to a ringing bell.

galvanometer. From the first plant he got no reaction whatsoever. The pen-recorder lapsed into a near straight-line tracing on the paper. Subsequent plants also failed to react.

Dumbfounded, Backster had a thought. "Does any part of your research involve harming plants?" he asked his visitor.

"Yes," she replied. "I terminate all the plants I work with. I put them in an oven and roast them to obtain their dry weight for my analysis."

Forty-five minutes after the visitor was safely on her way to the airport, Backster's plants once more responded normally.

In still another series of experiments, Backster established the fact that a special communion, or bond of affinity, exists between a plant and its keeper, no matter the distance separating them.

With the use of automated equipment and carefully synchronized stopwatches, Backster was able to note that his plants continued to react to his thoughts and attention from the next room, from down the hall, and even from several buildings away.

Back from a fifteen-mile trip to New Jersey, Backster established that his plants had perked up and shown definite and positive signs of response at the very moment he had decided to return to New York.

To see if he could get a reaction from plants from a distance of over a thousand miles, Backster checked a friend tuned to her own plants on a three-thousand-mile plane ride across the United States. From synchronized clocks they found the plants reacted strongly to her emotional stress at each takeoff and landing.

Backster has no idea what kind of energy wave may carry a man's thoughts or internal feelings to a plant. He has tried to screen a plant by placing it in a Faraday cage,[8] as well as in a lead container. Neither shield appeared in any way to block or jam the communication channel linking the plant to a human being. The carrier wave, he concluded, whatever it is, must somehow operate beyond the electromagnetic spectrum. "We're in another dimension," says Backster, "a scientific twilight in which something can go from point to point without going between, and without consuming time to get there. . . ."

Generally, the reaction of academic scientists to Backster's discoveries has been surprisingly positive. To date, more than seven thousand scientists have asked for reprints of Backster's original research. Between twenty and thirty universities are said to be replicating his principal experiments, and various foundations have expressed interest in funding further work.

An engineer from the Xerox Company—launched with funds from a psychic research enthusiast—has been studying Backster's phenomena in order to stimulate a plant into tripping a light switch by mere thought control.

More sensational are the experiments accomplished by Paul Sauvin, an electronics technician and inventor. Modifying the schematics in an article by L. George Lawrence (the reported pseudonym of a secret

---

8. *Faraday cage*, a screen that protects an area from electrostatic fields.

government worker) in *Popular Electronics* of June 1971, Sauvin was able to build sophisticated equipment to mentally trigger a device through a plant at considerable distance. Setting a philodendron on a laboratory bench two-and-a-half miles from his New Jersey home, Sauvin sent a strong emotion to the plant. When the philodendron received his telepathic message, it triggered a radio signal that turned on the ignition of an automobile in the laboratory parking lot, starting the motor.

The instants of Sauvin's thought transmission and of its reception by the plant were timed as synchronous by a shortwave radio station at Boulder, Colorado, two thousand miles away. Under less precise conditions Sauvin measured apparent synchronism in a plant's ability to turn on a switch when the plant was as far away from him as seventy miles. Sauvin believes that with the expert advice of certain design specialists he will be able to perform the same feat cross-country and determine for the first time whether the energy of ESP travels either at, or faster than, the speed of light. . . .

Actually, Backster is by no means the first investigator to conclude that plants have feelings similar to those of human beings or to record the reactions of plants on laboratory instruments.

Early in this century, the eminent Indian physiologist Sir Jagadis Chunder Bose, founder of the Bose Institute in Calcutta, demonstrated that plants have a perfectly good nervous system and a mechanism like a heart for pumping sap.

Probing plants with a fine needle attached to a galvanometer, Bose charted a sophisticated nervous system in plants by which they transform sensations into motor impulses. In a dozen fascinating books on plant physiology he detailed the mechanisms whereby leaves and twigs respond to electrical, chemical, and thermal stimuli, showing that the conduction of excitation in plants is fundamentally the same as that in animals. One apparatus he devised enabled an audience to see how a turnip, pricked on one side, shuddered on the other, indicating not only sensation but its transmission.

Pursuing Charles Darwin's observations on the waking and sleeping habits of plants, Bose noted that plants suffer from fatigue just as humans and animals do. He discovered that plants are so somnolent at times that they are practically insensitive, whereas at others—usually from midday on—they are easily excitable for a period of several hours.

(Some plants are so accurately scheduled that Carl Linnaeus, the eighteenth-century Swedish botanist, whose *Genera Plantorum* is considered the starting point of modern systematic botany, could tell the time of day by the different openings and closings of such common flowers as daisies, dandelions, primroses, and wild roses.)

Wondering how stimulants, depressants, and poisons affected plants, Bose injected several varieties with caffein, alcohol, musk, chloroform, and strychnine. The effects he obtained were similar to those in human beings. Caffein proved to be a stimulant. Spirits produced excitability followed by depression. Plants injected with alcohol swayed like drunkards. Chloroform tranquilized trees to the point that Bose was able successfully to transplant a large tree without the normal trauma of its being uprooted.

With a galvanometer, Bose discovered that plants go through a death spasm similar to the death throes of animals. At the moment of death, intense excitation is produced in a plant together with a powerful discharge of electricity. The spasm itself is caused by contractions of the dying cells.

Placing electrodes in the center and on the periphery of an ordinary green pea at the moment of its death, Bose registered a discharge of half a volt. If five hundred pairs of half peas were wired in series, said Bose, the electric discharge at the moment of their killing would amount to five hundred volts, more than enough to explode a human being. Luckily, Bose added, cooks need not be apprehensive, for peas in the pot are seldom connected in series, and the current has minimal amperage.

That plants will adapt themselves to human wishes was indicated—though generally ignored—by the experiments of Luther Burbank, the New England geneticist and experimenter with plants who gave his name to Burbank, California, where he moved at the beginning of the century to develop the pitless orange and such horticultural anomalies as an apple sweet on one side and sour on the other.

Burbank said he was able to build plants to a form mocked up in his mind, that plants responded to his mental images, indicating some form of intelligence and transmission of thought.

Contemplating the desert one day, Burbank reminded himself that every plant growing there was either bitter, poisonous, or spiny, and that each of these properties must have been developed over the course of millennia for purposes of self-defense against threatening predators. If a spiny cactus were given a human cultivator's love and protection, Burbank reasoned, it might abandon as unnecessary the urge to grow spines.

While conducting his experiments to make "spineless" cacti, Burbank talked to his plants to create a vibration of love. "You have nothing to fear," Burbank would tell his cacti. "You don't need your defensive thorns. I will protect you."

Gradually the plants of the desert evolved into a thornless variety. In Santa Rosa, Burbank told Swami Yogananda: "The secret of improved plant breeding, apart from scientific knowledge, is love."

Burbank also proved that the natural evolution of a plant could be telescopically speeded up. Experimenting with a walnut tree that normally would have taken more than thirty years to reach a state of abundant nut production, he was able to make it bear abundantly in half that time. "I now see humanity as one vast plant," said Burbank, "needing for its highest fulfillment only love, the natural blessings of the great outdoors, and intelligent crossing and selection. . . ."

But the most amazing recent experiment with plants is perhaps the one being carried out on a windblown patch of land surrounded on three sides by the North Sea on the east coast of Scotland, on Findhorn Bay in Moray. There, on a half acre of soil that is mostly sand and gravel, a nature-loving group is growing forty-pound cabbages and stunningly beautiful flowers by "communicating with the spirits that animate their plants." Peter and Elixir Caddy, the originators of the experiment, maintain they have entered into spiritual communication with the primordial architects of the plant world, the ancient devas[9] who control the universal laws of plant growth.

In their first season, the Caddys grew sixty-five different kinds of vegetables, twenty-one fruits, and forty-two herbs in ground that agricultural experts considered worthless for growing anything but gorse.[10] R. Lindsay Robb, professor of agriculture and former chief of a U.N. Food and Agriculture mission, after inspecting the garden, found that "the vigor, health and bloom of the plants in midwinter on land which is almost barren sand cannot be explained by the application of any known cultural methods of organic husbandry."

The devotees of the Findhorn garden say that what makes a desert bloom, more than water or fertilizer, is communion with the living plants. Man's most important contributions, they say, are the radiations such as love he puts into the soil while cultivating it. According to the Caddys, each plant species has a different guiding spirit that persists despite the growth, flowering, and demise of the individual plants. These spirits, say the Caddys, take pleasure when the exquisite flavor of a raspberry or brilliance of a dahlia is appreciated by a human being, and do their best when their efforts are most happily acknowledged. Happiness and joy in what one is doing, say the Caddys, are the prime requisites for success in any venture.

Because of the modern emphasis on rationality, the possibilities of a spirit life in plants were neglected until the advent of experiments such as those of the Caddys, Cleve Backster, and Marcel Vogel[11]; but in ancient times a whole kingdom of nature spirits was commonly accepted. To clairvoyants among the Celts,[12] such a world of elves and fauns and the great god Pan[13] was a matter of direct vision and experience.

Now, say the Findhorn gardeners, times are changing; a new "Aquarian" age is upon us, one in which this plundered planet may yet revert to an approximation of the Biblical Garden of Eden, where, they suggest, an original sin may have been to eat an apple without acknowledging and appreciating its full cycle of creation. ∎

---

9. *devas,* angels or gods in Hinduism and Buddhism. 10. *gorse,* a low, prickly evergreen shrub. 11. *Marcel Vogel,* an IBM research chemist in Los Gatos, California, who repeated Backster's experiments with the help of a group of IBM engineers. They found that plants reacted differently depending on the engineers' subject of conversation, and that they reacted differently to various kinds of music. 12. *Celts,* a race of people made up of the Irish, Scottish Highlanders, Welsh, and Bretons. 13. *Pan,* the ancient Greek god of forests, pastures, flocks, and shepherds.

5

VIEW
FROM
ON
HIGH

PUPPET SHOW

Fredric Brown

HORROR CAME TO CHERRYBELL at a little after noon on a blistering hot day in August.

Perhaps that is redundant; *any* August day in Cherrybell, Arizona, is blistering hot. It is on Highway 89, about forty miles south of Tucson and about thirty miles north of the Mexican border. It consists of two filling stations, one on each side of the road to catch travelers going in both directions, a general store, a beer-and-wine-license-only tavern, a tourist-trap-type trading post for tourists who can't wait until they reach the border to start buying serapes and huaraches, a deserted hamburger stand, and a few 'dobe houses inhabited by Mexican-Americans who work in Nogales, the border town to the south, and who, for God knows what reason, prefer to live in Cherrybell and commute, some of them in Model T Fords. The sign on the highway says, CHERRYBELL, POP. 42, but the sign exaggerates; Pop died last year—Pop Anders, who ran the now-deserted hamburger stand—and the correct figure should be 41.

Horror came to Cherrybell mounted on a burro led by an ancient, dirty and gray-bearded desert rat of a prospector who later gave the name of Dade Grant. Horror's name was Garvane. He was approximately nine feet tall but so thin, almost a stickman, that he could not have weighed over a hundred pounds. Old Dade's burro carried him easily, despite the fact that his feet dragged in the sand on either side.

"Puppet Show" by Fredric Brown. Originally appeared in PLAYBOY Magazine; copyright © 1962 by Elizabeth C. Brown. Reprinted by permission of Mrs. Elizabeth C. Brown and Scott Meredith Literary Agency, Inc., 580 Fifth Avenue, New York, N.Y. 10036.

Being dragged through the sand for, as it later turned out, well over five miles hadn't caused the slightest wear on the shoes—more like buskins, they were—which constituted all that he wore except for a pair of what could have been swimming trunks, in robin's-egg blue. But it wasn't his dimensions that made him horrible to look upon, it was his *skin*. It looked red, raw. It looked as though he had been skinned alive and the skin replaced raw side out. His skull, his face were equally narrow or elongated; otherwise, in every visible way, he appeared human—or at least humanoid. Unless you count such little things as the fact that his hair was robin's-egg blue to match his trunks, as were his eyes and his boots. Blood red and light blue.

Casey, owner of the tavern, was the first one to see them coming across the plain from the direction of the mountain range to the east. He'd stepped out of the back door of his tavern for a breath of fresh, if hot, air. They were about a hundred yards away at that time, and already he could see the utter alienness of the figure on the led burro. Just alienness at that distance; the horror came only at closer range. Casey's jaw dropped and stayed down until the strange trio was about fifty yards away; then he started slowly toward them. There are people who run at the sight of the unknown, others who advance to meet it. Casey advanced, slowly, to meet it.

Still in the wide open, twenty yards from the back of the little tavern, he met them. Dade Grant stopped and dropped the rope by which he was leading the burro. The burro stood still and dropped its head. The stickman stood up simply by planting his feet solidly and standing astride the burro. He stepped one leg across it and stood a moment, leaning his weight against his hands on the burro's back, and then sat down in the sand. "High-gravity planet," he said. "Can't stand long."

"Kin I get water fer my burro?" the prospector asked Casey. "Must be purty thirsty by now. Hadda leave water bags, some other things so it could carry——" He jerked a thumb toward the red and blue horror.

Casey was just realizing that it *was* a horror. At a distance the color combination seemed only mildly hideous, but close up—the skin was rough and seemed to have veins on the outside and looked moist (although it wasn't) and *damn* if it didn't look just like he had his skin peeled off and put back on inside out. Or just peeled off, period. Casey had never seen anything like it and hoped he wouldn't ever see anything like it again.

Casey felt something behind him and looked over his shoulder. Others had seen now and were coming, but the nearest of them, a pair of boys, were ten yards behind him. *"Muchachos,"* he called out. *"Agua por el burro. Un pozal. Pronto."*[1]

He looked back and said, "What—— Who——"

"Name's Dade Grant," said the prospector, putting out a hand, which Casey took absently. When he let go of it, it jerked back over the desert

---

1. *"Muchachos . . . Pronto."* "Boys," he called out. "Water for the burro. A bucketful. At once." [*Spanish*]

rat's shoulder, thumb indicating the thing that sat on the sand. *"His name's Garvane, he tells me.* He's an extra something or other, and he's some kind of minister."

Casey nodded at the stickman and was glad to get a nod in return instead of an extended hand. "I'm Manuel Casey," he said. "What does he mean, an extra something?"

The stickman's voice was unexpectedly deep and vibrant. "I am an extraterrestrial. And a minister plenipotentiary."[2]

Surprisingly, Casey was a moderately well educated man and knew both of those phrases; he was probably the only person in Cherrybell who would have known the second one. Less surprisingly, considering the speaker's appearance, he believed both of them.

"What can I do for you, sir?" he asked. "But first, why not come in out of the sun?"

"No, thank you. It's a bit cooler here than they told me it would be, but I'm quite comfortable. This is equivalent to a cool spring evening on my planet. And as to what you can do for me, you can notify your authorities of my presence. I believe they will be interested."

Well, Casey thought, by blind luck he's hit the best man for his purpose within at least twenty miles. Manuel Casey was half Irish, half Mexican. He had a half brother who was half Irish and half assorted American, and the half brother was a bird colonel at Davis-Monthan Air Force Base in Tucson.

He said, "Just a minute, Mr. Garvane, I'll telephone. You, Mr. Grant, would you want to come inside?"

"Naw, I don't mind sun. Out in it all day ever' day. An' Garvane here, he ast me if I'd stick with him till he was finished with what he's gotta do here. Said he'd gimme somethin' purty vallable if I did. Somethin'—a 'lectrononic——"

"An electronic battery-operated portable ore indicator," Garvane said. "A simple little device, indicates presence of a concentration of ore up to two miles, indicates kind, grade, quantity and depth."

Casey gulped, excused himself and pushed through the gathering crowd into his tavern. He had Colonel Casey on the phone in one minute, but it took him another four minutes to convince the colonel that he was neither drunk nor joking.

Twenty-five minutes after that, there was a noise in the sky, a noise that swelled and then died as a four-man helicopter sat down and shut off its rotors a dozen yards from an extraterrestrial, two men and a burro. Casey alone had had the courage to rejoin the trio from the desert; there were other spectators, but they still held well back.

Colonel Casey, a major, a captain and a lieutenant who was the helicopter's pilot all came out and ran over. The stickman stood up, all nine feet of him; from the effort it cost him to stand you could tell that he was used to a much lighter gravity than Earth's. He bowed,

---

2. *extraterrestrial . . . minister plenipotentiary.* An extraterrestrial is someone or something that comes from someplace other than Earth (terra). A minister plenipotentiary is a diplomat who has full power or authority.

repeated his name and the identification of himself as an extraterrestrial and a minister plenipotentiary. Then he apologized for sitting down again, explained why it was necessary and sat down.

The colonel introduced himself and the three who had come with him. "And now, sir, what can we do for you?"

The stickman made a grimace that was probably intended as a smile. His teeth were the same light blue as his hair and eyes.

"You have a cliché, 'Take me to your leader.' I do not ask that. In fact, I *must* remain here. Nor do I ask that any of your leaders be brought here to me. That would be impolite. I am perfectly willing for you to represent them, to talk to you and let you question me. But I do ask one thing.

"You have tape recorders. I ask that before I talk or answer questions, you have one brought. I want to be sure that the message your leaders eventually receive is full and accurate."

"Fine," the colonel said. He turned to the pilot. "Lieutenant, get on the radio in the whirlybird and tell them to get us a tape recorder faster than possible. It can be dropped by para—— No, that'd take longer, rigging it for a drop. Have them send it by another helicopter." The lieutenant turned to go. "Hey," the colonel said, "also fifty yards of extension cord. We'll have to plug it in inside Manny's tavern."

The lieutenant sprinted for the helicopter.

The others sat and sweated a moment and then Manuel Casey stood up. "That's a half-an-hour wait," he said, "and if we're going to sit here in the sun, who's for a bottle of cold beer? You, Mr. Garvane?"

"It is a cold beverage, is it not? I am a bit chilly. If you have something hot——"

"Coffee, coming up. Can I bring you a blanket?"

"No, thank you. It will not be necessary."

Casey left and shortly returned with a tray with half a dozen bottles of cold beer and a cup of steaming coffee. The lieutenant was back by then. Casey put the tray down and served the stickman first, who sipped the coffee and said, "It is delicious."

Colonel Casey cleared his throat, "Serve our prospector friend next, Manny. As for us—well, drinking is forbidden on duty, but it was a hundred and twelve in the shade in Tucson, and this is hotter and also is *not* in the shade. Gentlemen, consider yourselves on official leave for as long as it takes you to drink one bottle of beer or until the tape recorder arrives, whichever comes first."

The beer was finished first, but by the time the last of it had vanished, the second helicopter was within sight and sound. Casey asked the stickman if he wanted more coffee. The offer was politely declined. Casey looked at Dade Grant and winked, and the desert rat winked back; so Casey went in for two more bottles, one apiece for the civilian terrestrials. Coming back, he met the lieutenant arriving with the extension cord and returned as far as the doorway to show him where to plug it in.

When he came back, he saw that the second helicopter had brought its full complement of four, besides the tape recorder. There were, besides the pilot who had flown it, a technical sergeant who was skilled in its operation and who was now making adjustments on it and a lieutenant colonel and a warrant officer who had come along for the ride or because they had been made curious by the *request* for a tape recorder to be rushed to Cherrybell, Arizona, by air. They were standing gaping at the stickman, and whispered conversations were going on.

The colonel said, "Attention," quietly, but it brought complete silence. "Please sit down, gentlemen. In a rough circle. Sergeant, if you rig your mike in the center of the circle, will it pick up clearly what any one of us may say?"

"Yes, sir. I'm almost ready."

Ten men and one extraterrestrial humanoid sat in a rough circle, with the microphone hanging from a small tripod in the approximate center. The humans were sweating profusely; the humanoid shivered slightly. Just outside the circle, the burro stood dejectedly, its head low. Edging closer, but still about five yards away, spread out now in a semicircle, was the entire population of Cherrybell who had been at home at the time; the stores and the filling stations were deserted.

The technical sergeant pushed a button and the tape recorder's reel started to turn. "Testing . . . testing," he said. He held down the rewind button for a second and then pushed the playback button. "Testing . . . testing," said the recorder's speaker. Loud and clear. The sergeant pushed the rewind button, then the erase one to clear the tape. Then the stop button.

"When I push the next button, sir," he said to the colonel, "we'll be recording."

The colonel looked at the tall extraterrestrial, who nodded, and then the colonel nodded at the sergeant. The sergeant pushed the recording button.

"My name is Garvane," said the stickman slowly and clearly. "I am from a planet of a star which is not listed in your star catalogs, although the globular cluster in which it is one of ninety thousand stars is known to you. It is, from here, in the direction of the center of the galaxy at a distance of over four thousand light-years.

"However, I am not here as a representative of my planet or my people, but as minister plenipotentiary of the Galactic Union, a federation of the enlightened civilizations of the galaxy, for the good of all. It is my assignment to visit you and decide, here and now, whether or not you are to be welcomed to join our federation.

"You may now ask questions freely. However, I reserve the right to postpone answering some of them until my decision has been made. If the decision is favorable, I will then answer all questions, including the ones I have postponed answering meanwhile. Is that satisfactory?"

"Yes," said the colonel. "How did you come here? A spaceship?"

"Correct. It is overhead right now, in orbit twenty-two thousand miles out, so it revolves with the Earth and stays over this one spot. I am under observation from it, which is one reason I prefer to remain here in the open. I am to signal it when I want it to come down to pick me up."

"How do you know our language so fluently? Are you telepathic?"[3]

"No, I am not. And nowhere in the galaxy is any race telepathic except among its own members. I was taught your language for this purpose. We have had observers among you for many centuries—by *we,* I mean the Galactic Union, of course. Quite obviously, I could not pass as an Earthman, but there are other races who can. Incidentally, they are not spies or agents; they have in no way tried to affect you; they are observers and that is all."

"What benefits do we get from joining your union, if we are asked and if we accept?" the colonel asked.

"First, a quick course in the fundamental social sciences which will end your tendency to fight among yourselves and end or at least control your aggressions. After we are satisfied that you have accomplished that and it is safe for you to do so, you will be given space travel and many other things as rapidly as you are able to assimilate them."

"And if we are not asked or refuse?"

"Nothing. You will be left alone; even our observers will be withdrawn. You will work out your own fate—either you will render your planet uninhabited and uninhabitable within the next century or you will master social science yourselves and again be candidates for membership and again be offered membership. We will check from time to time, and if and when it appears certain that you are not going to destroy yourselves, you will again be approached."

"Why the hurry, now that you're here? Why can't you stay long enough for our leaders, as you call them, to talk to you in person?"

"Postponed. The reason is not important but it is complicated, and I simply do not wish to waste time explaining."

"Assuming your decision is favorable, how will we get in touch with you to let you know *our* decision? You know enough about us, obviously, to know that *I* can't make it."

"We will know your decision through our observers. One condition of acceptance is full and uncensored publication in your newspapers of this interview, verbatim from the tape we are now using to record it. Also of all deliberations and decisions of your government."

"And other governments? We can't decide unilaterally for the world."

"Your government has been chosen for a start. If you accept, we shall furnish the techniques that will cause the others to fall in line quickly—and those techniques do not involve force or the threat of force."

"They must be *some* techniques," said the colonel wryly, "if they'll make one certain country I don't have to name fall into line without even a threat."

"Sometimes the offer of reward is more significant than the use of a threat. Do you think the country you do not wish to name would like

---

3. *telepathic,* able to communicate mind to mind without using speech.

your country colonizing planets of far stars before they even reach the Moon? But that is a minor point, relatively. You may trust the techniques."

"It sounds almost too good to be true. But you said that you are to decide, here and now, whether or not we are to be invited to join. May I ask on what factors you will base your decision?"

"One is that I am—was, since I already have—to check your degree of xenophobia. In the loose sense in which you use it, that means fear of strangers. We have a word that has no counterpart in your vocabulary; it means fear of and revulsion toward *aliens.* I—or at least a member of my race—was chosen to make the first overt contact with you. Because I am what you would call roughly humanoid—as you are what I would call roughly humanoid—I am probably more horrible, more repulsive, to you than many completely different species would be. Because to you I am a caricature of a human being, I am more horrible to you than a being who bears no remote resemblance to you.

"You may think you *do* feel horror at me, and revulsion, but believe me, you have passed that test. There *are* races in the galaxy who can never be members of the federation, no matter how they advance otherwise, because they are violently and incurably xenophobic; they could never face or talk to an alien of any species. They would either run screaming from him or try to kill him instantly. From watching you and these people"—he waved a long arm at the civilian population of Cherrybell not far outside the circle of the conference—"I know you feel revulsion at the sight of me, but believe me, it is relatively slight and certainly curable. You have passed that test satisfactorily."

"And are there other tests?"

"One other. But I think it is time that I——" Instead of finishing the sentence, the stickman lay back flat on the sand and closed his eyes.

The colonel started to his feet. "What in *hell?*" he said. He walked quickly around the mike's tripod and bent over the recumbent extraterrestrial, putting an ear to the bloody-appearing chest.

As he raised his head, Dade Grant, the grizzled prospector, chuckled. "No heartbeat, Colonel, because no heart. But I may leave him as a souvenir for you and you'll find much more interesting things inside him than heart and guts. Yes, he is a puppet whom I have been operating, as your Edgar Bergen operates his—what's his name?—oh, yes, Charlie McCarthy.[4] Now that he has served his purpose, he is deactivated. You can go back to your place, Colonel."

Colonel Casey moved back slowly. "*Why?*" he asked.

Dade Grant was peeling off his beard and wig. He rubbed a cloth across his face to remove make-up and was revealed as a handsome young man. He said, "What he told you, or what you were told through him, was true as far as it went. He is only a simulacrum,[5] yes, but he is an exact duplicate of a member of one of the intelligent races of the galaxy, the one toward whom you would be disposed—if you were

---

4. *Edgar Bergen . . . Charlie McCarthy*. Edgar Bergen was a popular ventriloquist. His starring puppet was named Charlie McCarthy. 5. *simulacrum,* something formed in the likeness of a being.

violently and incurably xenophobic—to be most horrified by, according to our psychologists. But we did not bring a real member of his species to make first contact because they have a phobia of their own, agoraphobia—fear of space. They are highly civilized and members in good standing of the federation, but they never leave their own planet.

"Our observers assure us you don't have *that* phobia. But they were unable to judge in advance the degree of your xenophobia, and the only way to test it was to bring along something in lieu of someone to test it against and presumably to let him make the initial contact."

The colonel sighed audibly. "I can't say this doesn't relieve me in one way. We could get along with humanoids, yes, and we will when we have to. But I'll admit it's a relief to learn that the master race of the galaxy is, after all, human instead of only humanoid. What is the second test?"

"You are undergoing it now. Call me——" He snapped his fingers. "What's the name of Bergen's second-string puppet, after Charlie McCarthy?"

The colonel hesitated, but the tech sergeant supplied the answer. "Mortimer Snerd."

"Right. So call me Mortimer Snerd, and now I think it is time that I——" He lay back flat on the sand and closed his eyes just as the stickman had done a few minutes before.

The burro raised its head and put it into the circle over the shoulder of the tech sergeant.

"That takes care of the puppets, Colonel," it said. "And now, what's this bit about it being important that the master race be human or at least humanoid? What is a master race?"

RANDOM SAMPLE

T. P. Caravan

IF YOU DON'T GIVE ME ANOTHER piece of candy I'll cry. You'd be surprised how loud I can cry. Mother wouldn't like that.

Thank you. I just love candy.

I'm very polite for my age; everybody says so. I can get more candy that way. Old ladies are best. I'm also a very intelligent little girl, but I suppose you found that out from your tests. They gave me the same kind of tests, but they didn't give me any candy, so I was bad and didn't answer anything right.

Thank you. I'll take two this time. Do you have any hard candies? The heat's melted these chocolates a little.

My father says to get all I can out of you, because all you Viennese head-thumpers[1] are quacks. He says you cost an awful lot of money. He says only an old fraud would have a beard like a billy goat. He says . . .

Are you getting angry?

All right, then, if you give me just one more piece of candy I'll tell you all about it.

Merci. That's French, you know.

My brother Johnny and I were out in the backyard, stomping ants, when the spaceship came down. It's fun sometimes to watch ants, they run around so hopefully going about their business, carrying little bits of twigs and things in their mouths; and they don't even seem to know you're there until your foot just about touches them. Then they run away, waving their feelers before they squish. But the big red ants are the really good ones. You can jump right spang on them and they don't even seem to notice it. I guess they sink into the ground a little ways, because if you pound one between two rocks he squishes without any trouble. They taste funny. Once Johnny saw a red one fighting a black one and they kept on fighting until he burned them both up with his magnifying glass.

Will you buy me a magnifying glass if I tell you about it? I'd just love to have a magnifying glass. I bet the ant thinks the sun is spread out over the whole sky. I bet he thinks the whole world is burning up. I bet

"Random Sample" by T. P. Caravan. Copyright 1953 Mercury Press, Inc., © 1973 by Charles C. Munoz. Reprinted from The Magazine of FANTASY AND SCIENCE FICTION. Reprinted by permission of Charles C. Munoz.

1. *Viennese head-thumpers.* The caricatured picture of a psychiatrist is a Viennese with a goatee. Vienna was the home of Sigmund Freud, often called the father of psychoanalysis.

it hurts. I bet I could burn up more ants than Johnny can, even though I'm a whole year younger. He's ten.

Please, can I have a magnifying glass? Please? Please? Can I? Can I? I'll cry.

When can I have it?

Thank you.

It was his birthday so I let him take the ones near the ant hill. I'm really very generous at times. You let them get almost down the hole before you jump on them. That's the most fun. I was watching one I'd pulled the legs off, waiting to see if the others would eat it, when Johnny yelled for me to come quick and I went running over. He showed me one ant carrying another on its back, trying to get it down into the ant hill before we squished it. We were just about to stomp on its little head when we heard the noise in the sky. It was the kind of skreeky sound I make when I pull my fingernail along the blackboard in school and make old Miss Cooper get the shivers. I hate Miss Cooper. She doesn't give me any candy—thank you—and I never answer any questions for her.

We looked up and saw the rocket ship coming down for a landing in the woods. It didn't look like a ship to me, but that's what Johnny says it was. It looked like a big washing machine to me. Father says it was a hallucination—I like big words—but he didn't even see it, so how could he know?

Sometimes I hate Father. Are you writing that down? Was that the right thing to say? Can I have some more candy?

Thank you.

This is very good, even if it is melted. I should think you could afford to have your office air conditioned, then the candy wouldn't melt at all. If you were smart you'd think of these things.

What happened? I've told it over and over but nobody believes me. Isn't that sad? I don't think I'll tell anybody else about it.

The whole box? For me? Thank you. I just love chocolates.

Your beard isn't really much like a billy goat's.

We saw it come down in the woods and we ran over to the place. Nobody else was there. The grass and underbrush was burning a little but they were putting it out, and when they saw us they stopped still and made little noises to each other. I held up my hand and I said, "I'm queen here. You must all bow down." And Johnny held up his hand and said, "I'm king." He never thinks of anything for himself.

I hate them. They didn't bow down to me. One of them picked up a squirrel that had been burned a little when they landed, and he was petting it and putting something on the burned place, and he didn't pay any attention to me. I hated him most of all, so I went over and kicked him. He was smaller than Johnny, so Johnny kicked him too. I kicked him first, though, and he was just my size.

What did they look like? They didn't look like little old billy goats.

They took us inside their spaceship, and they started to give us some tests like the one you gave me. They were very simple tests, but I didn't like them so I got them all wrong. Johnny got them all wrong too, because I told him I'd scratch his eyes out if he didn't. I remember some of them. They drew little triangles with boxes on two of the sides and then they gave me the pen and waited to see what I'd do. I fooled them. I took the pen and threw ink all over them. It wasn't a pen, exactly, but it was like one. Then they held up one little block, then two, then three, then four. They did this a few times, and then they held up one block, then two. Then they waited for me to pick up three. I picked up all the blocks and hit them over the head with them. I had a lot of fun. I was very bad.

They got Johnny off in a corner, and before you could say "boo!" he was telling them about all the people he'd killed in the war. He wasn't really in the war, of course, but he likes to pretend he was. He likes television best when they kill lots of people. I don't think they really knew what he was talking about, but they looked as if they did. He's a very good actor.

I suppose they thought we were grownups; they were pretty much the same size we are. Anyway, they paid a lot of attention to him, so I went over and punched him a couple of times. I'm afraid we broke up the insides of their spaceship a little.

They looked pretty mad. I guess they were disgusted with Johnny; a lot of people are. I always try to make a good impression on strangers, even when they don't give me any candy, so I took some of them outside and showed them how to stomp ants. It was very funny. One of them got sick. Johnny and I were still jumping up and down, stomping ants, when they took off. I hated them. They were nasty; they didn't bow down to me.

That's all. Nothing else happened.

Father says not to take up too much of your expensive old time. He says no honest man could afford a penthouse for his office. You have a very nice view, don't you? You can see all over the city from here.

My, isn't it hot? I wish I had a refrigerator to keep my candy in.

Look there. Look at the fires springing up across the river. Aren't they pretty? Look. Look. And some on this side.

Take me away from here. It's too hot.

Look at the sun. Look at it. It's spreading out over the whole sky. It's burning up the city. Billy goat, help me! Save me. I'm sorry I was bad.

ON
THE
WHEEL

Damon Knight

FROM HIS PERCH IN THE FORETOP of the *Vlakengros,* Akim could see almost straight down into the cargo well of the old tub, where half a dozen trogs were still scrambling about. Nearby stood his father and the shipmaster, Hizoor Niarefh. Akim could see the tops of their turbaned heads and the bright shafts of their lances. The trogs, black and foreshortened, were like clumsy insects. Akim blew out his breath impatiently and lifted his eyes to the horizon. Westward, above the low hills of the mainland, the sun lay behind veils of purple and gold. A faint offshore breeze roughened the water. To the east, above the ocean, one of the moons had already risen. It was the end of his watch; another day was gone, wasted. Nothing ever happened on the *Vlakengros.*

At last there was a stirring, a distant shout. The trogs were climbing over the rail into their catamarans. Akim waited, twitching with impatience, until a figure stepped leisurely toward the foot of the mast and began to climb.

It was his brother Ogo, who had pimples and never smiled. "Pig," said Akim. He swung himself down the side of the lookout without waiting for Ogo to climb in; his toes caught the rope ladder and he started down. Ogo's dark head appeared above him. "Squid!" Akim shook his fist and kept on descending.

"On the Wheel" by Damon Knight from NOVA 2. Reprinted by permission of Robert P. Mills Ltd.

The deck trembled faintly under his feet as he crossed toward the forecastle; the auxiliaries were on, they were under way. Smells of cooking came from the galley. Akim ran down the companionway, snatched a meat pie from the table and was out again, followed by the curses of the cooks. Eating as he went, he reached his cubby and shut the door behind him. He tossed his fire lance into the rack, pulled off turban and robe, and sank down in his chair before the viewer. Now, at last!

He remembered exactly where he had left off, but he thumbed the rewind, listened to the tape squeal for a few moments, then punched "play." The screen lighted. There he was, Edward Robinson, opening the door at the end of the long hall. Still chewing, Akim settled lower into his chair, careful not to move his eyes a millimeter from the screen. The room was large but divided by frosted glass partitions into a jungle of smaller spaces. Behind one of these partitions, looking out through a hole in it, sat a girl with pink and white skin. Over her glossy brown hair she wore a telephone headset. Somewhere in the labyrinth behind her, close and yet invisible, a voice was raised in anger. She looked at Robinson with weary indifference. "Yes, can I help you?"

He advanced, straightening his thin shoulders, and took a folded paper out of his pocket. He unfolded it and laid it on the counter. "Central Employment sent me."

"All right, fill this out." She handed him a card. Along the wall to his right were straight chairs in which three young men sat. One was biting his pencil and scowling. Robinson sat down and began filling out his card. Name. Address. Sex. Age. Race (crossed out by a heavy black line). Education. Previous Employment (list your last three jobs, with dates, duties performed, and reason for leaving). Robinson made up the education, the dates, the reasons, and one of the jobs. While he was doing this, one of the other young men was called. He walked down the corridor between the glass partitions and disappeared. Robinson finished his card and gave it to the girl behind the partition, who was filing her nails. A typewriter clattered somewhere. The second young man was called. Robinson looked around, saw a copy of *Time* on the table beside him, and picked it up. He read an article about dynamic Eric Woolmason who at the age of forty-one was forging a new empire in Pacific Northwest public utilities. The third young man stood up suddenly and crumpled his card. His face was pink. He glanced sidelong at Robinson, then walked out. The girl at the window looked after him with a faint one-sided smile. "Well, goodbye," she murmured.

Robinson began to read the ads in the back of the magazine. He did not think about the coming interview, but his heart was thumping and his palms were moist. At last the girl's voice said, "Mr. Robinson." He stood up. She pointed with her pencil. "Straight down. End of the hall."

"All hands! All hands!" He sat up with a jerk, his heart racing. The room was dark except for the tiny lighted screen. The bellowing voice went on. "All hands to stations! All hands!"

Akim staggered out of the chair, painfully confused. He got into his robe somehow, snatched up the fire lance. Where was his turban? In the screen, a tiny Robinson was walking between the rows of frost-white partitions. He hit the "off" button angrily and lurched out of the room.

Abovedecks, searchlights and the jets of fire lances were wavering across the windy darkness. Something heavy fell to the deck and lay snapping and squealing. A half-naked sailor ran up and hit it with an axe. Akim kept on going. He could see that the foretop was crowded already—three lances were spitting up there. There was another shriek from the sky, a pause, then a splash near the bow. He ran to the quarterdeck rail and found a place between his brother Emmuz and his uncle's cousin Hudny. A searchlight in the bow probed the sky like a skeletal finger. Something appeared in it and was gone. The beam swung, caught it again. Half a dozen lance flames spitted it. It fell, trailing oily smoke. There were more shrieks, splashes. Back toward the waist, there was a flurry of running feet, curses, shouts. Something was thrashing, tangled in the foremast shrouds. A voice screamed, "Don't shoot, you fool! Up the mast and chop it!"

Something came whistling through the darkness under the search-beam. Akim crouched, raised his lance, fired. The flame illuminated a ferocious tusked head, a pink hairless body, leathery wings. There was a shriek and a stench, and the thing plopped down beyond him like a sack of wet meal. Someone hit it with an axe.

The noise died away. The searchlights continued to swing across the darkness. After a time, one of them picked up another bright shape, but it was far away, swinging wide around the ship, and the lance-flames missed it. "Any more?" came a bellow from the deck.

"No, your worship," answered a voice from the foretop.

"All right then, secure."

Akim lingered glumly to watch the deckhands gather up the bodies and throw them over the side. Pigs were the only excitement in these latitudes; in the old days, it was said, ships had fought them for days with musket and cutlass. But now, not ten minutes since the first alarm, it was all over. A few sailors were swabbing the blood away with sea water, the rest were drifting back belowdecks.

Yawning, Akim went back to his cubby. He was tired, but too restless to go to bed. He wondered whether he was hungry and thought of going to the galley again, but it did not seem worth the effort. With a sigh, he sat in front of the viewer and switched it on.

There was Robinson, walking stiffly into a large area filled with desks cluttered with papers and typewriters. A heavy dark-haired man with black-rimmed glasses stood waiting. His white shirtsleeves were rolled to the elbow. "Robinson? I'm Mr. Beverly." At other desks, a few men glanced up, all pale, unsmiling. Beverly gave Robinson a brief, moist handshake and motioned to a chair. Robinson sat down and tried not to look self-conscious. Glancing at the card in his hand, Beverly said, "Not much experience in this line. Do you think you can handle it?"

Robinson said, "Yes, I think—well, I think I can handle it." He crossed his legs, then uncrossed them.

Beverly nodded, pursing his lips. He reached for a magazine on the desk, pushed it an inch closer. "You're familiar with this publication?"

The cover had a picture of a woman in a tramp's costume smoking a cigar, and a headline, "SMOKES TEN STOGIES A DAY." "Yes, I've seen it," Robinson answered. He tried to think of something else to say. "It's, uh, the kind of thing you read in barbershops, isn't it?"

Beverly nodded again, slowly. His expression did not change. Robinson crossed his legs. "Your job," Beverly said, "would involve choosing pictures for the magazine from photos like these." He pointed to the next desk; it was covered with disorderly heaps of photographs. "Do you think you could do that?"

Robinson stared at the topmost picture, which showed a young woman in what appeared to be a circus costume. He could see the powder caked on her dimpled face, and the beads of mascara on her eyelashes. "Yes, sure. I mean, I think I could handle it."

"Uh-huh. Okay Robinson, thanks for coming in. We'll let you know. Go out that way, if you don't mind." He gave Robinson another handshake and turned away.

Robinson walked to the elevator. He knew he was not going to get the job, and even if he did get it, he would hate it. In the street, he turned west and walked against a tide of blank-eyed, gum-chewing faces. A taxi went over a manhole cover, clink-clank. Steam was rising from an excavation at the corner. The world was like a puzzle with half the pieces missing. What was the point of all these drab buildings, this dirty sky?

In his room, he made some hash and eggs and ate it, reading the *Daily News* and listening to the radio. Then he poured a cup of instant coffee and took it to the easy chair in the corner. On the table beside him lay a paperback book. The cover showed a half-naked, red-skinned young man whose smooth muscles bulged as he struck with a scimitar at a monstrous flying boar. A maiden in metal breastplates cowered behind him, and there was ship's rigging in the background. Robinson found his place, bent the book's spine to flatten it, and began to read.

Sometime during the night (he read), the young crewman awoke with a start. He had fallen asleep in his chair, and his legs were cramped, his neck stiff. He got up and walked back and forth the few steps the cubby allowed, but it was not enough, and he went out into the passage. The ship was silent and dark. On an impulse, he climbed the companionway and emerged under a spectral sky. The deck was awash with moonlight. Up in the foretop, there was a wink of red as the lookout lighted his pipe. That would be Rilloj, his second cousin, a heavy, black-browed man who had the same oxlike face as his father, and his uncle Zanid, and all the rest. On the whole ship there was not one of them he could talk to, not one who understood his yearnings.

Hugging himself for warmth, he walked over to the lee rail. A few stars shone above the dim horizon. Up there, somewhere, unreachable and unknown, there must be worlds of mystery, worlds where a man could *live*. Gigantic cities thronged with people, exotic machines, ancient wisdom. . . .

And he was Akim, seventeen years old, a crewman on the *Vlaken-gros*. As he turned, he felt a queer loss of balance for an instant; the world seemed to split, and he had a glimpse of a ragged crack with grayness showing through it. Then it was gone, but it had frightened him. What could cause such a thing?

Back in his cubby, he sat down heavily in front of the screen. He would be sorry for it in a few hours, when the watch turned him out, but after all, what else was there? He turned on the machine. There was Robinson, reading in his chair. A cigarette beside him in the ashtray had burned to a long gray ash. The alarm clock read two-thirty. It was the gray turning point of the night, when the eyes are dry and the blood flows thin. Robinson yawned, read another line without interest, then shut the book and tossed it aside. He began to realize how tired he really was. He shut off the viewer, pulled his bunk down out of the wall, stripped off his robe. He got up and headed for the bathroom, unbuttoning his shirt as he went. He brushed his teeth, wound the alarm clock (but did not set it), undressed and got in between the rumpled sheets. He went to the head, made sure his door was secure, then rolled into the bunk. As he lay there between sleep and waking, the events of the day got all mixed up somehow with the story he had been viewing. Tomorrow they would be at their next port of call, and he would pick up his unemployment check. Maybe he would get a job. The ship was rolling gently. Under the edge of the blind, the neons winked red-blue, red-green, red-blue. Good night, good night. Sleep tight, don't let the seapigs bite.

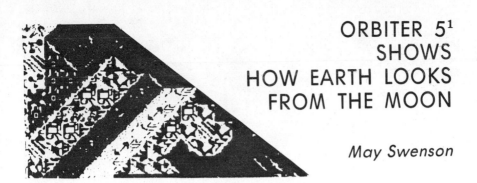

ORBITER 5[1]
SHOWS
HOW EARTH LOOKS
FROM THE MOON

May Swenson

There's a woman in the earth,
sitting on her heels.
You see her from the back,
in three-quarter profile.
5   She has a flowing pigtail.
She's holding something

in her right hand—
some holy jug.
Her left arm is thinner,
10   in a gesture like a dancer.
She's the Indian Ocean.
Asia is light

swirling up out of her vessel.
Her pigtail points to Europe,
15   and her dancer's arm
is the Suez Canal.
She is a woman
in a square kimono,[2]

bare feet tucked
20   beneath the tip of Africa.
Her tail of long hair
is the Arabian Peninsula.
A woman in the earth,
a man in the moon.

"Orbiter 5 Shows How Earth Looks from the Moon" is reprinted by permission of Charles Scribner's Sons from ICONOGRAPHS by May Swenson. Copyright © 1969 May Swenson.
1. *Orbiter 5.* The fifth Orbiting Solar Observatory was launched in January 1969 to study the sun's influence on Earth's atmosphere. **2.** *kimono,* a Japanese robelike garment held closed with a wide sash.

THE KING OF THE BEASTS

Philip José Farmer

THE BIOLOGIST WAS SHOWING the distinguished visitor through the zoo and laboratory.

"Our budget," he said, "is too limited to re-create all known extinct species. So we bring to life only the higher animals, the beautiful ones that were wantonly exterminated. I'm trying, as it were, to make up for brutality and stupidity. You might say that man struck God in the face every time he wiped out a branch of the animal kingdom."

He paused, and they looked across the moats and the force fields. The quagga[1] wheeled and galloped, delight and sun flashing off his flanks. The sea otter poked his humorous whiskers from the water. The gorilla peered from behind bamboo. Passenger pigeons strutted. A rhinoceros trotted like a dainty battleship. With gentle eyes a giraffe looked at them, then resumed eating leaves.

"There's the dodo.[2] Not beautiful but very droll. And very helpless. Come. I'll show you the re-creation itself."

In the great building, they passed between rows of tall and wide tanks. They could see clearly through the windows and the jelly within.

"Those are African elephant embryos," said the biologist. "We plan to grow a large herd and then release them on the new government preserve."

"You positively radiate," said the distinguished visitor. "You really love the animals, don't you?"

"I love all life."

"Tell me," said the visitor, "where do you get the data for re-creation?"

"The King of the Beasts" by Philip José Farmer. Reprinted by permission of the Author and Scott Meredith Literary Agency, Inc., 580 Fifth Avenue, New York, N.Y. 10036.

1. *quagga,* a South African animal related to the horse and zebra, which became extinct during the nineteenth century. 2. *dodo,* a large, flightless bird which has been extinct since the seventeenth century.

"Mostly, skeletons and skins from the ancient museums. Excavated books and films that we succeeded in restoring and then translating. Ah, see those huge eggs? The chicks of the giant moa[3] are growing within them. These, almost ready to be taken from the tank, are tiger cubs. They'll be dangerous when grown but will be confined to the preserve."

The visitor stopped before the last of the tanks.

"Just one?" he said. "What is it?"

"Poor little thing," said the biologist, now sad. "It will be so alone But I shall give it all the love I have."

"Is it so dangerous?" said the visitor. "Worse than elephants, tigers and bears?"

"I had to get special permission to grow this one," said the biologist His voice quavered.

The visitor stepped sharply back from the tank. He said, "Then it must be. . . . But you wouldn't dare!"

The biologist nodded.

"Yes. It's a man."

---

3. *moa,* a recently extinct flightless bird of New Zealand, which is similar to the ostrich.

UFO DETECTIVE SOLVES 'EM ALL— WELL, ALMOST

Philip J. Hilts

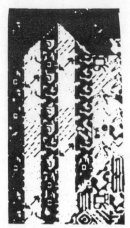

WASHINGTON——THE PHOTOS ARE CLEAR enough: It is a normal suburban home and backyard, and hovering above the normal backyard is a flying saucer.

"It looked like a good solid case," says Stuart Nixon. The photos were taken by a teen-age boy, and his skeptical father had quickly taken them to scientists at the government lab where he worked. He figured the scientists would find the flaws, and that would be it; he didn't want his son to start believing in such nonsense as flying saucers. But the scientists couldn't debunk the pictures. No hoax, they said. They had picked the photos apart carefully, studying them with sophisticated microscopes. They found nothing wrong.

The boy's father, skepticism rapidly receding, turned the pictures and the boy's report over to Stuart Nixon for a final opinion. Nixon is a UFO man, checking up on unidentified flying objects for the National Investigations Committee on Aerial Phenomena, which has three full-time and two part-time investigators and an auxiliary legion of enthusiasts ranging from scientists to science-fiction fans.

With typical caution, Nixon went over the photos and finally, in one greatly enlarged print, he noticed a faint shadow. He magnified the negatives for a closer look, and this time, the faint shadow appeared as a sharp line above the saucer.

Nixon checked one more thing. He went over the boy's report of how the saucer had moved: slowly downward until it was almost directly over the youngster's head. Nixon then pieced together the negatives, laying them out in the order they were shot. There was no progressive movement downward. The saucer sequence was alternately close and far away, as if the saucer were stationary and the photographer moving.

On the evening Nixon arrived at the boy's suburban home to deliver his report, he found the family all sitting round the living room, waiting confidently for another astounding confirmation.

"UFO Detective Solves 'Em All—Well, Almost" by Philip J. Hilts. © The Washington Post, 1973. Reprinted by permission of The Washington Post.

Quickly assessing the situation, Nixon changed from UFO man to family counselor. Before delivering his verdict, he took the boy photographer out to the garage and told the youngster what he found, that examination of the photos had revealed the thread—that faint shadow—by which the phony saucer had been suspended. It would be better to confess, he told the culprit.

After some forty-five minutes of friendly persuasion, the boy ran into the house and up the stairs. Nixon walked back to the house, and a few minutes later, the boy crept shyly down the staircase, hiding something behind his back. Finally, he whipped out a little model of a flying saucer and mumbled something about a friend who made him do it.

For Stuart Nixon, a thin and lively man who animates stories with gestures and pencil drawings, this is what it's like, most of the time. He blasts probably nine out of ten of the UFO reports that come across his cluttered desk.

Nixon thinks of himself as a journalist and investigative writer. Before coming to NICAP six years ago, he had worked as a copyboy, then as a writer for *Space Business Daily,* an aeronautics and space trade journal. He has also been a free-lance writer.

When Nixon worked at Space Publications, UFOs were a running topic among the writers and editors. Actually, UFOs were mostly a running joke. Nixon was puzzled by the reports that appeared on the newswires, and in office conversation found himself alternately defending and attacking the pro-UFO position.

He stopped by NICAP's office one afternoon to find out something about the group and heard a job would soon open up here. He agreed to work on some special projects in the beginning but finally moved in full-time.

NICAP, a private group with a $40,000 budget supplied by 3,500 dues-paying members and the sale of literature on outer space, survived the breakup of the flying saucer romance in the late sixties partly because of its skeptical approach. "Also," says Nixon, "it attracts people who are willing to support it emotionally as well as intellectually."

So thirty-one-year-old bachelor Stuart Nixon sits behind a desk piled up with photos and drawings of extraterrestrial craft,[1] cluttered with articles and books on weird lights, hisses and bangs from saucers, eggs, rockets and giant cigars.

In the files are seventeen years' worth of these reports, perhaps fifteen thousand of them. They come in steadily still, from NICAP members, from people who have read about NICAP, from people who've been referred by their local Air Force base.

The Washington area, Nixon noted, has had some of the great UFO sightings of all time, including the famed incidents of July, 1952. Late one night seven blips appeared on radar screens at National Airport and Andrews Air Base. Ground observers spotted the UFOs as bright

1. *extraterrestrial craft,* ships from other planets.

moving lights in the sky. Commercial pilots coming and going from National spotted the lights, which seemed to cluster around plane wings. The Air Force scrambled jets to chase the UFOs, which zipped across the radar screens for hours.

A week later the whole scene was repeated.

A recent case which promises to be a classic in the lore of UFOers is the case of the Virginia Giant. It happened near Fredericksburg about a year and a half ago, when three teen-agers were out hunting in a field. After roaming the area for a while, two of the youngsters headed off to a nearby house, leaving a seventeen-year-old and his dog to tromp through the grass.

The youngsters at the house waited for the boy and his dog. When they didn't return, the youngsters went back to the field. They found the dog gone and the boy lying in the weeds in a state of shock. He told his friends he had seen "a thing" come out of the sky, put out legs and land in the field near him. Out of the craft came a huge creature. The young man saw it silhouetted against the horizon, and watched it hulk toward him. He dropped to the ground, but the creature kept coming. The boy's dog fled. The creature came a little closer, then finally turned and moved back to the craft. It took off and disappeared.

Several days later, four people in the area reported a similar craft following their car.

"It's kind of bizarre," says Nixon. "We haven't finished our investigation of the incident, so we don't have a conclusion yet."

Perhaps the most convincing of UFO witnesses were the U.S. astronauts on Gemini missions. An Air Force report lists three sightings:

1. Gemini 4, Astronaut McDivitt. Observation of a cylindrical object with a protuberance.

2. Gemini 4, Astronaut McDivitt. Observation of a moving bright light at a higher level than the Gemini spacecraft.

3. Gemini 7, Astronaut Borman saw what he referred to as a "Bogey"[2] flying in formation with the spacecraft.

McDivitt's cylindrical object was not only sighted but photographed with both still and movie cameras. The North American Air Defense Command checked to see if it corresponded with any possible satellites, meteors or space debris which might be in the area. Negative. The weird object in the NASA photos is still without explanation.

Stuart Nixon is now working on a breakthrough project. It's called Project Access, based on the idea that all the UFO men have at the moment, and all they are likely to get, is raw data from thousands of sightings. So NICAP is designing a computer program to turn the data bits into patterns and trends.

At the end of 1969 and beginning of 1970, things looked pretty bad for the serious UFO investigators. The Air Force issued a report summing up its twenty-one years of UFO investigation. The summary said nothing had been gained in those years, and that UFOs weren't

---

2. "Bogey," a slang term for an unidentified aircraft.

worth studying. NICAP quickly lost half its membership and public interest seemed to dim considerably.

But now, things have begun popping again. 1972 had more sightings than many previous years, new books on the subject have been published, Project Access is underway and then there is a new UFO device: On a shelf behind Nixon's desk is an upside-down glass jar about eight inches high. In this glass jar you can see wire filaments, a tiny metal structure that looks like an oil derrick and a few other items which look like they belong to somebody's radio.

"That's a UFO detector," Nixon says.

He explains that it is a very sensitive magnetometer which reacts to the slightest changes in the electromagnetic field around it. When there is a disturbance in the magnetic field, a little needle touches a loop, completing an electric circuit wired up to a bell.

The device has so far only been tested once. It may actually have detected some UFOs, but that is uncertain. Thirteen of the cosmic burglar alarms were put in homes around a small town in New Hampshire known for its UFO sightings.

"But the things kept going off constantly," Nixon says. "It seems that sunspots[3] set them off, too." A couple of times, though, the devices went off when there weren't any sunspots. And when there had been UFO reports in the area.

---

3. *sunspots*, dark spots that sometimes appear on the surface of the sun and are associated with disturbances of the Earth's magnetic field.

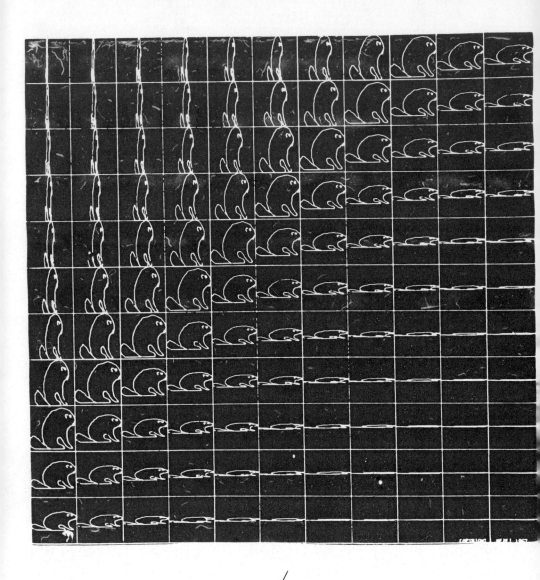

6

WHAT TIME NEXT TIME

THE
GOOD
PROVIDER

Marion Gross

MINNIE LEGGETY TURNED UP THE WALK of her Elm Street bungalow and saw that she faced another crisis. When Omar sat brooding like that, not smoking, not "studying," but just scrunched down inside of himself, she knew enough after forty years to realize that she was facing a crisis. As though it weren't enough just trying to get along on Omar's pension these days, without having to baby him through another one of his periods of discouragement! She forced a gaiety into her voice that she actually didn't feel.

"Why, hello there, Pa, what are you doing out here? Did you have to come up for air?" Minnie eased herself down beside Omar on the stoop and put the paper bag she had been carrying on the sidewalk. Such a little bag, but it had taken most of their week's food budget! Protein, plenty of lean, rare steaks and chops, that's what that nice man on the radio said old folks needed, but as long as he couldn't tell you how to buy it with steak at $1.23 a pound, he might just as well save his breath to cool his porridge. And so might she, for all the attention Omar was paying her. He was staring straight ahead as though he didn't even see her. This looked like one of his real bad spells. She took his gnarled hand and patted it.

"What's the matter, Pa? Struck a snag with your gadget?" The "gadget" filled three full walls of the basement and most of the floor space besides, but it was still a "gadget" to Minnie—another one of his ideas that didn't quite work.

Omar had been working on gadgets ever since they were married. When they were younger, she hotly sprang to his defense against her sisters-in-law: "Well, it's better than liquor, and it's cheaper than pinochle; at least I know where he is nights." Now that they were older, and Omar was retired from his job, his tinkering took on a new significance. It was what kept him from going to pieces like a lot of men who were retired and didn't have enough activity to fill their time and their minds.

"What's the matter, Pa?" she asked again.

"The Good Provider" by Marion Gross from 50 SHORT SCIENCE FICTION TALES. Copyright 1952 by Marion Gross. By permission of Barthold Fles, Literary Agent.

The old man seemed to notice her for the first time. Sadly he shook his head. "Minnie, I'm a failure. The thing's no good; it ain't practical. After all I promised you, Minnie, and the way you stuck by me and all, it's just not going to work."

Minnie never had thought it would. It just didn't seem possible that a body could go gallivanting back and forth the way Pa had said they would if the gadget worked. She continued to pat the hand she held and told him soothingly, "I'm not sure but it's for the best, Pa. I'd sure have gotten airsick, or timesick, or whatever it was. What're you going to work on now that you're giving up the Time Machine?" she asked anxiously.

"You don't understand, Min," the old man said. "I'm through. I've failed. I've failed at everything I've ever tried to make. They always *almost* work, and yet there's always something I can't get just right. I never knew enough, Min, never had enough schooling, and now it's too late to get any. I'm just giving up altogether. I'm through!"

This *was* serious. Pa with nothing to tinker at down in the basement, Pa constantly underfoot, Pa with nothing to keep him from just slipping away like old Mr. Mason had, was something she didn't like to think about. "Maybe it isn't as bad as all that," she told him. "All those nice parts you put into your gadget, maybe you could make us a television or something with them. Land, a television, that would be a nice thing to have."

"Oh, I couldn't do that, Min. I wouldn't know how to make a television; besides, I told you, it almost works. It's just that it ain't practical. It ain't the way I pictured it. Come down, I'll show you." He dragged her into the house and down into the basement.

The Time Machine left so little free floor space, what with the furnace and coal bin and washtubs, that Minnie had to stand on the stairway while Pa explained it to her. It needed explanation. It had more colored lights than a pinball machine, more plugs than the Hillsdale telephone exchange, and more levers than one of those newfangled voting booths.

"Now see," he said, pointing to various parts of the machine, "I rigged this thing up so we could move forward or back in time and space both. I thought we could go off and visit foreign spots, and see great things happening, and have ourselves an interesting old age."

"Well, I don't rightly know if I'd have enjoyed that, Pa," Minnie interrupted. "I doubt I'd know how to get along with all them foreigners, and their strange talk and strange ways and all."

Omar shook his head in annoyance. "The Holy Land. You'd have wanted to see the Holy Land, wouldn't you? You could have sat with the crowd at Galilee and listened to the Lord's words right from His lips. You'd have enjoyed that, wouldn't you?"

"Omar, when you talk like that you make the whole thing sound sacrilegious and against the Lord's ways. Besides, I suppose the Lord would have spoke in Hebrew, and I don't know one word of that and you don't either. I don't know but what I'm glad you couldn't get the thing to work," she said righteously.

"But Min, it does work!" Omar was indignant.

"But you said——"

"I never said it don't work. I said it ain't practical. It don't work good enough, and I don't know enough to make it work better."

Working on the gadget was one thing, but believing that it worked was another. Minnie began to be alarmed. Maybe folks had been right—maybe Omar had gone off his head at last. She looked at him anxiously. He seemed all right and, now that he was worked up at her, the depression seemed to have left him.

"What do you mean it works, but not good enough?" she asked him.

"Well, see here," Omar told her, pointing to an elaborate control board. "It was like I was telling you before you interrupted with your not getting along with foreigners, and your sacrilegion and all. I set this thing up to move a body in time and space any which way. There's a globe of the world worked in here, and I thought that by turning the globe and setting these time controls to whatever year you had in mind you could go wherever you had a mind to. Well, it don't work like that. I've been trying it out for a whole week and no matter how I set the globe, no matter how I set the time controls, it always comes out the same. It lands me over at Main and Center, right in front of Purdey's meat market."

"What's wrong with that?" Minnie asked. "That might be real convenient."

"You don't understand," Omar told her. "It isn't *now* when I get there, it's twenty years ago! That's the trouble, it don't take me none of the places I want to go, just Main and Center. And it don't take me none of the times I want to go, just twenty years ago, and I saw enough of the depression[1] so I don't want to spend my old age watching people sell apples. Then on top of that, this here timer don't work." He pointed to another dial. "It's supposed to set to how long you want to stay, wherever you want to go, but it don't work at all. Twenty minutes, and then woosh, you're right back here in the basement. Nothing works like I want it to."

Minnie had grown thoughtful as Omar recounted the faults of the machine. Wasn't it a caution the way even a smart man like Pa, a man smart enough to make a Time Machine, didn't have a practical ounce to his whole hundred and forty-eight pounds? She sat down heavily on the cellar steps and, emptying the contents of her purse on her broad lap, began examining the bills.

"What you looking for, Min?" Omar asked.

Minnie looked at him pityingly. Wasn't it a caution. . . .

Purdey the butcher was leaning unhappily against his chopping block. The shop was clean and shining, the floor was strewn with fresh sawdust, and Purdey himself, unmindful of the expense, had for the

---

1. *the depression.* The Great Depression was a widespread collapse of the American economy, which lasted from the stock market crash of 1929 up to the outbreak of World War II. At times, as many as seventeen million people were jobless, so that street vendors selling apples, pencils, and so on, became a common sight.

sake of his morale donned a fresh apron. But for all that, Purdey wished that he was hanging on one of his chromium-plated meat hooks.

The sky was blue and smogless, something it never was when the shops were operating and employing the valley's five thousand bread-winners. Such potential customers as were abroad had a shabby, threadbare look to them. Over in front of the Bijou old Mr. Ryan was selling apples.

While he watched, a stout, determined-looking woman appeared at the corner of Main and Center. She glanced quickly around, brushing old Mr. Ryan and his apples with her glance, and then came briskly toward Purdey's shop. Purdey straightened up.

"Afternoon, Ma'am, what can I do for you?" He beamed as though the light bill weren't three months overdue.

"I'll have a nice porterhouse," the lady said hesitantly. "How much is porterhouse?"

"Forty-five a pound, best in the house." Purdey held up a beauty, expecting her to change her mind.

"I'll take it," the lady said. "And six lamb chops. I want a rib roast for Sunday, but I can come back for that. No use carrying too much," she explained. "Could you please hurry with that? I haven't very much time."

"New in town?" Purdey asked as he turned to ring up the sale on the cash register.

"Yes, you might say so," the woman said. By the time Purdey turned back to ask her name, she was gone. But Purdey knew she'd be back. She wanted a rib roast for Sunday. "It just goes to show you," Purdey said to himself, surveying the satisfactory tab sticking up from the register, "there still is some money around. Two dollars, and she never even batted an eyelash. It goes to show you!"

A SOUND OF THUNDER

Ray Bradbury

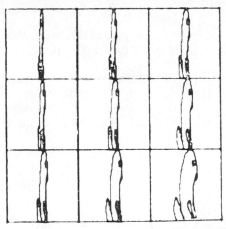

THE SIGN ON THE WALL SEEMED to quaver under a film of sliding warm water. Eckels felt his eyelids blink over his stare, and the sign burned in this momentary darkness:

TIME SAFARI, INC.
SAFARIS TO ANY YEAR IN THE PAST.
YOU NAME THE ANIMAL.
WE TAKE YOU THERE.
YOU SHOOT IT.

A warm phlegm gathered in Eckels' throat; he swallowed and pushed it down. The muscles around his mouth formed a smile as he put his hand slowly out upon the air, and in that hand waved a check for ten thousand dollars to the man behind the desk.

"Does this safari guarantee I come back alive?"

"We guarantee nothing," said the official, "except the dinosaurs." He turned. "This is Mr. Travis, your Safari Guide in the Past. He'll tell you what and where to shoot. If he says no shooting, no shooting. If you disobey instructions, there's a stiff penalty of another ten thousand dollars, plus possible government action on your return."

Eckels glanced across the vast office at a mass and tangle, a snaking and humming of wires and steel boxes, at an aurora that flickered now orange, now silver, now blue. There was a sound like a gigantic bonfire burning all of time, all the years and all the parchment calendars, all the hours piled high and set aflame.

A touch of the hand and this burning would, on the instant, beautifully reverse itself. Eckels remembered the wording in the advertisements to the letter. Out of chars and ashes, out of dust and coals, like golden salamanders, the old years, the green years, might leap; roses sweeten the air, white hair turn Irish-black, wrinkles vanish; all, everything fly back to seed, flee death, rush down to their beginnings, suns rise in western skies and set in glorious easts, moons eat themselves opposite to the custom, all and everything cupping one in another like Chinese boxes, rabbits into hats, all and everything

"A Sound of Thunder" by Ray Bradbury. Copyright 1952 by Ray Bradbury, reprinted by permission of Harold Matson Co., Inc.

returning to the fresh death, the seed death, the green death, to the time before the beginning. A touch of a hand might do it, the merest touch of a hand.

"Unbelievable." Eckels breathed, the light of the machine on his thin face. "A real Time Machine." He shook his head. "Makes you think. If the election had gone badly yesterday, I might be here now running away from the results. Thank God Keith won. He'll make a fine President of the United States."

"Yes," said the man behind the desk. "We're lucky. If Deutscher had gotten in, we'd have the worst kind of dictatorship. There's an anti-everything man for you, a militarist, anti-Christ, anti-human, anti-intellectual. People called us up, you know, joking but not joking. Said if Deutscher became President they wanted to go live in 1492. Of course it's not our business to conduct escapes, but to form safaris. Anyway, Keith's President now. All you got to worry about is——"

"Shooting my dinosaur," Eckels finished it for him.

"A *Tyrannosaurus rex*. The Tyrant Lizard, the most incredible monster in history. Sign this release. Anything happens to you, we're not responsible. Those dinosaurs are hungry."

Eckels flushed angrily. "Trying to scare me!"

"Frankly, yes. We don't want anyone going who'll panic at the first shot. Six safari leaders were killed last year, and a dozen hunters. We're here to give you the severest thrill a *real* hunter ever asked for. Traveling you back sixty million years to bag the biggest game in all of time. Your personal check's still there. Tear it up."

Mr. Eckels looked at the check. His fingers twitched.

"Good luck," said the man behind the desk. "Mr. Travis, he's all yours."

They moved silently across the room, taking their guns with them, toward the machine, toward the silver metal and the roaring light.

First a day and then a night and then a day and then a night, then it was day-night-day-night-day. A week, a month, a year, a decade! A.D. 2055. A.D 2019. 1999! 1957! Gone! The machine roared.

They put on their oxygen helmets and tested the intercoms.

Eckels swayed on the padded seat, his face pale, his jaw stiff. He felt the trembling in his arms and he looked down and found his hands tight on the new rifle. There were four other men in the machine. Travis, the safari leader, his assistant, Lesperance, and two other hunters, Billings and Kramer. They sat looking at each other, and the years blazed around them.

"Can these guns get a dinosaur cold?" Eckels felt his mouth saying.

"If you hit them right," said Travis on the helmet radio. "Some dinosaurs have two brains, one in the head, another far down the spinal column. We stay away from those. That's stretching luck. Put your first two shots into the eyes, if you can, blind them, and go back into the brain."

The machine howled. Time was a film run backward. Suns fled and ten million moons fled after them. "Think," said Eckels. "Every hunter that ever lived would envy us today. This makes Africa seem like Illinois."

The machine slowed; its scream fell to a murmur. The machine stopped.

The sun stopped in the sky.

The fog that had enveloped the machine blew away and they were in an old time, a very old time indeed, three hunters and two safari heads with their blue metal guns across their knees.

"Christ isn't born yet," said Travis. "Moses has not gone to the mountain to talk with God. The Pyramids are still in the earth, waiting to be cut out and put up. *Remember* that. Alexander, Caesar, Napoleon, Hitler—none of them exists."

The men nodded.

"That"—Mr. Travis pointed—"is the jungle of sixty million two thousand and fifty-five years before President Keith."

He indicated a metal path that struck off into green wilderness, over streaming swamp, among giant ferns and palms.

"And that," he said, "is the path, laid by Time Safari for your use. It floats six inches above the earth. Doesn't touch so much as one grass blade, flower, or tree. It's an anti-gravity metal. Its purpose is to keep you from touching this world of the past in any way. Stay on the path. Don't go off it. I repeat. *Don't go off.* For *any* reason! If you fall off, there's a penalty. And don't shoot any animal we don't okay."

"Why?" asked Eckels.

They sat in the ancient wilderness. Far birds' cries blew on a wind, and the smell of tar and an old salt sea, moist grasses, and flowers the color of blood.

"We don't want to change the future. We don't belong here in the past. The government doesn't *like* us here. We have to pay big graft to keep our franchise. A Time Machine is finicky business. Not knowing it, we might kill an important animal, a small bird, a roach, a flower even, thus destroying an important link in a growing species."

"That's not clear," said Eckels.

"All right," Travis continued, "say we accidentally kill one mouse here. That means all the future families of this one particular mouse are destroyed, right?"

"Right."

"And all the families of the families of the families of that one mouse! With a stamp of your foot, you annihilate first one, then a dozen, then a thousand, a million, a *billion* possible mice!"

"So they're dead," said Eckels. "So what?"

"So what?" Travis snorted quietly. "Well, what about the foxes that'll need those mice to survive? For want of ten mice, a fox dies. For want of ten foxes, a lion starves. For want of a lion, all manner of insects, vultures, infinite billions of life forms are thrown into chaos and destruction. Eventually it all boils down to this: Fifty-nine million years later, a caveman, one of a dozen on the *entire world*, goes hunting wild boar or saber-toothed tiger for food. But you, friend, have *stepped* on all the tigers in that region. By stepping on *one* single mouse. So the caveman starves. And the caveman, please note, is not just *any* expendable man, no! He is an *entire future nation.* From his loins would have sprung ten sons. From *their* loins one hundred sons, and thus onward to a civilization. Destroy this one man, and you destroy a race, a people, an entire history of life. It is comparable to slaying some of Adam's grandchildren. The stomp of your foot, on one mouse, could start an earthquake, the effects of which could shake our Earth and destinies down through time, to their very foundations. With the death of that one caveman, a billion others yet unborn are throttled in the womb. Perhaps Rome never rises on its seven hills. Perhaps Europe is forever a dark forest, and only Asia waxes healthy and teeming. Step on a mouse and you crush the Pyramids. Step on a mouse and you leave your print, like a Grand Canyon, across eternity. Queen Elizabeth might never be born, Washington might not cross the Delaware, there might never be a United States at all. So be careful. Stay on the path. *Never* step off!"

"I see," said Eckels. "Then it wouldn't pay for us even to touch the *grass?*"

"Correct. Crushing certain plants could add up infinitesimally. A little error here would multiply in sixty million years, all out of proportion. Of course maybe our theory is wrong. Maybe time *can't* be changed by us. Or maybe it can be changed only in little subtle ways. A dead mouse here makes an insect imbalance there, a population disproportion later, a bad harvest further on, a depression, mass starvation, and, finally, a change in *social* temperament in far-flung countries. Something much more subtle, like that. Perhaps only a soft breath, a whisper, a hair, pollen on the air, such a slight, slight change that unless you looked close you wouldn't see it. Who knows? Who really can say he knows? We don't know. We're guessing. But until we do know for certain whether our messing around in time *can* make a big roar or a little rustle in history, we're being careful. This machine, this path, your clothing and bodies, were sterilized, as you know, before the journey. We wear these oxygen helmets so we can't introduce our bacteria into an ancient atmosphere."

"How do we know which animals to shoot?"

"They're marked with red paint," said Travis. "Today, before our journey, we sent Lesperance here back with the machine. He came to this particular era and followed certain animals."

"Studying them?"

"Right," said Lesperance. "I track them through their entire existence, noting which of them lives longest. Very few. How many times they mate. Not often. Life's short. When I find one that's going to die when a tree falls on him, or one that drowns in a tar pit, I note the exact hour, minute, and second. I shoot a paint bomb. It leaves a red patch on his side. We can't miss it. Then I correlate our arrival in the past so that we meet the monster not more than two minutes before he would have died anyway. This way, we kill only animals with no future, that are never going to mate again. You see how *careful* we are?"

"But if you came back this morning in time," said Eckels eagerly, "you must've bumped into *us,* our safari! How did it turn out? Was it successful? Did all of us get through—alive?"

Travis and Lesperance gave each other a look.

"That'd be a paradox," said the latter. "Time doesn't permit that sort of mess—a man meeting himself. When such occasions threaten, time steps aside. Like an airplane hitting an air pocket. You felt the machine jump just before we stopped? That was us passing ourselves on the way back to the future. We saw nothing. There's no way of telling *if* this expedition was a success, *if we* got our monster, or whether all of us—meaning *you,* Mr. Eckels—got out alive."

Eckels smiled palely.

"Cut that," said Travis sharply. "Everyone on his feet!"

They were ready to leave the machine.

The jungle was high and the jungle was broad and the jungle was the entire world forever and forever. Sounds like music and sounds like flying tents filled the sky, and those were pterodactyls soaring with cavernous gray wings, gigantic bats of delirium and night fever. Eckels, balanced on the narrow path, aimed his rifle playfully.

"Stop that!" said Travis. "Don't even aim for fun, blast you! If your gun should go off——"

Eckels flushed. "Where's our *Tyrannosaurus?*"

Lesperance checked his wristwatch. "Up ahead. We'll bisect his trail in sixty seconds. Look for the red paint! Don't shoot till we give the word. Stay on the path. *Stay on the path!*"

They moved forward in the wind of morning.

"Strange," murmured Eckels. "Up ahead, sixty million years, Election Day over. Keith made President. Everyone celebrating. And here we are, a million years lost, and they don't exist. The things we worried about for months, a lifetime, not even born or thought of yet."

"Safety catches off, everyone!" ordered Travis. "You, first shot, Eckels. Second, Billings. Third, Kramer."

"I've hunted tiger, wild boar, buffalo, elephant, but now, this is *it,*" said Eckels. "I'm shaking like a kid."

"Ah," said Travis.

Everyone stopped.

Travis raised his hand. "Ahead," he whispered. "In the mist. There he is. There's His Royal Majesty now."

The jungle was wide and full of twitterings, rustlings, murmurs, and sighs.

Suddenly it all ceased, as if someone had shut a door.

Silence.

A sound of thunder.

Out of the mist, one hundred yards away, came *Tyrannosaurus rex.*

"It," whispered Eckels. "It . . ."

"Sh!"

It came on great oiled, resilient, striding legs. It towered thirty feet above half of the trees, a great evil god, folding its delicate watchmaker's claws close to its oily reptilian chest. Each lower leg was a piston, a thousand pounds of white bone, sunk in thick ropes of muscle, sheathed over in a gleam of pebbled skin like the mail of a terrible warrior. Each thigh was a ton of meat, ivory, and steel mesh. And from the great breathing cage of the upper body those two delicate arms dangled out front, arms with hands which might pick up and examine men like toys, while the snake neck coiled. And the head itself, a ton of sculptured stone, lifted easily upon the sky. Its mouth gaped, exposing a fence of teeth like daggers. Its eyes rolled, ostrich eggs, empty of all expression save hunger. It closed its mouth in a death grin. It ran, its pelvic bones crushing aside trees and bushes, its taloned feet clawing damp earth, leaving prints six inches deep wherever it settled its weight. It ran with a gliding ballet step, far too poised and balanced for its ten tons. It moved into a sunlit arena warily, its beautifully reptilian hands feeling the air.

"Why, why," Eckels twitched his mouth. "It could reach up and grab the Moon."

"Sh!" Travis jerked angrily. "He hasn't seen us yet."

"It can't be killed." Eckels pronounced this verdict quietly as if there could be no argument. He had weighed the evidence and this was his considered opinion. The rifle in his hands seemed a cap gun. "We were fools to come. This is impossible."

"Shut up!" hissed Travis.

"Nightmare."

"Turn around," commanded Travis. "Walk quietly to the machine. We'll remit one-half your fee."

"I didn't realize it would be this *big,*" said Eckels. "I miscalculated, that's all. And now I want out."

"It *sees* us!"

"There's the red paint on its chest!"

The Tyrant Lizard raised itself. Its armored flesh glittered like a thousand green coins. The coins, crusted with slime, steamed. In the slime, tiny insects wriggled, so that the entire body seemed to twitch and undulate, even while the monster itself did not move. It exhaled. The stink of raw flesh blew down the wilderness.

"Get me out of here," said Eckels. "It was never like this before. I was always sure I'd come through alive. I had good guides, good safaris, and safety. This time, I figured wrong. I've met my match and admit it. This is too much for me to get hold of."

"Don't run," said Lesperance. "Turn around. Hide in the machine."

"Yes." Eckels seemed to be numb. He looked at his feet as if trying to make them move. He gave a grunt of helplessness.

"Eckels!"

He took a few steps, blinking, shuffling.

"Not *that* way!"

The monster, at the first motion, lunged forward with a terrible scream. It covered one hundred yards in six seconds. The rifles jerked up and blazed fire. A windstorm from the beast's mouth engulfed them in the stench of slime and old blood. The monster roared, teeth glittering with sun.

Eckels, not looking back, walked blindly to the edge of the path, his gun limp in his arms, stepped off the path, and walked, not knowing it, in the jungle. His feet sank into green moss. His legs moved him, and he felt alone and remote from the events behind.

The rifles cracked again. Their sound was lost in shriek and lizard thunder. The great level of the reptile's tail swung up, lashed sideways. Trees exploded in clouds of leaf and branch. The monster twitched its jeweler's hands down to fondle at the men, to twist them in half, to crush them like berries, to cram them into its teeth and its screaming throat. Its boulder-stone eyes leveled with the men. They saw themselves mirrored. They fired at the metallic eyelids and the blazing black iris.

Like a stone idol, like a mountain avalanche, *Tyrannosaurus* fell. Thundering, it clutched trees, pulled them with it. It wrenched and tore the metal path. The men flung themselves back and away. The body hit, ten tons of cold flesh and stone. The guns fired. The monster lashed its armored tail, twitched its snake jaws, and lay still. A fount of blood spurted from its throat. Somewhere inside, a sac of fluids burst. Sickening gushes drenched the hunters. They stood, red and glistening.

The thunder faded.

The jungle was silent. After the avalanche, a green peace. After the nightmare, morning.

Billings and Kramer sat on the pathway and threw up. Travis and Lesperance stood with smoking rifles, cursing steadily.

In the Time Machine, on his face, Eckels lay shivering. He had found his way back to the path, climbed into the machine.

Travis came walking, glanced at Eckels, took cotton gauze from a metal box, and returned to the others, who were sitting on the path.

"Clean up."

They wiped the blood from their helmets. They began to curse too. The monster lay, a hill of solid flesh. Within, you could hear the sighs and murmurs as the furthest chambers of it died, the organs malfunctioning, liquids running a final instant from pocket to sac to spleen, everything shutting off, closing up forever. It was like standing by a wrecked locomotive or a steam shovel at quitting time, all valves being released or levered tight. Bones cracked; the tonnage of its own flesh, off balance, dead weight, snapped the delicate forearms, caught underneath. The meat settled, quivering.

Another cracking sound. Overhead, a gigantic tree branch broke from its heavy mooring, fell. It crashed upon the dead beast with finality.

"There," Lesperance checked his watch. "Right on time. That's the giant tree that was scheduled to fall and kill this animal originally." He glanced at the two hunters. "You want the trophy picture?"

"What?"

"We can't take a trophy back to the future. The body has to stay right here where it would have died originally, so the insects, birds, and bacteria can get at it, as they were intended to. Everything in balance. The body stays. But we *can* take a picture of you standing near it."

The two men tried to think, but gave up, shaking their heads.

They let themselves be led along the metal path. They sank wearily into the machine cushions. They gazed back at the ruined monster, the stagnating mound, where already strange reptilian birds and golden insects were busy at the steaming armor.

A sound on the floor of the Time Machine stiffened them. Eckels sat there, shivering.

"I'm sorry," he said at last.

"Get up!" cried Travis.

Eckels got up.

"Go out on that path alone," said Travis. He had his rifle pointed. "You're not coming back in the machine. We're leaving you here!"

Lesperance seized Travis' arm. "Wait——"

"Stay out of this!" Travis shook his hand away. "This fool nearly killed us. But it isn't *that* so much, no. It's his *shoes!* Look at them! He ran off the path. That *ruins* us! We'll forfeit! Thousands of dollars of insurance! We guarantee no one leaves the path. He left it. Oh, the fool! I'll have to report to the government. They might revoke our license to travel. Who knows *what* he's done to time, to history!"

"Take it easy, all he did was kick up some dirt."

"How do we *know?*" cried Travis. "We don't know anything! It's all a mystery! Get out of here, Eckels!"

Eckels fumbled in his shirt. "I'll pay anything. A hundred thousand dollars!"

Travis glared at Eckels' checkbook and spat. "Go out there. The monster's next to the path. Stick your arms up to your elbows in his mouth. Then you can come back with us."

"That's unreasonable!"

"The monster's dead, you idiot. The bullets! The bullets can't be left behind. They don't belong in the past; they might change anything. Here's my knife. Dig them out!"

The jungle was alive again, full of the old tremorings and bird cries. Eckels turned slowly to regard the primeval garbage dump, that hill of nightmares and terror. After a long time, like a sleepwalker he shuffled out along the path.

He returned, shuddering, five minutes later, his arms soaked and red to the elbows. He held out his hands. Each held a number of steel bullets. Then he fell. He lay where he fell, not moving.

"You didn't have to make him do that," said Lesperance.

"Didn't I? It's too early to tell." Travis nudged the still body. "He'll live. Next time he won't go hunting game like this. Okay." He jerked his thumb wearily at Lesperance. "Switch on. Let's go home."

1492. 1776. 1812.

They cleaned their hands and faces. They changed their caking shirts and pants. Eckels was up and around again, not speaking. Travis glared at him for a full ten minutes.

"Don't look at me," cried Eckels. "I haven't done anything."

"Who can tell?"

"Just ran off the path, that's all, a little mud on my shoes—what do you want me to do—get down and pray?"

"We might need it. I'm warning you, Eckels, I might kill you yet. I've got my gun ready."

"I'm innocent. I've done nothing!"

1999. 2000. 2055.

The machine stopped.

"Get out," said Travis.

The room was there as they had left it. But not the same as they had left it. The same man sat behind the same desk. But the same man did not quite sit behind the same desk.

Travis looked around swiftly. "Everything okay here?" he snapped.

"Fine. Welcome home!"

Travis did not relax. He seemed to be looking at the very atoms of the air itself, at the way the sun poured through the one high window.

"Okay, Eckels, get out. Don't ever come back."

Eckels could not move.

"You heard me," said Travis. "What're you *staring* at?"

Eckels stood smelling of the air, and there was a thing to the air, a chemical taint so subtle, so slight, that only a faint cry of his subliminal senses warned him it was there. The colors, white, gray, blue, orange, in the wall, in the furniture, in the sky beyond the window, were . . . were. . . . And there was a *feel*. His flesh twitched. His hands twitched. He stood drinking the oddness with the pores of his body. Somewhere, someone must have been screaming one of those whistles that only a dog can hear. His body screamed silence in return. Beyond this room, beyond this wall, beyond this man who was not quite the same man seated at this desk that was not quite the same desk . . . lay an entire world of streets and people. What sort of world it was now, there was no telling. He could feel them moving there, beyond the walls, almost, like so many chess pieces blown in a dry wind. . . .

But the immediate thing was the sign painted on the office wall, the same sign he had read earlier today on first entering.

Somehow, the sign had changed:

TYME SEFARI INC.

SEFARIS TU ANY YEER EN THE PAST.

YU NAIM THE ANIMALL.

WEE TAEKYUTHAIR.

YU SHOOT ITT.

Eckels felt himself fall into a chair. He fumbled crazily at the thick slime on his boots. He held up a clod of dirt, trembling, "No, it *can't* be. Not a *little* thing like that. No!"

Embedded in the mud, glistening green and gold and black, was a butterfly, very beautiful and very dead.

"Not a little thing like *that!* Not a butterfly!" cried Eckels.

It fell to the floor, an exquisite thing, a small thing that could upset balances and knock down a line of small dominoes and then big dominoes and then gigantic dominoes, all down the years across time. Eckels' mind whirled. It *couldn't* change things. Killing one butterfly couldn't be *that* important! Could it?

His face was cold. His mouth trembled, asking: "Who—who won the presidential election yesterday?"

The man behind the desk laughed. "You joking? You know very well. Deutscher, of course! Who else? Not that fool weakling Keith. We got an iron man now, a man with guts!" The official stopped. "What's wrong?"

Eckels moaned. He dropped to his knees. He scrabbled at the golden butterfly with shaking fingers. "Can't we," he pleaded to the world, to himself, to the officials, to the machine, "can't we take it *back,* can't we *make* it alive again? Can't we start over? Can't we——"

He did not move. Eyes shut, he waited, shivering. He heard Travis breathe loud in the room; he heard Travis shift his rifle, click the safety catch, and raise the weapon.

There was a sound of thunder.

WHO'S CRIBBING?

Jack Lewis

April 2, 1952

Mr. Jack Lewis
90–26 219 St.
Queens Village, N.Y.

Dear Mr. Lewis:

We are returning your manuscript "The Ninth Dimension." At first glance, I had figured it a story well worthy of publication. Why wouldn't I? So did the editors of *Cosmic Tales* back in 1934 when the story was first published.

As you no doubt know, it was the great Todd Thromberry who wrote the story you tried to pass off on us as an original. Let me give you a word of caution concerning the penalties resulting from plagiarism.

It's not worth it. Believe me.

Sincerely,
Doyle P. Gates
Science Fiction Editor
Deep Space Magazine

April 5, 1952

Mr. Doyle P. Gates, Editor
Deep Space Magazine
New York, N.Y.

Dear Mr. Gates:

I do not know, nor am I aware of the existence of any Todd Thromberry. The story you rejected was submitted in good faith, and I resent the inference that I plagiarized it.

"Who's Cribbing?" by Jack Lewis. Copyright 1952 by Better Publications Inc.; by arrangement with the author's agent, Forrest J Ackerman, 2495 Glendower Ave., Hollywood/CA 90027.

"The Ninth Dimension" was written by me not more than a month ago, and if there is any similarity between it and the story written by this Thromberry person, it is purely coincidental.

However, it has set me thinking. Some time ago, I submitted another story to *Stardust Scientifiction* and received a penciled notation on the rejection slip stating that the story was, "too thromberrish."

Who in the hell is Todd Thromberry? I don't remember reading anything written by him in the ten years I've been interested in science fiction.

Sincerely,
Jack Lewis

April 11, 1952

Mr. Jack Lewis
90–26 219 St.
Queens Village, N.Y.

Dear Mr. Lewis:

Re: Your letter of April 5.

While the editors of this magazine are not in the habit of making open accusations and are well aware of the fact in the writing business there will always be some overlapping of plot ideas, it is very hard for us to believe that you are not familiar with the works of Todd Thromberry.

While Mr. Thromberry is no longer among us, his works, like so many other writers', only became widely recognized after his death in 1941. Perhaps it was his work in the field of electronics that supplied him with the bottomless pit of new ideas so apparent in all his works. Nevertheless, even at this stage of science fiction's development it is apparent that he had a style that many of our so-called contemporary writers might do well to copy. By "copy," I do not mean rewrite word for word one or more of his works, as you have done. For while you state this has been accidental, surely you must realize that the chance of this phenomenon actually happening is about a million times as great as the occurrence of four pat royal flushes[1] on one deal.

Sorry, but we're not that naive.

Sincerely yours,
Doyle P. Gates
Science Fiction Editor
Deep Space Magazine

---

1. *pat royal flushes,* the highest possible set of cards in a standard poker game. The hand contains the Ace, King, Queen, Jack, and ten, all of the same suit (spades, hearts, diamonds, or clubs). *Pat* means that the player would get the whole sequence on the first deal.

April 14, 1952

Mr. Doyle P. Gates, Editor
Deep Space Magazine
New York, N.Y.

Sir:

Your accusations are typical of the rag you publish.
Please cancel my subscription immediately.

Sincerely,
Jack Lewis

April 14, 1952

Science Fiction Society
144 Front Street
Chicago, Ill.

Gentlemen:

I am interested in reading some of the works of the late Todd
Thromberry.
I would like to get some of the publications that feature his stories.

Respectfully,
Jack Lewis

April 22, 1952

Mr. Jack Lewis
90–26 219 St.
Queens Village, N.Y.

Dear Mr. Lewis:

So would we. All I can suggest is that you contact the publishers if
any are still in business, or haunt your second-hand bookstores.

If you succeed in getting any of these magazines, please let us know.
We'll pay you a handsome premium on them.

Yours,
Ray Albert
President
Science Fiction Society

May 11, 1952

Mr. Sampson J. Gross, Editor
Strange Worlds Magazine
St. Louis, Mo.

Dear Mr. Gross:

I am enclosing the manuscript of a story I have just completed. As you see on the title page, I call it "Wreckers of Ten Million Galaxies." Because of the great amount of research that went into it, I must set the minimum price on this one at not less than two cents a word.

Hoping you will see fit to use it for publication in your magazine, I remain,

Respectfully,
Jack Lewis

May 19, 1952

Mr. Jack Lewis
90–26 219 St.
Queens Village, N.Y.

Dear Mr. Lewis:

I'm sorry, but at the present time we won't be able to use "Wreckers of Ten Million Galaxies." It's a great yarn though, and if at some future date we decide to use it we will make out the reprint check directly to the estate of Todd Thromberry.

That boy sure could write.

Cordially,
Sampson J. Gross
Editor
Strange Worlds Magazine

May 23, 1952

Mr. Doyle P. Gates, Editor
Deep Space Magazine
New York, N.Y.

Dear Mr. Gates:

While I said I would never have any dealings with you or your magazine again, a situation has arisen which is most puzzling.

It seems all my stories are being returned to me by reason of the fact that except for the byline, they are exact duplicates of the works of this Todd Thromberry person.

In your last letter you aptly described the odds on the accidental occurrence of this phenomenon in the case of one story. What would you consider the approximate odds on no less than half a dozen of my writings?

I agree with you—astronomical!

Yet in the interest of all mankind, how can I get the idea across to you that every word I have submitted was actually written *by me!* I have never copied any material from Todd Thromberry, nor have I ever seen any of his writings. In fact, as I told you in one of my letters, up until a short while ago I was totally unaware of his very existence.

An idea has occurred to me however. It's a truly weird theory, and one that I probably wouldn't even suggest to anyone but a science-fiction editor. But suppose—just suppose—that this Thromberry person, what with his experiments in electronics and everything, had in some way managed to crack through this time-space barrier mentioned so often in your magazine. And suppose—egotistical as it sounds—he had singled out my work as being the type of material he had always wanted to write.

Do you begin to follow me? Or is the idea of a person from a different time cycle looking over my shoulder while I write too fantastic for you to accept?

Please write and tell me what you think of my theory.

Respectfully,
Jack Lewis

May 25, 1952

Mr. Jack Lewis
90–26 219 St.
Queens Village, N.Y.

Dear Mr. Lewis:

We think you should consult a psychiatrist.

Sincerely,
Doyle P. Gates
Science Fiction Editor
Deep Space Magazine

June 3, 1952

Mr. Sam Mines
Science Fiction Editor
Standard Magazines Inc.
New York 16, N.Y.

Dear Mr. Mines:

While the enclosed is not really a manuscript at all, I am submitting this series of letters, carbon copies, and correspondence, in the hope that you might give some credulity to this seemingly unbelievable happening.

The enclosed letters are all in proper order and should be self-explanatory. Perhaps if you publish them, some of your readers might have some idea how this phenomenon could be explained.

I call the entire piece "Who's Cribbing?"

Respectfully,
Jack Lewis

June 10, 1952

Mr. Jack Lewis
90–26 219 St.
Queens Village, N.Y.

Dear Mr. Lewis:

Your idea of a series of letters to put across a science-fiction idea is an intriguing one, but I'm afraid it doesn't quite come off.

It was in the August 1940 issue of *Macabre Adventures* that Mr. Thromberry first used this very idea. Ironically enough, the story title also was "Who's Cribbing?"

Feel free to contact us again when you have something more original.

Yours,
Samuel Mines
Science Fiction Editor
Standard Magazines Inc.

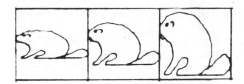

THE
THIRD
LEVEL

Jack Finney

THE PRESIDENTS OF THE New York Central and the New York, New Haven and Hartford railroads will swear on a stack of timetables that there are only two. But I say there are three, because I've *been* on the third level at Grand Central Station. Yes, I've taken the obvious step: I talked to a psychiatrist friend of mine, among others. I told him about the third level at Grand Central Station, and he said it was a waking-dream wish fulfillment. He said I was unhappy. That made my wife kind of mad, but he explained that he meant the modern world is full of insecurity, fear, war, worry, and all the rest of it, and that I just want to escape. Well, hell, who doesn't? Everybody I know wants to escape, but they don't wander down into any third level at Grand Central Station.

But that's the reason, he said, and my friends all agreed. Everything points to it, they claimed. My stamp collecting, for example—that's a "temporary refuge from reality." Well, maybe, but my grandfather didn't need any refuge from reality; things were pretty nice and peaceful in his day, from all I hear, and he started my collection. It's a nice collection, too, blocks of four of practically every U.S. issue, first-day covers, and so on. President Roosevelt collected stamps, too, you know.

Anyway, here's what happened at Grand Central. One night last summer I worked late at the office. I was in a hurry to get uptown to my apartment, so I decided to subway from Grand Central because it's faster than the bus.

Now, I don't know why this should have happened to me. I'm just an ordinary guy named Charley, thirty-one years old, and I was wearing a tan gabardine suit and a straw hat with a fancy band—I passed a dozen men who looked just like me. And I wasn't trying to escape from anything; I just wanted to get home to Louisa, my wife.

I turned into Grand Central from Vanderbilt Avenue and went down the steps to the first level, where you take trains like the Twentieth

"The Third Level" by Jack Finney. Copyright 1950 by Jack Finney, reprinted by permission of Harold Matson Co., Inc.

Century. Then I walked down another flight to the second level, where the suburban trains leave from, ducked into an arched doorway heading for the subway—and got lost. That's easy to do. I've been in and out of Grand Central hundreds of times, but I'm always bumping into new doorways and stairs and corridors. Once I got into a tunnel about a mile long and came out in the lobby of the Roosevelt Hotel. Another time I came up in an office building on Forty-sixth Street, three blocks away.

Sometimes I think Grand Central is growing like a tree, pushing out new corridors and staircases like roots. There's probably a long tunnel that nobody knows about feeling its way under the city right now, on its way to Times Square, and maybe another to Central Park. And maybe—because for so many people through the years Grand Central *has* been an exit, a way of escape—maybe that's how the tunnel I got into . . . but I never told my psychiatrist friend about that idea.

The corridor I was in began angling left and slanting downward and I thought that was wrong, but I kept on walking. All I could hear was the empty sound of my own footsteps and I didn't pass a soul. Then I heard that sort of hollow roar ahead that means open space, and people talking. The tunnel turned sharp left; I went down a short flight of stairs and came out on the third level at Grand Central Station. For just a moment I thought I was back on the second level, but I saw the room was smaller, there were fewer ticket windows and train gates, and the information booth in the center was wood and old-looking. And the man in the booth wore a green eyeshade and long black sleeve-protectors. The lights were dim and sort of flickering. Then I saw why: They were open-flame gaslights.

There were brass spittoons on the floor, and across the station a glint of light caught my eye: A man was pulling a gold watch from his vest pocket. He snapped open the cover, glanced at his watch, and frowned. He wore a dirty hat, a black four-button suit with tiny lapels, and he had a big, black, handlebar mustache. Then I looked around and saw that everyone in the station was dressed like 1890 something; I never saw so many beards, sideburns and fancy mustaches in my life. A woman walked in through the train gate; she wore a dress with leg-of-mutton sleeves and skirts to the top of her high-buttoned shoes. Back of her, out on the tracks, I caught a glimpse of a locomotive, a very small Currier & Ives locomotive with a funnel-shaped stack. And then I knew.

To make sure, I walked over to a newsboy and glanced at the stack of papers at his feet. It was the *World;* and the *World* hasn't been published for years. The lead story said something about President Cleveland. I've found that front page since, in the public library files, and it was printed June 11, 1894.

I turned toward the ticket windows knowing that here—on the third level at Grand Central—I could buy tickets that would take Louisa and me anywhere in the United States we wanted to go. In the year 1894. And I wanted two tickets to Galesburg, Illinois.

Have you ever been there? It's a wonderful town still, with big old frame houses, huge lawns, and tremendous trees whose branches meet overhead and roof the streets. And in 1894, summer evenings were twice as long, and people sat out on their lawns, the men smoking cigars and talking quietly, the women waving palm-leaf fans, with the fireflies all around, in a peaceful world. To be back there with the First World War still twenty years off, and World War II over forty years in the future . . . I wanted two tickets for that.

The clerk figured the fare—he glanced at my fancy hatband, but he figured the fare—and I had enough for two coach tickets, one way. But when I counted out the money and looked up, the clerk was staring at me. He nodded at the bills. "That ain't money, Mister," he said, "and if you're trying to skin me you won't get very far," and he glanced at the cash drawer beside him. Of course the money was old-style bills, half again as big as the money we use nowadays, and different-looking. I turned away and got out fast. There's nothing nice about jail, even in 1894.

And that was that. I left the same way I came, I suppose. Next day, during lunch hour, I drew three hundred dollars out of the bank, nearly all we had, and bought old-style currency (that *really* worried my psychiatrist friend). You can buy old money at almost any coin dealer's, but you have to pay a premium. My three hundred dollars bought less than two hundred dollars in old-style bills, but I didn't care; eggs were thirteen cents a dozen in 1894.

But I've never again found the corridor that leads to the third level at Grand Central Station, although I've tried often enough.

Louisa was pretty worried when I told her all this and didn't want me to look for the third level anymore, and after a while I stopped; I went back to my stamps. But now we're *both* looking, every weekend, because now we have proof that the third level is still there. My friend Sam Weiner disappeared! Nobody knew where, but I sort of suspected because Sam's a city boy, and I used to tell him about Galesburg—I went to school there—and he always said he liked the sound of the place. And that's where he is, all right. In 1894.

Because one night, fussing with my stamp collection, I found—well, do you know what a first-day cover is? When a new stamp is issued, stamp collectors buy some and use them to mail envelopes to themselves on the very first day of sale; and the postmark proves the date. The envelope is called a first-day cover. They're never opened; you just put blank paper in the envelope.

That night, among my oldest first-day covers, I found one that shouldn't have been there. But there it was. It was there because someone had mailed it to my grandfather at his home in Galesburg; that's what the address on the envelope said. And it had been there since July 18, 1894—the postmark showed that—yet I didn't remember it at all. The stamp was a six-cent, dull brown, with a picture of President Garfield. Naturally, when the envelope came to Granddad in the mail, it went right into his collection and stayed there—till I took it out and opened it.

The paper inside wasn't blank. It read·

941 Willard Street
July 18, 1894
Galesburg, Illinois

Charley:
I got to wishing that you were right. Then I got to *believing* you were
right. And, Charley, it's true: I found the third level! I've been here two
weeks, and right now, down the street at the Dalys', someone is playing a
piano, and they're all out on the front porch singing "Seeing Nellie Home."
And I'm invited over for lemonade. Come on back, Charley and Louisa.
Keep looking till you find the third level! It's worth it, believe me!

The note is signed Sam.

At the stamp and coin store I go to, I found out that Sam bought
eight hundred dollars worth of old-style currency. That ought to set
him up in a nice little hay, feed, and grain business; he always said
that's what he really wished he could do, and he certainly can't go back
to his old business. Not in Galesburg, Illinois, in 1894. His old
business? Why, Sam was my psychiatrist.

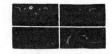

SPEED

Josephine Miles

A light year[1] is a cell year.
Nothing harries it on but its own speed,
Nothing halts it but its round roll.
It rushes through space as through a lifetime of
                                        incarceration.[2]

5 Unconscionable[3] to me is the speed of a light year
Which I cannot follow with my mind's eye
Or hear rushing and rattling with my heart's ear,
But stands still around me in the perpetual moment of
                                        the universe.

In the real year into which I was born,
10 Autumn succeeds summer and every flower
Lives hastily through the steps of its day
Filled with the clamor of seconds and happenings.

How can I fathom the millennial[4] views
Of sky from cell walls which appertain
15 To eternity, when here at hand
Gardens of time happen, come into bloom, fade,
                                  happen again?

"Speed" from POEMS: 1930–1960 by Josephine Miles. Copyright © 1960 by Josephine Miles. Reprinted by permission of Indiana University Press.

1. *light year,* the distance that light, moving through a vacuum, travels in one year; about six trillion miles. 2. *incarceration,* imprisonment. 3. *Unconscionable,* beyond reason, or unbearable. 4. *millennial,* covering thousands of years. *Millennial* is also the term for a vision of some future thousand-year age, when human society will at last have reached peace and perfection.

THE INN
OUTSIDE
THE WORLD

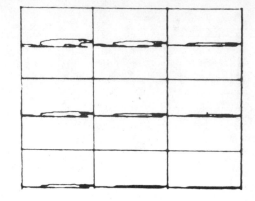

Edmond Hamilton

MERRILL FELT DISCOURAGED TONIGHT, though not for himself. His despondency was for the old man in the next room of this dingy Balkan[1] hotel, the thin, gray, spectacled old man who was one of the four most important people in postwar Europe.

Carlus Guinard had come back from exile to lead a stricken nation out of its chaotic misery, and he was the only statesman who could do it. But, tonight, even Guinard had been so crushed by defeat that he had admitted his helplessness to hold back his people from the abyss.

"Too much intolerance, too many old grudges, too many ambitious men," he said wearily to Merrill when his last conference of the day was over. "I fear it is hopeless."

Merrill was only an unimportant lieutenant, assigned by U.S. Military Intelligence to guard Guinard, but he and the old statesman had become friends in these last weeks.

"You're tired, sir," he had said, awkwardly encouraging. "Things won't look so black in the morning."

"I fear that the night over this part of Europe is to be a long, long night," murmured Guinard. His thin shoulders were sagging, his ordinarily twinkling, friendly eyes now dull and haggard.

He whispered, "Perhaps *they* could help me. It is against our laws, but——" Then, aware of the staring Merrill, he broke off. "Good night, Lieutenant."

Merrill had been worried and restless ever since. He liked and respected the world-famous old statesman, and was downcast by the other's defeat and despair. He knew what a herculean task the tired old man was attempting.

He went to the open window. Across the dark, bomb-shattered city out there moaned a chill wind. Away northward, the river glistened beneath the stars. Few lights had yet come back on in this land, though the war was over. Perhaps the lights would never come back if Guinard failed?

What had the old man whispered about "they" helping him? Some-

"The Inn Outside the World" by Edmond Hamilton from WEIRD TALES Magazine, (July 1945). Reprinted by permission of the author and his agents, Scott Meredith Literary Agency, Inc., 580 Fifth Avenue, New York, N.Y. 10036.

1. *Balkan,* any of the five nations, including Yugoslavia and Greece, which lie on the southeastern Balkan peninsula of Europe, between Italy and Turkey.

thing that was against the "laws"? Was Guinard planning a secret conference of some kind? Did he intend to slip out without his American bodyguard for that purpose?

Merrill felt sudden alarm. And it wasn't because he might lose his commission if he failed to guard the statesman. It was because he liked Guinard, and knew there were many out in that dark city who would assassinate him if they could. Guinard mustn't try to go out alone——

He went to Guinard's door and listened. And he heard a soft step inside the bedroom. It increased his apprehensions. Guinard had retired an hour before. Then he *was* trying to slip out secretly?

Merrill softly opened the door. What he saw was so unexpected and amazing that for a moment he just stood and stared.

Guinard stood, his back toward the American, in the center of the room. The old man was holding his watch above his head, and was fingering its heavy, jeweled case.

Had Guinard suddenly gone crazy from strain? It seemed so to Merrill. Yet there seemed sober purpose in Guinard's madness.

He'd noticed the old statesman's watch before this. It was a curious, massive gold one, with a complex pattern of big jewels inset on its back.

Guinard was pressing the jewels, one after another, as he held the watch above his head. There was something so oddly suggestive of the ominous about it, that Merrill impulsively strode forward.

Guinard turned, startled, as Merrill reached his side. The old man yelled in sharp alarm.

"Get back, Lieutenant—don't——"

It all happened together. As he shouted, as Merrill reached him, from the upheld watch there dropped toward the two men a thin, wavering thread of blinding light.

It struck them and Merrill was dazed and blinded by a shock of force. It seemed to him that the floor beneath his feet vanished and that he was falling——

Merrill did not lose consciousness. But the world seemed to disappear from around him as he plunged through bellowing blackness. And then there was a sharp shock, and he was standing staggering on firm footing again.

But the hotel room was gone. The walls, the floor, the lights, had vanished as by witchcraft. The only thing remaining of all that was Carlus Guinard, whose thin arm he had been clutching.

"What——" choked Merrill. He couldn't form or speak more words than that one.

He was standing on grassy ground in a strange misty darkness. He was in the open air, but there was nothing to see. Nothing but a swirling mist through which filtered a faint green glow of light.

In that green glow, Guinard's thin face was close to him and was staring at him aghast.

"You came through with me!" Guinard exclaimed, thunderstruck. "But this—it's never happened before. It's forbidden! You don't belong!"

"Guinard, what happened?" Merrill asked hoarsely. He looked wildly around the greenish, silent mists. A gruesome possibility shook him. "Was it an explosion? Are we—dead?"

"No, no!" the old statesman hastily denied. His face was a study in perplexity and anxiety. He seemed to ignore their surroundings entirely in his concentration on Merrill. "But you, Lieutenant—you should not be in this place. Had I known you were behind me——"

Then Guinard pulled himself together. "I shall have to take you to the others," he muttered distractedly. "It's all I can do now. And they will have to decide about you. If they don't understand——"

Distress came into his fine, haggard face at some thought that he did not voice as he looked at Merrill.

The American could not understand. He wanted to say something but he couldn't. It was too sudden, too overwhelming.

He could only stand, staring stupidly about him. There was not a sound. Nor any movement. Nothing but the curling, greenish mists whose cool, damp tendrils silently caressed their faces.

Guinard spoke urgently. "Lieutenant, you must understand me! You have inadvertently blundered into a place where you have no right to be, into the greatest and most closely guarded of secrets."

"What is this place?" Merrill asked hoarsely. "And how did we get here like that? *How?*"

Guinard spoke slowly, trying to penetrate his dazed mind. "Listen, Lieutenant. I must tell you, since you are here. This is not our Earth. This is another world."

Merrill's brain groped for understanding. "Another world? You mean, we're on one of the other planets?"

Guinard shook his gray head quickly. "No, not any planet of any universe known to science. A different universe, a different space-time continuum,[2] entirely."

He looked baffled. "How shall I tell you? I am a statesman, not a physicist. I only know myself what Rodemos and Zyskyn and the others have told me.

"But listen. This world, in its other space-time frame, is always close to Earth, contiguous. Held there—what did Zyskyn say?—by interdimensional gravitation. Meshed forever with Earth, yet forever invisible and untouchable to Earthmen."

Merrill's throat was dry, but his heart began to beat faster. A little of this, at least, he could understand.

"I've read speculations on such an interlocking world," he said slowly. "But if that's what it is, how did we get here?"

Guinard showed his watch, with its curious pattern of big jewels on the back. "This brought us through, Lieutenant. It isn't a watch,

---

2. *space-time continuum.* A space (or the bodies in it) cannot exist in no time at all; nor can any time (or the events in it) happen except within some space. Therefore, in modern physics, the universe is pictured as stretching out not merely through the dimensions of length, width, and height, but as stretching out through the interlocked dimensions of time and space. The continuum is the single uninterrupted pattern of existence within which all objects and events of our universe have positions and move in time as well as in space. If other such space-time patterns exist, then a world in one of them would move along a path of space-time entirely unconnected to that of our universe.

though it looks like one. It is a compact instrument which can project enough force to thrust matter from Earth into this world."

The old man talked rapidly. "This world, and the way into it, have been known for thousands of years. A scientist of ancient Atlantis[3] found the way first. He passed the secret down to a chosen few of each generation."

"You mean"—Merrill struggled to comprehend—"you mean that in every stage of the world's history, there have been a few people who knew about *this?*"

And he made a wild gesture toward the unearthly landscape of solemn green mists that surrounded them.

Guinard's gray head bobbed. "Yes. A few of the greatest men in each age have been admitted into the secret and have been bequeathed the jeweled Signs which are the key to entrance here. I don't claim to be worthy of belonging to the world's greatest—but they thought me so and admitted me to their brotherhood."

He went on: "And all the members of our secret brotherhood, the greatest men of every age of Earth in past and future, come often into this world and gather at our meeting-place here."

Merrill was stunned. "You mean, men of the past, present and future *meet* in this world? But——"

Guinard reminded, "I told you that this world is outside Earth's space-time. A thousand years on Earth is but a few days here. Time is different."

He elaborated hastily. "Think of the different ages of Earth as rooms along a corridor. You can't go from one room into another, from one age into another. But the occupants of all the rooms, of all the ages, can, if they have the key, come out and meet together in the corridor which is common to them all."

The old statesman's face was haggard as he concluded. "I came here tonight to seek help from the others of our brotherhood! Help that could enable me to pull my people and nation out of the abyss of anarchy. It's the only hope I have left now. Always, it's been against the laws of our brotherhood to give each other such help. But now——"

He clutched Merrill's wrist and pulled him forward. "I can't delay here longer. You will have to come with me, even though you are not of the initiated."

Merrill found himself being hurried along by the old statesman, through the greenish mists. The grassy ground rolled in low swales, and they crossed little streams. They could see little but the enfolding mists, and there was no sign or sound of life.

The American felt as though he walked in a weird dream. His brain was staggering at the implications of what Guinard had just told him.

A secret brotherhood of the world's greatest men of all ages, an esoteric tradition that held the key to entrance into an alien world

---

3. *Atlantis,* in an ancient tradition, the world's first and yet most advanced civilization. Atlantis was supposedly an island continent in mid-Atlantic, which was swallowed by the sea in a vast earthquake about 10,000 B.C. Many scholars think the story is pure legend, but others think it may be a confused account of a later historical empire.

where all those men of many ages could mix and meet! Incredible, surely——

A clear voice called suddenly from close behind them. *"Est Guinard? Salve!"*[4]

Guinard stopped, peering back into the mists. *"Salve frater! Quis est?"*[5]

He murmured rapidly to Merrill. "We have to have some common language, of course. And we use Latin. Those who didn't know it, learned it. You know it?"

Merrill mumbled numbly, "I was a medical student before the war. But who——"

A figure emerged from the mists, overtaking them, and gave cheerful greeting.

"I hoped to see you this visit, Guinard," he said in rattling Latin. "How go things in that strange century of yours?"

"Not well, Ikhnaton," answered the old statesman. "It's why I've come. I've got to have help."

"Help? From us others?" repeated the man called Ikhnaton. "But you know that's impossible——"

He broke off suddenly, staring at Merrill. And Merrill in turn was gazing at him with even more wonder.

The man was young, with a thin, dark, intellectual face and luminous eyes. But his costume was outlandish. A linen cloak over a short tunic, a snake-crested gold fillet around his dark hair, a flaming disk hanging around his neck with the curious jeweled pattern of the Sign in its face.

"Ikhnaton, King of Egypt in the fourteenth century, B.C.," Guinard was explaining hurriedly. "Even if you don't know much history you must have heard of him."

Ikhnaton! Merrill stared unbelievingly. He'd heard of the Egyptian ruler who had been called the first great man in history, the reformer who had dreamed of universal brotherhood, back in time's dawn.

The Egyptian was frankly puzzled. "This man doesn't belong to us. Why did you bring him?"

"I didn't intend to, it was all a mistake," Guinard said hastily. "I'll explain when we reach the inn."

"There it is," Ikhnaton nodded ahead. "And it sounds like a good gathering this time. I hope so—last time I came, there was nobody here but Darwin and that stiff-necked Luther,[6] and our argument never ended."

Warm, ruddy light glowed in the mists ahead, beckoning to them. The light came from the oblong windows of a low, squat building.

It was a curious structure, this place they called "the inn." One-storied and built of dark stone, with timber gables, it looked dreamlike

---

4. *"Est Guinard? Salve!"* "Is that Guinard? Welcome!" 5. *"Salve frater! Quis est?"* "Welcome brother! Who's there?" 6. *Darwin . . . Luther.* Charles Darwin (1809-1882) was an English naturalist, whose theory of the evolution of life led to great debates about religion and science. Martin Luther (1483-1546) left the Roman Catholic Church to lead the Protestant Reformation in Germany.

and unreal here in the silent mists. There were vineyards and gardens around it, Merrill saw.

Guinard opened the door. Ruddy light and warmth and the clamor of disputing voices struck their faces. Men hailed them in Latin.

"Ho, Guinard! Come in and listen to this! Zyskyn and old Socrates[7] are at it again!"

Merrill stood and stared. Most of the inn was a big common room, stone-flagged, with heavy, timbered walls. A huge fireplace at one side held a leaping blaze, and its flickering light joined the reddish glow of torches in wall sockets to illuminate the room.

There were long tables down the center. Grouped around the longest table, with their winecups standing unheeded upon it now, were the most motley group of men possible to imagine.

A tall Roman in bronze sat beside a man in supermodern zipper garments, a grave, bearded man in Elizabethan ruff and hose beside a withered, ancient Chinese, a merry fellow in the gaudy clothes of sixteenth-century France beside a stout, sober man in the drab brown of an American Colonial. At the far end of the table, silent and brooding, sat a man wrapped in dark robe and cowllike hood, a man with a pale, young-old face.

All this fantastically variegated company, except that brooding, cowled listener, were eagerly joining in an argument. The two chief disputants were a handsome young man in a strange, glittering garment of woven metal and a bald, stocky Greek with shrewd eyes and a broken nose. Then, Merrill thought numbly, these two disputants were Zyskyn and—Socrates?

A fat, jolly, moon-faced fellow in the costume of old Babylon[8] waddled up to them. That he was the master of the inn, Merrill knew by the brimming winecups he was carrying as he greeted them.

"Welcome, friend Guinard!" he boomed. "And you too, Ikhnaton—but remember, no more arguments about theology."

His eyes fell on Merrill, behind them. And he stiffened. "But this man is not one of us!"

The booming words rang out so suddenly loud that they cut across the argument in the room, and all heads turned toward them.

The tall, bald, bleak-eyed Roman put down his goblet and strode up to them. He faced Merrill.

"How came you here?" he demanded sharply. "Do you have the Sign?"

"Wait, Caesar," begged Guinard urgently. "He doesn't have the Sign. But it's not his fault that he's here."

Caesar? Julius Caesar? Merrill could only stare at the Roman and then at the others.

The quiet, grave-faced man in Elizabethan costume interposed himself into the argument.

---

7. *Socrates* (470?-399 B.C.), one of the greatest Greek philosophers during the Golden Age of Athens.
8. *Babylon,* in early Biblical times, the luxurious capital of the Babylonian empire that ruled part of southwest Asia.

"You remember me, Guinard? Francis Bacon.[9] May I ask where you and Ikhnaton found this man?"

The Egyptian king made a gesture of denial. "I never saw him until a few minutes ago."

"His name is Merrill, and he came with me," Carlus Guinard said rapidly. His voice rose with tension. "It's my fault that he's here. I was not careful enough about being alone when I came through, and he got caught in the force of the Sign and was swept with me."

Guinard hurried on. "If there's any blame for his coming, it attaches to my carelessness. But I was half-crazy tonight with worry. Back in my time, my people reel on the brink of anarchy and destruction. I have to save them. And so I have come to you others—for help."

The handsome young man in the queer flexible metal garment stared at him incredulously.

"For our help? You know we can't help you to do anything in your own time, Guinard!"

"Zyskyn is right," nodded Francis Bacon. "You surely should have known that, Guinard."

"But I *must* have help!" Guinard exclaimed feverishly. "Some of you are from times future to my own, and your greater science and wisdom can save millions of my people. At least, let me tell you!"

Caesar's curt voice cut into the excited babble that followed. "Let's take things in order. This is a serious thing you propose, Guinard. For the time being, we'll pass over the matter of this man you chanced to bring with you. His fate can be decided later. Sit down, all of you, and we'll hear what Guinard has to say."

Merrill could see that Guinard's proposal had thrown a bombshell into this group. As they returned to the table, all were still excitedly talking, all except the brooding, cowled man who had not stirred.

Merrill found himself pushed into a seat at the table by Ikhnaton. The young Egyptian king looked at him with a friendly glance.

"It must seem strange to you, eh?" Ikhnaton said, over the excited clamor. "It did to me, when I first came through. I was almost afraid to use the Sign."

"How did you get the Sign?" Merrill asked him. "How were you initiated into—this?"

Ikhnaton explained. "Rodemos of Atlantis—he isn't here tonight—was the first to find a way into this world. He passed down the secret, which is imparted to only a few men in each generation."

The Egyptian continued. "I imagine you have heard of most of these here tonight. Though some, of course, are still in your future."

Merrill learned that the handsome Zyskyn was a great scientist of the thirty-first-century Antarctican civilization. The old Chinese was Lao-tse[10] of the sixth century B.C. and the swarthy, slender man beside him was the Dutch philosopher Spinoza.

---

9. *Francis Bacon* (1561-1626), an English statesman and author who helped to modernize many areas of philosophy and scientific thought. 10. *Lao-tse* (lou′ tse′), the probable founder of Taoism, a religious philosophy which teaches the humble and simple life as the way to peace and harmony with the Tao, the essential principle of the universe.

Stout, pawky Benjamin Franklin sat beside the great Buddhist emperor Asoka. Next to them was John Loring, a famous space explorer of the twenty-fifth century, and across from them the merry face of François Rabelais.[11]

"It's incredible," Merrill said hoarsely. "I've read and heard of most of these men—Caesar, yourself—I know how long you lived and how you died."

Ikhnaton interrupted sharply. "Don't mention anything like that! It's considered bad taste to talk here of a man's personal future, even when you know it from history. It would be disconcerting, you know."

Merrill gestured past the excitedly clamoring group toward the cowled man who sat strangely silent and unmoved at the end of the table.

His face fascinated Merrill. It was smooth and young, but his dark, watching eyes had something infinitely old about them.

"Who is that?" he asked the Egyptian.

Ikhnaton shrugged. "That's Su Suum, who never talks about himself. We know only that he comes from some far future time, farther even than Zyskyn's age. He comes often, but just sits and listens."

The clamor of discussion that had been unloosed by Guinard's proposal was quelled again by the crisp voice of Julius Caesar.

"Will you not be quiet enough so that we may at least hear what Guinard has to say?" he demanded.

The uproar quieted. Men sat back down and looked toward Guinard. Franklin polished his steel-rimmed spectacles with a silk handkerchief, while Rabelais drained his winecup and set it down with a sigh.

Merrill looked back and forth along the faces. From Ikhnaton of old Egypt, beside him, to the farthest end of the table where sat the silent figure of Su Suum, man of the remotest future.

Guinard was speaking urgently. "I know the laws of our brotherhood as well as you. First, to keep this world and our meetings always secret. Second, to give the Sign which is our badge of fellowship only to those who are above petty self-seeking. And third, that one age of Earth must never through us directly influence another age.

"Nevertheless," he continued earnestly. "I desire tonight that you grant an exception to that third law. I come here for my people, seeking aid to save my twentieth-century land and race from utter misery."

He went on, telling them of his war-stricken land and of the danger that anarchy and terror would crush its millions. He pictured his own helplessness to halt the tide.

Loring, the space explorer of the twenty-fifth, interrupted. "But from what I've read of your century's history, those convulsions of which you speak will finally end."

"They will end, yes, but before then millions of my people will have

11. *François Rabelais* (fräN swä′ rab′ə lä), a sixteenth-century Frenchman, the author of zestful, good-humored satires which praise a joyous love of people and of life, including the pleasures of food and drink.

lived starved and stunted lives!" Guinard exclaimed. "It is to prevent that that I appeal to you for help."

"Let us be clear," said Socrates keenly. "Just what sort of help do you desire?"

Guinard looked toward Zyskyn, and John Loring, and the silent man called Su Suum.

"You three," he told them, "come from far future times when scientific progress is great. Could none of you suggest any scientific means of psychologically pacifying my people into good will and cooperation?"

Merrill saw that Su Suum remained silent, watching abstractedly and making no sign of assent. But young Zyskyn answered slowly.

"Why, yes, down in Antarctica our psychomechanists long ago solved that problem. We have certain apparatus whose subtle radiation we use to manipulate the psychology of backward peoples, and twist their thinking toward peace and cooperation."

"Give me the secret of that apparatus and with it I can save millions in my time from misery!" cried Guinard.

That the proposal was disturbing, Merrill could see. The group were silent, looking troubledly at each other.

Then old Lao-tse spoke, using the unfamiliar language slowly and with difficulty.

"I am opposed to doing that. For it would violate the laws of time and infinity which separate the ages of our Earth. It would introduce a confusion of eras which might bring on cosmic disaster."

Ikhnaton retorted warmly. "What harm could it do? Guinard would keep his use of the apparatus secret. And it would save many. I say, let us make an exception to our law and help him."

Loring, the space explorer, looked anxiously at the bald Greek next to him. "Socrates, you're one of the wisest of us. What do you say?"

The Greek rubbed his nose thoughtfully. "It is my belief that all outward things are but forms and shadows of the ideal, and I cannot credit that the ideal laws of the universe would permit transgressing the bounds of Earthly time without dire results."

Francis Bacon spoke precisely and calmly. "I hold the other opinion. Once I wrote that our object should be to extend man's dominion over all the universe. Why not conquer time as space has been conquered?"

Spinoza and Franklin shook their heads doubtfully, and then Caesar interrupted restlessly.

"Talk, talk—we have too much of it here. What Guinard wants is action and help. Are we to give it to him?"

"I say again, let us help him!" Ikhnaton exclaimed. "Why should not the future aid the past, as the past has always aided its future?"

Rabelais shook his head sorrowfully. "Men are fools. Guinard's people would have no more troubles if they forgot their hatreds and hopes and stuck to their drinking."

Zyskyn spoke troubledly to the old statesman. "Guinard, they seem to feel there is too much danger in what you ask."

Guinard's thin shoulders sagged. "Then I shall never be able to steer my people out of their misery."

Uproar of argument broke out again. Merrill ignored it. The desperation, the hopelessness, in the old statesman's face had wakened a fierce resolve in the young American.

"Guinard, there's one way to get what you want," he muttered. "This way!"

And Merrill snatched out the flat pistol inside his jacket and leveled it at Zyskyn.

"I hate to do this," he said to the dumbfounded group. "But I've *seen* the misery that Guinard is trying to relieve. He's got to have your help. You'll promise him the apparatus he needs, or——"

"Or what, man of the past?" said young Zyskyn, smiling faintly at Merrill.

He made a swift motion with his hand. From a bracelet on his wrist leaped a little tongue of green light.

It hit Merrill's arm with paralyzing shock. The pistol dropped from his nerveless fingers.

The silence was broken by Caesar's laugh. "I like that young fool. At least, he doesn't just talk—he tries to act."

"He has shown that the people of his age are too barbaric to be trusted with Zyskyn's science," snapped the space explorer, Loring.

Guinard looked down strickenly at the American. "Lieutenant, you shouldn't have done that!"

And then suddenly, through the increased uproar of disputing voices that followed Merrill's impulsive action and defeat, there came a slow chill voice.

"Will you listen to me, brothers?"

It was the man at the farthest end of the long table who was speaking. The cowled figure of Su Suum, always before silent.

Zyskyn, Caesar, Franklin—all in the room were stricken to silence by the unexpected voice. They stared wonderingly at Su Suum.

"You have often wondered about me," Su Suum said quietly. "I told you that I came from Earth's far future, but I did not tell you more than that. I preferred to listen. But now, I think, I must speak.

"I come from a time far in Earth's future, indeed. By your reckoning, it would be the 14,000th century."

"That far?" whispered Zyskyn, astounded. "But——"

Su Suum, his strange young-old face quiet and passionless, continued. "As to who I am—*I am the last.*"

A terrible realization came to Merrill, of the meaning of those quiet words. "You mean——?" Socrates was murmuring astoundedly.

"Yes," said Su Suum. "I mean that I am the last man of all men. The final survivor of the race to whose past you all belong."

His brooding eyes looked beyond them into infinite space and time. "All the history of our race, I know. I could tell you all of it, how the first star-colonists left Earth in the thirty-fourth century, how the cooling Earth was itself evacuated in the 108th, how for thousands on thousands of years our race spread out through the galaxies and founded a cosmic empire of power and splendor you could not even imagine.

"And I could tell you, too, of how with the long ages that empire finally shrunk and withered as the galaxies faded and died. Of how the mighty realm and the trillioned races of men fell in inevitable decline, shrinking with the eras to fewer worlds, until at last but a remnant of them were left on a dying world far across the galaxy.

"I was the last of that remnant," Su Suum continued. "The last of all men left in a dying, darkened universe. With me, human history concludes its glorious span as we all knew that somewhere and someday it must conclude itself."

The cowled man made a gesture. "I was lonely, in that dying, haunted universe. And before I died I wanted to come back to the little world from which our race sprang, the Earth. Dead, icy and forlorn it is in my era—and I the only man upon it.

"That is why, by means of the Sign that descended through the ages to me, I came among you. I have sat here many times with you men of the past, listening to your talk of the ages. And to me, it has been as though I relived the wonderful saga of our race."

The men—these men from as many different ages—stared at Su Suum as though he were indeed a ghost from beyond death.

Merrill finally heard old Lao-tse ask, "Then, last of men, what is your word as to the decision we must make on Guinard's request?"

Su Suum spoke slowly. "My word is this: Even though it were possible to transgress the bounds of Earth's ages without disaster, even though you were able thus to save your peoples from confusion and struggle, would it be great gain?

"I tell you this—no matter what great powers you win, no matter how high you carry human achievement, in the end it must all conclude with *me*. Must end with a perished race, humanity's story told, all the great goals you struggled toward fallen to dust and nothingness.

"So, it is not important that you may not attain the goals toward which you struggle. What is important is the way in which you carry on that struggle, your own courage and kindness from day to day. Though you attain the most glittering Utopia[12] of your dreams, yet it will someday perish. But the mere passing days of struggle that you make splendid by your courage, the record that you write in the pages of the past, that can *never perish.*"

Merrill saw Guinard stand up, and in the midst of a deep silence speak unsteadily.

"I am answered from the world's end," said the old statesman. "And you have given me the courage of which you speak."

He looked around the silent group. "I shall return now. May my young friend return with me? I guarantee his silence."

---

12. *Utopia,* an ideal society, with perfect peace and justice for everyone.

There was a moment's hesitation, and then Caesar made a gesture. 'Let him go, friends. Guinard's guarantee is good."

Guinard held his medallion-watch above himself and Merrill, pressed the jewels on its back. The thread of blinding light from the instrument struck the American and he knew nothing.

Merrill awoke with sun streaming into his eyes. He sat up dazedly and found himself on the couch in Guinard's shabby hotel room.

The old man was bending over him. "I fear that you fell asleep in here last night, Lieutenant."

Merrill sprang to his feet. "Guinard! We're back on Earth, then! They let me come back!"

Guinard frowned at him in perplexity. "Back on Earth? I don't understand. I'm afraid you've been dreaming."

Merrill clutched his arm. "It was no dream! You were there with me, with Caesar, Socrates, all of them! And that man Su Suum—good God, the last of the human race——"

Guinard soothingly patted his shoulder. "There, Lieutenant, you've apparently had a nightmare of some kind."

Merrill stared at him. Then he spoke slowly. "I think I understand. You guaranteed my silence. You know that if you pretend it all never happened, I'll *have* to keep silent, since nobody would ever believe me."

The old statesman shook his head. "I'm sorry. I don't know what you're talking about."

Merrill felt staggered. Had it all then really been mere fabric of dream, that brotherhood of the ages? If it were——

Guinard was speaking. "Enough of this. There's work to do. Work that may or may not pull my people together. But it's got to be tried."

"But last night you were so hopeless," Merrill said wonderingly.

"That was my weakness," Guinard said quietly. "I forgot that it is not whether we win or lose the struggle that matters most, but how we bear ourselves in the fight. I shall not weaken again."

The words of Su Suum re-echoed in Merrill's mind. And he knew now that it had been no dream, even though Guinard would never admit it, even though he'd never be able to convince anyone.

And Guinard knew he knew, for the statesman's eyes met his in a long, quiet look. Then the old man turned toward the door.

"Come, Lieutenant. Our work is waiting for us."

A Matter of Relativity

ON THE RELATIVITY OF TIME

Wolfgang Pauli

WE MAY BEGIN WITH A SCENE as it appears to us, a pond surrounded by pines. It is night, and the stars are out in space. With their great speeds so far away, they look like motionless, brilliant pinpoints in the familiar constellations. Fireflies weave against the pines and the sky, and all these patterns, still or moving, are reflected in the pond. A frog is croaking and mosquitoes whine. The Earth is solid underfoot, and the world seems stable and peaceful.

These are things we hear, see and feel with our senses. But how much of this is an extension of our minds? The interpretation of time, as of space, depends upon the viewpoint. In the tempo of everyday life, a thousand years seem a long time. But to someone who studies paleontology,[1] thirty thousand years may seem but an instant, and this amount in a geologic era[2] is no time at all. It seems quite certain, though, that the length of our life largely determines whether we consider something slow or fast.

To see how this may be, let us invent imaginary people with exaggeratedly brief and long life spans and call them *Minim* and *Chronos,* respectively. Minim's life span shall be as fast as the fraction of a thought. While we wink an eye, four or five of his generations pass. If he stood by the pond, here is how he might describe what he saw:

"The universe is an immense black expanse of space, studded with many specks of light. Some of these specks are nestled among the spearlike, still matter called grass. Others are suspended in the air all about me, held there by an invisible force, while still others appear to

---

"On the Relativity of Time" by Wolfgang Pauli from THE WORLD OF LIFE: A General Biology. Copyright 1949 by Houghton Mifflin Company. Reprinted by permission of the author.

1. *paleontology,* the science that reconstructs from fossils the types of plants and animals which lived in prehistoric ages. 2. *geologic era,* any of the five main stages in the development of the Earth's physical structure. According to paleontologists, our present era, the shortest so far, has already lasted about seventy million years.

be suspended far out in space, no doubt held there by the same mysterious force. Huge dark masses of inert and apparently everlasting matter, called *trees*, surround me. A peculiarly formed, still, and motionless lump of matter called *man* forms a mound beneath the trees. No sign of motion or life has ever been detected in any of these objects. All of them are as unchanging and unresponsive as the things called *stones* which also lie all about. In fact, the world is motionless, unchanging. We, the Minims, appear to be the only creatures who have life and motion."

Thus Minim might describe his universe, and what a different universe he sees! His world is black because his life span happens to come at night. To him the fireflies are as motionless as the stars, because in the 1/100 part of a second that he lives, the streaking fireflies do not move enough for their motion to be noticed. Wind, the quivering of a leaf, or of a blade of grass, don't exist for Minim. No sound within the range of human hearing would be heard by him. Stories of the far-off period when the world was in sunlight would not, even in the form of myth, come down to the night-living Minim generations. There is no more motion in such a world than in a photograph.

Now imagine a time far slower than human time, and a person as sluggish and long-lived to man as man is to Minim. We shall call this creature of near eternity *Chronos*, and just one of his slow-moving hours would in our reckoning be twenty-five million years. This is how the same pond might look to him:

"Everything in the universe flashes and squirms with great speed. Most things exist but a moment and flash out of existence. There is no fixed, firm point on which to rest the eye. A moment ago as I sat down (it took him fifteen thousand of our years to do so) there was one of those ephemeral things called a *pond* before me. By the time I was seated it had disappeared, as such mirages do. The Earth is a thick fluid that moves constantly in a series of waves or hills. Valleys are dangerous with wicked writhing streams that tear into the land. Most of the surface of this heaving Earth is covered with a turbulent green stuff, which may persist some minutes and then disappear completely, only to flash back again for an instant the next second. A few minutes ago, the world was covered briefly with a white fluff, but this too faded away. Overhead is a great expanse of space, divided into distinct halves. One half is a uniform gray; the other is bright and shining. In the gray area I dimly see a squirming pattern of spirals and circles. The shining half of the sky is bright and unchanging, and a warm light comes from it. On the Earth I see no moving object, no organized creature with a life span or any life such as mine."

This is the world of Chronos, to whom seven thousand years are but a second. How could his world be the same as man's or Minim's? Actually, all three worlds have the same setting in space, but are differently set in time. Hence the three subjective impressions are totally different. To us a pond is as lasting as the light of the firefly is to Minim, but for Chronos it would probably have vanished as soon as he glimpsed it. The average tree germinates, matures, decays, and dies in less than 1/50 of one of his seconds. He would not even see the long-lived sequoia; only the green haze which spreads and then disappears.

To Chronos, the slow process of erosion, the grinding away of mountains by wind and water, frost and heat, would be a visible flowing and sliding. Night and day and the seasons would not exist for him. In one of his seconds the sun rises and sets two million times. He would have lived through the last ice age in a moment, but it would not have lasted long enough to produce a chill in his frame. He would not see the sun, but an arched band of light; or the stars, but weaving spirals.

Finally, to Chronos, all the life that populates the Earth is less than fleeting shadows, invisible and beyond the range of his senses.

RELATIVITY
WINS
AGAIN

AFTER A FIFTY-EIGHT HOUR and five minute jaunt aboard a 747 jetliner, physicist Joseph Hafele and astronomer Richard Keating tentatively think that Einstein was at least partly right.

Essentially, the scientists set out to beat the clock and confirm one of Einstein's paradoxical theories. The paradox stems from Einstein's Special Theory of Relativity postulated in 1905 which implies that time passes more slowly for a rapidly moving object than for an object at rest. Put another way, it means that time itself is different on board a moving locomotive than for one standing at a station.

With four extremely accurate atomic clocks on loan from the U.S. Naval Observatory, Hafele and Keating made two circumnavigations of the globe, one in an easterly direction and the other in a westerly one. On the eastbound trip, the clocks would be moving faster than a reference clock on the Earth's surface (which spins in an easterly direction at one thousand miles per hour). By Einstein's equation, the clocks on board should lose about one hundred billionths of a second compared with a clock left behind on Earth. On the westbound flight, however, the clock on Earth would be moving faster to an observer than the one in the jet since the plane would be flying against the Earth's rotation.

Hafele and Keating's results seem to confirm Einstein's theory. The scientists are currently reviewing their data and will issue a more definitive statement in the near future.

"Relativity Wins Again" reprinted with permission of *Science Digest*. © The Hearst Corp.; January 1972. All Rights Reserved.

A
MATTER
OF OVERTIME

ON HIS TRIUMPHANT TOUR of Europe last month, Apollo 8 astronaut
Frank Borman amused his audiences by insisting that he, James
Lovell and William Anders were older than they would have been had
they not flown to the moon. "I think we should get overtime for that,"
he complained. Borman was joking about his pay, but he was quite
serious about his aging. During their Moon mission, the astronauts
aged about three hundred microseconds (three hundred millionths of a
second) more than the people they left behind on Earth.

Borman was informed of his overtime by University of Maryland
physicist Carroll Alley who, at the request of NASA officials, calculated the effects on the astronauts of two phenomena described by
Einstein's relativity equations: 1) time actually runs slower for an
object as its speed increases—the so-called "time dilation" effect, and
2) time speeds up for an object as it moves away from a body (like the
Earth) exerting a gravitational force.

While Apollo 8 was within four thousand miles of the Earth, Alley
found, the spacecraft's speed was the predominant factor; time slowed
up and the astronauts actually aged more slowly than mere Earth-
lings. But beyond that distance, as the effects of Earth's gravity
lessened, Apollo's time began running fast. Over the entire journey,
Alley says, Apollo's time passed more quickly than Earth time by the
three hundred microseconds.

Despite Alley's calculations, Borman's tongue-in-cheek overtime
demand is valid only for Astronaut Anders, who made his first space
flight in Apollo 8. When Borman and Lovell were crewmates on the
two-week orbital mission of Gemini 7, the time dilation effect was
dominant for the entire period; the two astronauts thus aged less than
those on Earth by approximately four hundred microseconds. Lovell's
time also slowed down by about one hundred microseconds during the
four-day flight of Gemini 12.

Thus, during all their missions in space, Lovell and Borman respectively spent two hundred and one hundred microseconds less time than
was recorded on Earth—which means that they were paid for more
time than they actually worked.

"A Matter of Overtime" from TIME, March 7, 1969. Reprinted by permission from TIME, The
Weekly Newsmagazine; Copyright Time Inc.

7

EPITAPH

THERE WILL COME
SOFT RAINS

Ray Bradbury

IN THE LIVING ROOM the voice-clock sang, *Tick-tock, seven o'clock, time to get up, time to get up, seven o'clock!* as if it were afraid that nobody would. The morning house lay empty. The clock ticked on, repeating and repeating its sounds into the emptiness. *Seven-nine, breakfast time, seven-nine!*

In the kitchen the breakfast stove gave a hissing sigh and ejected from its warm interior eight pieces of perfectly browned toast, eight eggs sunnyside up, sixteen slices of bacon, two coffees, and two glasses of milk.

"Today is August 4, 2026," said a second voice from the kitchen ceiling, "in the city of Allendale, California." It repeated the date three times for memory's sake. "Today is Mr. Featherstone's birthday. Today is the anniversary of Tilita's marriage. Insurance is payable, as are the water, gas, and light bills."

Somewhere in the walls, relays clicked, memory tapes glided under electric eyes.

Eight-one, tick-tock, eight-one o'clock, off to school, off to work, run, run, eight-one! But no doors slammed, no carpets took the soft tread of rubber heels. It was raining outside. The weather box on the front door sang quietly: "Rain, rain, go away; rubbers, raincoats for today. . . ." And the rain tapped on the empty house, echoing.

Outside, the garage chimed and lifted its door to reveal the waiting car. After a long wait the door swung down again.

At eight-thirty the eggs were shriveled and the toast was like stone. An aluminum wedge scraped them into the sink, where hot water whirled them down a metal throat which digested and flushed them away to the distant sea. The dirty dishes were dropped into a hot washer and emerged twinkling dry.

"There Will Come Soft Rains" by Ray Bradbury. Copyright 1950 by Ray Bradbury, reprinted by permission of Harold Matson Co., Inc.

Nine-fifteen, sang the clock, *time to clean.*

Out of warrens in the wall, tiny robot mice darted. The rooms were acrawl with the small cleaning animals, all rubber and metal. They thudded against chairs, whirling their mustached runners, kneading the rug nap, sucking gently at hidden dust.

Then, like mysterious invaders, they popped into their burrows. Their pink electric eyes faded. The house was clean.

Ten o'clock. The sun came out from behind the rain. The house stood alone in a city of rubble and ashes. This was the one house left standing. At night the ruined city gave off a radioactive glow which could be seen for miles.

Ten-fifteen. The garden sprinklers whirled up in golden founts, filling the soft morning air with scatterings of brightness. The water pelted windowpanes, running down the charred west side where the house had been burned evenly free of its white paint. The entire west face of the house was black, save for five places. Here the silhouette in paint of a man mowing a lawn. Here, as in a photograph, a woman bent to pick flowers. Still farther over, their images burned on wood in one titanic instant, a small boy, hands flung into the air; higher up, the image of a thrown ball; and opposite him a girl, hands raised to catch a ball which never came down.

The five spots of paint—the man, the woman, the children, the ball—remained. The rest was a thin charcoaled layer.

The gentle sprinkler rain filled the garden with falling light.

Until this day, how well the house had kept its peace. How carefully it had inquired, "Who goes there? What's the password?" and, getting no answer from lonely foxes and whining cats, it had shut up its windows and drawn shades in an old-maidenly preoccupation with self-protection which bordered on a mechanical paranoia.

It quivered at each sound, the house did. If a sparrow brushed a window, the shade snapped up. The bird, startled, flew off! No, not even a bird must touch the house!

The house was an altar with ten thousand attendants, big, small, servicing, attending, in choirs. But the gods had gone away, and the ritual of the religion continued senselessly, uselessly.

Twelve noon.

A dog whined, shivering, on the front porch.

The front door recognized the dog voice and opened. The dog, once huge and fleshy, but now gone to bone and covered with sores, moved in and through the house, tracking mud. Behind it whirred angry mice, angry at having to pick up mud, angry at inconvenience.

For not a leaf fragment blew under the door but what the wall panels flipped open and the copper scrap rats flashed swiftly out. The offending dust, hair, or paper, seized in miniature steel jaws, was raced back to the burrows. There, down tubes which fed into the cellar, it was dropped into the sighing vent of an incinerator which sat like evil Baal[1] in a dark corner.

The dog ran upstairs, hysterically yelping to each door, at last realizing, as the house realized, that only silence was here.

It sniffed the air and scratched the kitchen door. Behind the door, the stove was making pancakes which filled the house with a rich baked odor and the scent of maple syrup.

The dog frothed at the mouth, lying at the door, sniffing, its eyes turned to fire. It ran wildly in circles, biting at its tail, spun in a frenzy, and died. It lay in the parlor for an hour.

Two o'clock, sang a voice.

Delicately sensing decay at last, the regiments of mice hummed out as softly as blown gray leaves in an electrical wind.

Two-fifteen.

The dog was gone.

In the cellar, the incinerator glowed suddenly and a whirl of sparks leaped up the chimney.

Two-thirty-five.

Bridge tables sprouted from patio walls. Playing cards fluttered onto pads in a shower of pips. Martinis manifested on an oaken bench with egg-salad sandwiches. Music played.

But the tables were silent and the cards untouched.

At four o'clock the tables folded like great butterflies back through the paneled walls.

Four-thirty.

The nursery walls glowed.

Animals took shape: yellow giraffes, blue lions, pink antelopes, lilac panthers cavorting in crystal substance. The walls were glass. They looked out upon color and fantasy. Hidden films clocked through well-oiled sprockets, and the walls lived. The nursery floor was woven to resemble a crisp cereal meadow. Over this ran aluminum roaches and iron crickets, and in the hot still air butterflies of delicate red tissue wavered among the sharp aroma of animal spoors! There was the sound like a great matted yellow hive of bees within a dark bellows, the lazy bumble of a purring lion. And there was the patter of okapi[2] feet and the murmur of a fresh jungle rain, like other hoofs, falling upon the summer-starched grass. Now the walls dissolved into distances of parched weed, mile on mile, and warm endless sky. The animals drew away into thorn brakes and water holes.

It was the children's hour.

---

1. *Baal* (ba'əl), an idol; the local god of the ancient people of Syria and Palestine. Often young flocks were offered to Baal as burnt sacrifice. 2. *okapi,* an African animal, giraffelike but smaller and with a shorter neck.

Five o'clock. The bath filled with clear hot water.

Six, seven, eight o'clock. The dinner dishes manipulated like magic tricks, and in the study a *click*. In the metal stand opposite the hearth where a fire now blazed up warmly, a cigar popped out, half an inch of soft gray ash on it, smoking, waiting.

Nine o'clock. The beds warmed their hidden circuits, for nights were cool here.

Nine-five. A voice spoke from the study ceiling: "Mrs. McClellan, which poem would you like this evening?"

The house was silent.

The voice said at last, "Since you express no preference, I shall select a poem at random." Quiet music rose to back the voice. "Sara Teasdale. As I recall, your favorite. . . .

There will come soft rains and the smell of the ground,
And swallows circling with their shimmering sound;

And frogs in the pools singing at night,
And wild plum trees in tremulous white;

Robins will wear their feathery fire
Whistling their whims on a low fence-wire;

And not one will know of the war, not one
Will care at last when it is done.

Not one would mind, neither bird nor tree
If mankind perished utterly;

And Spring herself, when she woke at dawn,
Would scarcely know that we were gone."*

The fire burned on the stone hearth and the cigar fell away into a mound of quiet ash on its tray. The empty chairs faced each other between the silent walls, and the music played.

At ten o'clock the house began to die.

The wind blew. A falling tree bough crashed through the kitchen window. Cleaning solvent, bottled, shattered over the stove. The room was ablaze in an instant!

"Fire!" screamed a voice. The house lights flashed, water pumps shot water from the ceilings. But the solvent spread on the linoleum, licking, eating, under the kitchen door, while the voices took it up in chorus: "Fire, fire, fire!"

---

*"There Will Come Soft Rains" reprinted with permission of Macmillan Publishing Co., Inc. from COLLECTED POEMS by Sara Teasdale. Copyright 1920 by Macmillan Publishing Co., Inc., renewed 1948 by Mamie T. Wheless.

The house tried to save itself. Doors sprang tightly shut, but the windows were broken by the heat and the wind blew and sucked upon the fire.

The house gave ground as the fire in ten billion angry sparks moved with flaming ease from room to room and then up the stairs. While scurrying water rats squeaked from the walls, pistoled their water, and ran for more. And the wall sprays let down showers of mechanical rain.

But too late. Somewhere, sighing, a pump shrugged to a stop. The quenching rain ceased. The reserve water supply which had filled baths and washed dishes for many quiet days was gone.

The fire crackled up the stairs. It fed upon Picassos and Matisses[3] in the upper halls, like delicacies, baking off the oily flesh, tenderly crisping the canvases into black shavings.

Now the fire lay in beds, stood in windows, changed the colors of drapes!

And then, reinforcements.

From attic trap doors, blind robot faces peered down with faucet mouths gushing green chemical.

The fire backed off, as even an elephant must at the sight of a dead snake. Now there were twenty snakes whipping over the floor, killing the fire with a clear cold venom of green froth.

But the fire was clever. It had sent flame outside the house, up through the attic to the pumps there. An explosion! The attic brain which directed the pumps was shattered into bronze shrapnel on the beams.

The fire rushed back into every closet and felt of the clothes hung there.

The house shuddered, oak bone on bone, its bared skeleton cringing from the heat, its wire, its nerves revealed as if a surgeon had torn the skin off to let the red veins and capillaries quiver in the scalded air. "Help, help! Fire! Run, run!" Heat snapped mirrors like the first brittle winter ice. And the voices wailed "Fire, fire, run, run," like a tragic nursery rhyme, a dozen voices, high, low, like children dying in a forest, alone, alone. And the voices fading as the wires popped their sheathings like hot chestnuts. One, two, three, four, five voices died.

In the nursery the jungle burned. Blue lions roared, purple giraffes bounded off. The panthers ran in circles, changing color, and ten million animals, running before the fire, vanished off toward a distant steaming river. . . .

Ten more voices died. In the last instant under the fire avalanche, other choruses, oblivious, could be heard announcing the time, playing music, cutting the lawn by remote-control mower, or setting an umbrella frantically out and in the slamming and opening front door, a thousand things happening, like a clock shop when each clock strikes the hour insanely before or after the other, a scene of maniac

---

3. *Picassos and Matisses*, paintings by the Spanish-born impressionist artist Pablo Picasso (1881-1973) and the French impressionist artist Henri Matisse (1869-1954).

confusion, yet unity; singing, screaming, a few last cleaning mice darting bravely out to carry the horrid ashes away! And one voice, with sublime disregard for the situation, read poetry aloud in the fiery study, until all the film spools burned, until all the wires withered and the circuits cracked.

The fire burst the house and let it slam flat down, puffing out skirts of spark and smoke.

In the kitchen, an instant before the rain of fire and timber, the stove could be seen making breakfasts at a psychopathic rate, ten dozen eggs, six loaves of toast, twenty dozen bacon strips, which, eaten by fire, started the stove working again, hysterically hissing!

The crash. The attic smashing into kitchen and parlor. The parlor into cellar, cellar into subcellar. Deepfreeze, armchair, film tapes, circuits, beds, and all like skeletons thrown in a cluttered mound deep under.

Smoke and silence. A great quantity of smoke.

Dawn showed faintly in the east. Among the ruins, one wall stood alone. Within the wall, a last voice said, over and over again and again, even as the sun rose to shine upon the heaped rubble and steam:

"Today is August 5, 2026, today is August 5, 2026, today is . . ."

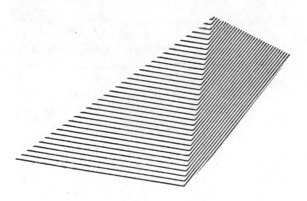

THE FORGOTTEN ENEMY

Arthur C. Clarke

THE THICK FURS THUDDED SOFTLY to the ground as Professor Millward jerked himself upright on the narrow bed. This time, he was sure, it had been no dream; the freezing air that rasped against his lungs still seemed to echo with the sound that had come crashing out of the night.

He gathered the furs around his shoulders and listened intently. All was quiet again: from the narrow windows on the western walls long shafts of moonlight played upon the endless rows of books, as they played upon the dead city beneath. The world was utterly still; even in the old days the city would have been silent on such a night, and it was doubly silent now.

With weary resolution Professor Millward shuffled out of bed and doled a few lumps of coke into the glowing brazier. Then he made his way slowly toward the nearest window, pausing now and then to rest his hand lovingly on the volumes he had guarded all these years.

He shielded his eyes from the brilliant moonlight and peered out into the night. The sky was cloudless: the sound he had heard had not been thunder, whatever it might have been. It had come from the north, and even as he waited it came again.

Distance had softened it, distance and the bulk of the hills that lay beyond London. It did not race across the sky with the wantonness of thunder, but seemed to come from a single point far to the north. It was like no natural sound that he had ever heard, and for a moment he dared to hope again.

Only Man, he was sure, could have made such a sound. Perhaps the dream that had kept him here among these treasures of civilization for more than twenty years would soon be a dream no longer. Men were returning to England, blasting their way through the ice and snow with the weapons that science had given them before the coming of the dust.[1] It was strange that they should come by land, and from the north, but he thrust aside any thoughts that would quench the newly kindled flame of hope.

"The Forgotten Enemy" by Arthur C. Clarke. Copyright 1953 by Avon Publications, Inc. Reprinted by permission of the Author and his agents, Scott Meredith Literary Agency, Inc., 580 Fifth Avenue, New York, N.Y. 10036.

1. *the dust*, cosmic dust, fine particles in outer space. The Earth, in the story, is apparently passing through a belt of dense cosmic dust which has screened the power of the sun.

Three hundred feet below, the broken sea of snow-covered roofs lay bathed in the bitter moonlight. Miles away the tall stacks of Battersea Power Station glimmered like thin white ghosts against the night sky. Now that the dome of St. Paul's[2] had collapsed beneath the weight of snow, they alone challenged his supremacy.

Professor Millward walked slowly back along the bookshelves, thinking over the plan that had formed in his mind. Twenty years ago he had watched the last helicopters climbing heavily out of Regent's Park, the rotors churning the ceaselessly falling snow. Even then, when the silence had closed around him, he could not bring himself to believe that the North had been abandoned forever. Yet already he had waited a whole generation, among the books to which he had dedicated his life.

In those early days he had sometimes heard, over the radio which was his only contact with the South, of the struggle to colonize the now-temperate lands of the Equator. He did not know the outcome of that far-off battle, fought with desperate skill in the dying jungles and across deserts that had already felt the first touch of snow. Perhaps it had failed; the radio had been silent now for fifteen years or more. Yet if men and machines were indeed returning from the north—of all directions—he might again be able to hear their voices as they spoke to one another and to the lands from which they had come.

Professor Millward left the University building perhaps a dozen times a year, and then only through sheer necessity. Over the past two decades he had collected everything he needed from the shops in the Bloomsbury area, for in the final exodus vast supplies of stocks had been left behind through lack of transport. In many ways, indeed, his life could be called luxurious; no professor of English literature had ever been clothed in such garments as those he had taken from an Oxford Street furrier's.

The sun was blazing from a cloudless sky as he shouldered his pack and unlocked the massive gates. Even ten years ago packs of starving dogs had hunted in this area, and though he had seen none for years he was still cautious and always carried a revolver when he went into the open. The sunlight was so brilliant that the reflected glare hurt his eyes; but it was almost wholly lacking in heat. Although the belt of cosmic dust through which the Solar System was now passing had made little visible difference to the sun's brightness, it had robbed it of all strength. No one knew whether the world would swim out into the warmth again in ten or a thousand years, and civilization had fled southward in search of lands where the word *summer* was not an empty mockery.

The latest drifts had packed hard and Professor Millward had little difficulty in making the journey to Tottenham Court Road. Sometimes it had taken him hours of floundering through the snow, and one year he had been sealed in his great concrete watchtower for nine months.

---

2. *the dome of St. Paul's.* The dome of St. Paul's Cathedral, the largest cathedral of the Church of England, long dominated the skyline of London.

He kept away from the houses with their dangerous burdens of snow and their Damoclean[3] icicles, and went north until he came to the shop he was seeking. The words above the shattered windows were still bright: "Jenkins & Sons. Radio and Electrical. Television A Specialty."

Some snow had drifted through a broken section of roofing, but the little upstairs room had not altered since his last visit a dozen years ago. The all-wave radio still stood on the table, and empty tins scattered on the floor spoke mutely of the lonely hours he had spent here before all hope had died. He wondered if he must go through the same ordeal again.

Professor Millward brushed the snow from the copy of *The Amateur Radio Handbook for 1965,* which had taught him what little he knew about wireless. The test-meters and batteries were still lying in their half-remembered places, and to his relief some of the batteries still held their charge. He searched through the stock until he had built up the necessary power supplies, and checked the radio as well as he could. Then he was ready.

It was a pity that he could never send the manufacturers the testimonial they deserved. The faint "hiss" from the speaker brought back memories of the BBC,[4] of the nine o'clock news and symphony concerts, of all the things he had taken for granted in a world that was gone like a dream. With scarcely controlled impatience he ran across the wavebands, but everywhere there was nothing save that omnipresent hiss. That was disappointing, but no more; he remembered that the real test would come at night. In the meantime he would forage among the surrounding shops for anything that might be useful.

It was dusk when he returned to the little room. A hundred miles above his head, tenuous and invisible, the Heaviside layer[5] would be expanding outward toward the stars as the sun went down. So it had done every evening for millions of years, and for half a century only, Man had used it for his own purposes, to reflect around the world his messages of hate or peace, to echo with trivialities or to sound with music once called immortal.

Slowly, with infinite patience, Professor Millward began to traverse the shortwave bands that a generation ago had been a babel of shouting voices and stabbing Morse. Even as he listened, the faint hope he had dared to cherish began to fade within him. The city itself was no more silent than the once-crowded oceans of ether. Only the faint crackle of thunderstorms half the world away broke the intolerable stillness. Man had abandoned his latest conquest.

Soon after midnight the batteries faded out. Professor Millward did not have the heart to search for more, but curled up in his furs and fell

---

3. *Damoclean.* According to Greek legend, when Damocles, a courtier, was invited to a feast by Dionysius, the king of Syracuse, he found suspended above his chair a sword hanging by a single hair. This was to teach Damocles a lesson about the constant peril of a king's life. Today when something is described as *Damoclean,* it means that the item represents imminent danger. 4. *BBC,* British Broadcasting Corporation. 5. *Heaviside layer,* a layer of electrically charged atmosphere, also called the *ionosphere.* When a sky wave hits the Heaviside layer, part of the wave bends toward the Earth. Shortwave-radio operators use the Heaviside layer to send radio waves long distances.

into a troubled sleep. He got what consolation he could from the thought that if he had not proved his theory, he had not disproved it either.

The heatless sunlight was flooding the lonely white road when he began the homeward journey. He was very tired for he had slept little, and his sleep had been broken by the recurring fantasy of rescue.

The silence was suddenly broken by the distant thunder that came rolling over the white roofs. It came—there could be no doubt now—from beyond the northern hills that had once been London's playground. From the buildings on either side little avalanches of snow went swishing out into the wide street; then the silence returned.

Professor Millward stood motionless, weighing, considering, analyzing. The sound had been too long-drawn to be an ordinary explosion—he was dreaming again—it was nothing less than the distant thunder of an atomic bomb, burning and blasting away the snow a million tons at a time. His hopes revived, and the disappointments of the night began to fade.

That momentary pause almost cost him his life. Out of a side street something huge and white moved suddenly into his field of vision. For a moment his mind refused to accept the reality of what he saw; then the paralysis left him and he fumbled desperately for his futile revolver. Padding toward him across the snow, swinging its head from side to side with a hypnotic, serpentine motion, was a huge polar bear.

He dropped his belongings and ran, floundering over the snow toward the nearest buildings. Providentially the Underground[6] entrance was only fifty feet away. The steel grille was closed, but he remembered breaking the lock many years ago. The temptation to look back was almost intolerable, for he could hear nothing to tell how near his pursuer was. For one frightful moment the iron lattice resisted his numbed fingers. Then it yielded reluctantly and he forced his way through the narrow opening.

Out of his childhood there came a sudden, incongruous memory of an albino ferret he had once seen weaving its body ceaselessly across the wire netting of its cage. There was the same reptile grace in the monstrous shape, almost twice as high as a man, that reared itself in baffled fury against the grille. The metal bowed but did not yield beneath the pressure; then the bear dropped to the ground, grunted softly and padded away. It slashed once or twice at the fallen haversack, scattering a few tins of food into the snow, and vanished as silently as it had come.

A very shaken Professor Millward reached the University three hours later, after moving in short bounds from one refuge to the next. After all these years he was no longer alone in the city. He wondered if there were other visitors, and that same night he knew the answer. Just before dawn he heard, quite distinctly, the cry of a wolf from somewhere in the direction of Hyde Park.

By the end of the week he knew that the animals of the North were

---

6. *the Underground,* the London subway.

on the move. Once he saw a reindeer running southward, pursued by a pack of silent wolves, and sometimes in the night there were sounds of deadly conflict. He was amazed that so much life still existed in the white wilderness between London and the Pole. Now something was driving it southward, and the knowledge brought him a mounting excitement. He did not believe that these fierce survivors would flee from anything save Man.

The strain of waiting was beginning to affect Professor Millward's mind, and for hours he would sit in the cold sunlight, his furs wrapped around him, dreaming of rescue and thinking of the way in which men might be returning to England. Perhaps an expedition had come from North America across the Atlantic ice. It might have been years upon its way. But why had it come so far north? His favorite theory was that the Atlantic ice packs were not safe enough for heavy traffic further to the south.

One thing, however, he could not explain to his satisfaction. There had been no air reconnaissance; it was hard to believe that the art of flight had been lost so soon.

Sometimes he would walk along the ranks of books, whispering now and then to a well-loved volume. There were books here that he had not dared to open for years, they reminded him so poignantly of the past. But now, as the days grew longer and brighter, he would sometimes take down a volume of poetry and reread his old favorites. Then he would go to the tall windows and shout the magic words over the rooftops, as if they would break the spell that had gripped the world.

It was warmer now, as if the ghosts of lost summers had returned to haunt the land. For whole days the temperature rose above freezing, while in many places flowers were breaking through the snow. Whatever was approaching from the north was nearer, and several times a day that enigmatic roar would go thundering over the city, sending the snow sliding upon a thousand roofs. There were strange, grinding undertones that Professor Millward found baffling and even ominous. At times it was almost as if he were listening to the clash of mighty armies, and sometimes a mad but dreadful thought came into his mind and would not be dismissed. Often he would wake in the night and imagine he heard the sound of mountains moving to the sea.

So the summer wore away, and as the sound of that distant battle drew steadily nearer Professor Millward was the prey of ever more violently alternating hopes and fears. Although he saw no more wolves or bears—they seemed to have fled southward—he did not risk leaving the safety of his fortress. Every morning he would climb to the highest window of the tower and search the northern horizon with field glasses. But all he ever saw was the stubborn retreat of the snows above Hampstead, as they fought their bitter rearguard action against the sun.

His vigil ended with the last days of the brief summer. The grinding thunder in the night had been nearer than ever before, but there was still nothing to hint at its real distance from the city. Professor

Millward felt no premonition as he climbed to the narrow window and raised his binoculars to the northern sky.

As a watcher from the walls of some threatened fortress might have seen the first sunlight glinting on the spears of an advancing army, so in that moment Professor Millward knew the truth. The air was crystal-clear, and the hills were sharp and brilliant against the cold blue of the sky. They had lost almost all their snow. Once he would have rejoiced at that, but it meant nothing now.

Overnight, the enemy he had forgotten had conquered the last defenses and was preparing for the final onslaught. As he saw that deadly glitter along the crest of the doomed hills, Professor Millward understood at last the sound he had heard advancing for so many months. It was little wonder he had dreamed of mountains on the march.

Out of the North, their ancient home, returning in triumph to the lands they had once possessed, the glaciers had come again.

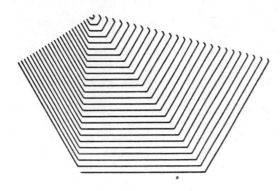

EARTHMEN BEARING GIFTS

Fredric Brown

DHAR RY SAT ALONE IN HIS ROOM, meditating. From outside the door he caught a thought wave equivalent to a knock, and, glancing at the door, he willed it to slide open.

It opened. "Enter, my friend," he said. He could have projected the idea telepathically; but with only two persons present, speech was more polite.

Ejon Khee entered. "You are up late tonight, my leader," he said.

"Yes, Khee. Within an hour the Earth rocket is due to land, and I wish to see it. Yes, I know, it will land a thousand miles away, if their calculations are correct. Beyond the horizon. But if it lands even twice that far the flash of the atomic explosion should be visible. And I have waited long for first contact. For even though no Earthman will be on that rocket, it will still be first contact—for them. Of course our telepath teams have been reading their thoughts for many centuries, but—this will be the first *physical* contact between Mars and Earth."

Khee made himself comfortable on one of the low chairs. "True," he said. "I have not followed recent reports too closely, though. Why are they using an atomic warhead? I know they suppose our planet is uninhabited, but still——"

"They will watch the flash through their lunar telescopes and get a—what do they call it?—a spectroscopic analysis.[1] That will tell them more than they know now (or think they know; much of it is erroneous) about the atmosphere of our planet and the composition of its surface. It is—call it a sighting shot, Khee. They'll be here in person within a few oppositions. And then——"

"Earthmen Bearing Gifts" by Fredric Brown. Reprinted by permission of Mrs. Elizabeth C. Brown and Scott Meredith Literary Agency, Inc., 580 Fifth Avenue, New York, N.Y. 10036.

1. *spectroscopic analysis.* When substances are heated to a high temperature, they give off a light which can be separated into a pattern of colors by passing it through a prism. Each substance makes its own pattern of colors. By analyzing the patterns, the spectroscope operator can determine the substances that are present.

Mars was holding out, waiting for Earth to come. What was left of Mars, that is; this one small city of about nine hundred beings. The civilization of Mars was older than that of Earth, but it was a dying one. This was what remained of it: one city, nine hundred people. They were waiting for Earth to make contact, for a selfish reason and for an unselfish one.

Martian civilization had developed in a quite different direction from that of Earth. It had developed no important knowledge of the physical sciences, no technology. But it had developed social sciences to the point where there had not been a single crime, let alone a war, on Mars for fifty thousand years. And it had developed fully the parapsychological sciences of the mind, which Earth was just beginning to discover. Mars could teach Earth much. How to avoid crime and war to begin with. Beyond those simple things lay telepathy, telekinesis, empathy[2] . . . .

And Earth would, Mars hoped, teach them something even more valuable to Mars: how, by science and technology—which it was too late for Mars to develop now, even if they had the type of minds which would enable them to develop these things—to restore and rehabilitate a dying planet, so that an otherwise dying race might live and multiply again.

Each planet would gain greatly, and neither would lose.

And tonight was the night when Earth would make its first sighting shot. Its next shot, a rocket containing Earthmen, or at least an Earthman, would be at the next opposition, two Earth years, or roughly four Martian years, hence. The Martians knew this, because their teams of telepaths were able to catch at least some of the thoughts of Earthmen, enough to know their plans. Unfortunately, at that distance, the connection was one-way. Mars could not ask Earth to hurry its program. Or tell Earth scientists the facts about Mars' composition and atmosphere which would have made this preliminary shot unnecessary.

Tonight Ry, the leader (as nearly as the Martian word can be translated), and Khee, his administrative assistant and closest friend, sat and meditated together until the time was near. Then they drank a toast to the future—in a beverage based on menthol, which had the same effect on Martians as alcohol on Earthmen—and climbed to the roof of the building in which they had been sitting. They watched toward the north, where the rocket should land. The stars shone brilliantly and unwinkingly through the atmosphere.

In Observatory No. 1 on Earth's moon, Rog Everett, his eye at the eyepiece of the spotter scope, said triumphantly, "Thar she blew, Willie. And now, as soon as the films are developed, we'll know the

---

2. *telepathy, telekinesis, empathy,* examples of parapsychology. Telepathy is communicating mind to mind without using speech; telekinesis is causing objects to move without using physical power; and empathy is entering into another's feelings.

score on that old planet Mars." He straightened up—there'd be no more to see now—and he and Willie Sanger shook hands solemnly. It was an historical occasion.

"Hope it didn't kill anybody. Any Martians, that is. Rog, did it hit dead center in Syrtis Major?"

"Near as matters. I'd say it was maybe a thousand miles off, to the south. And that's damn close on a fifty-million-mile shot. Willie, do you really think there are any Martians?"

Willie thought a second and then said, "No."

He was right.

THE
IFTH
OF
OOFTH

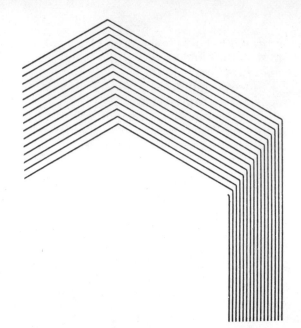

Walter Tevis

FARNSWORTH HAD INVENTED A NEW DRINK that night. He called it a mulled sloe gin toddy. Exactly as fantastic as it sounds—ramming a red-hot poker into a mugful of warm red gin, cinnamon, cloves and sugar, and then *drinking* the fool thing—but like many of Farnsworth's ideas, it managed somehow to work out. In fact, its flavor had become completely acceptable to me after the third one.

When he finally set the end of his steaming poker back on the coals for rest and regeneration, I leaned back warmly in my big leather chair—the one he had rigged up so that it would gently rock you to sleep if you pressed the right button—and said, "Oliver, your ingenuity is matched only by your hospitality."

Farnsworth blushed and smiled. He is a small, chubby man and blushes easily. "Thank you," he said. "I have another new one. I call it a jelled vodka fizz—you eat it with a spoon. You may want to try it later. It's—well—exceptional."

I suppressed a shudder at the thought of eating jelled vodka and said, "Interesting, very interesting," and since he didn't reply, we both stared at the fire for a while, letting the gin continue its pleasant work. Farnsworth's bachelor's home was very comfortable and relaxing, and I always enjoyed my Wednesday night visits there thoroughly. I suppose most men have a deep-seated love for open fires and liquor—however fantastically prepared—and deep, comfortable leather armchairs.

Then, after several minutes, Farnsworth abruptly bounced to his feet and said, "There's a thing I wanted to show you. Made it last week. Didn't pull it off too well, though."

"The Ifth of Ooth" by Walter Tevis. Copyright © 1957 by Galaxy Publishing Corp. Reprinted by permission of the author.

"Really?" I said. I'd thought the drinks had been his usual weekly brainchild. They seemed quite enough.

"Yes," he said, trotting over to the door of the study. "It's downstairs in the shop. I'll get it." And he bounced out of the room, the paneled door closing as it had opened, automatically, behind him.

I turned back to the fire again, pleased that he had made something in the machine shop—the carpentry shop was in a shed in the backyard; the chemistry and optical labs in the attic—for he was his most proficient with his lathe and milling machines. His self-setting, variable-twist thumb bolt had been a beautiful piece of work and its patent had netted him, as had several other machined devices, a remarkable sum.

He returned in a minute, carrying a very odd-looking thing with him, and set it on the table beside my chair. I examined it silently for a minute while Farnsworth stood over me, half smiling, his little green eyes wide, sparkling in the reflected, flickering light from the fire. I knew he was suppressing his eagerness for my comment, but I was uncertain what to say.

The thing, upon examination, appeared simple: a more or less cross-shaped construction of several dozen one-inch cubes, half of them of thin, transparent plastic, the other half made of thin little sheets of aluminum. Each cube seemed to be hinged to two others very cunningly and the arrangement of them all was somewhat confusing.

Finally, I said, "How many cubes?" I had tried to count them, but kept getting lost.

"Sixty-four," he said. "I think."

"You *think?*"

"Well—" He seemed embarrassed. "At least I *made* sixty-four cubes, thirty-two of each kind; but somehow I haven't been able to count them since. They seem to . . . get lost, or shift around, or something."

"Oh?" I was becoming interested. "May I pick it up?"

"Certainly," he said, and I took the affair, which was surprisingly lightweight, in my hands and began folding the cubes around on their hinges. I noticed then that some were open on one side and that certain others would fit into these if their hinging arrangements would allow them to.

I began folding them absently and said, "You could count them by marking them one at a time. With a crayon, for instance."

"As a matter of fact," he admitted, blushing again, "I tried that. Didn't seem to work out. When I finished, I found I had marked six cubes with the number one and on none of them could I find a two or three, although there were two fours, one of them written in reverse and in green." He hesitated. "I had used a red marking pencil." I saw him shudder slightly as he said it, although his voice had been casual-sounding enough. "I rubbed the numbers off with a damp cloth and didn't . . . try it again."

"Well," I said. And then, "What do you call it?"

"A pentaract."

He sat back down again in his armchair. "Of course, that name really isn't accurate. I suppose a pentaract should really be a four-dimensional pentagon, and this is meant to be a picture of a five-dimensional[1] cube."

"A *picture?*" It didn't look like a picture to me.

"Well, it couldn't *really* have five-dimensionality—length, width, breadth, ifth and oofth—or I don't think it could." His voice faltered a little at that. "But it's supposed to illustrate what you might call the layout of an object that did have those."

"What kind of object would that be?" I looked back at the thing in my lap and was mildly surprised to see that I had folded a good many of the cubes together.

"Suppose," he said, "you put a lot of points in a row, touching; you have a line—a one-dimensional figure. Put four lines together at right angles and on a plane; a square—two-dimensional. Six squares at right angles and extended into real space give you a cube—three dimensions. And eight cubes extended into four physical dimensions give you a tesseract, as it's called——"

"And eight tesseracts make a pentaract," I said. "Five dimensions."

"Exactly. But naturally this is just a picture of a pentaract, in that sense. There probably isn't any ifth and oofth at all."

"I still don't know what you mean by a *picture,*" I said, pushing the cubes around interestedly.

"You don't?" he asked, pursing his lips. "It's rather awkward to explain, but . . . well, on the surface of a piece of paper, you can make a very realistic picture of a cube—you know, with perspective and shading and all that kind of thing—and what you'd actually be doing would be illustrating a three-dimensional object, the cube, by using only two dimensions to do it with."

"And of course," I said, "you could *fold* the paper into a cube. Then you'd have a real cube."

He nodded. "But you'd have to *use* the third dimension—by folding the flat paper *up*—to do it. So, unless I could fold my cubes up through ifth or oofth, my pentaract will have to be just a poor picture. Or, really, eight pictures. Eight tesseracts, pictures of four-dimensional objects, stuck together to make a picture of five dimensions."

"Well!" I said, a bit lost. "And what do you plan to use it for?"

"Just curiosity." And then, abruptly, looking at me now, his eyes grew wide and he bumped up out of his chair. He said breathlessly, "What have you done to it?"

I looked down at my hands. I was holding a little structure of eight cubes, joined together in a small cross. "Why, nothing," I said, feeling a little foolish. "I only folded most of them together."

"That's impossible! There were only twelve open ones to begin with! All of the others were six-sided!"

---

1. *four-dimensional . . . five-dimensional.* Most scientists and philosophers agree to the existence of three dimensions. The first dimension is length; the second is height; and the third is depth. Some people have speculated about the possibility of there being more than three dimensions. Albert Einstein suggested that the fourth dimension might be time. And in this story, Walter Tevis suggests a fifth dimension, "a most peculiar kind of space, one that distorted sizes quite strangely."

Farnsworth made a grab for it, apparently beside himself, and the gesture was so sudden that I drew back. It made Farnsworth miss his grab and the little object flew from my hands and hit the floor, solidly, on one of its corners. There was a slight bump as it hit, and a faint clicking noise, and the thing seemed to crumple in a very peculiar way. And sitting in front of us on the floor was one little one-inch cube, and nothing else.

For at least a full minute, we stared at it. Then I stood up and looked in my chair seat, looked around the floor of the room, even got down on my knees and peered under the chair. Farnsworth was watching me, and when I finished and sat down again, he asked, "No others?"

"No other cubes," I said, "anywhere."

"I was afraid of that." He pointed an unsteady finger at the one cube in front of us. "I suppose they're all in there." Some of his agitation had begun to wear off—you can, I suppose, get used to anything—and after a moment he said thoughtfully, "What was that you said about folding the paper to make a cube?"

I looked at him and managed an apologetic smile. I had been thinking the same thing. "What was that *you* said about having to go into another dimension to do it?"

He didn't smile back, but he got up and said, "Well, I doubt if it can bite," and bent over and picked the cube up, hefting its weight carefully in his hand. "It seems to weigh the same as the—sixty-four did," he said, quite calmly now. Then he looked at it closely and suddenly became agitated again. "Good heavens! Look at this!" He held it up. On one side, exactly in the center, was a neat little hole, about a half-inch across.

I moved my head closer to the cube and saw that the hole was not really circular. It was like the iris diaphragm of a camera, a polygon made of many overlapping, straight pieces of metal, allowing an opening for light to enter. Nothing was visible through the hole; I could see only an undefined blackness.

"I don't understand how . . ." I began, and stopped.

"Nor I," he said. "Let's see if there's anything in here."

He put the cube up to his eye and squinted and peered for a minute. Then he carefully set it on the table, walked to his chair, sat down and folded his hands over his fat little lap.

"George," he said, "there *is* something in there." His voice now was very steady and yet strange.

"What?" I asked. What else do you say?

"A little ball," he said. "A little round ball. Quite misted over, but nonetheless a ball."

"Well!" I said.

"George, I'll get the gin."

He was back from the sideboard in what seemed an incredibly short time. He had the sloe gin in highball glasses, with ice and water. It tasted horrible.

When I finished mine, I said, "Delicious. Let's have another," and we did. After I drank that one, I felt a good deal more rational.

I set my glass down. "Farnsworth, it just occurred to me. Isn't the fourth dimension supposed to be *time,* according to Einstein?"

He had finished his second sloe gin highball, unmulled, by then. "Supposed to be, yes, according to Einstein. I call it ifth—or oofth—take your pick." He held up the cube again, much more confidently now, I noticed. "And what about the *fifth* dimension?"

"Beats me," I said, looking at the cube, which was beginning to seem vaguely sinister to me. "Beats the hell out of me."

"Beats me, too, George," he said almost gaily—an astonishing mood for old Farnsworth. He turned the cube around with his small, fat fingers. "This is probably all wrapped up in time in some strange way. Not to mention the very peculiar kind of space it appears to be involved with. Extraordinary, don't you think?"

"Extraordinary," I nodded.

"George, I think I'll take another look." And he put the cube back to his eye again. "Well," he said, after a moment of squinting, "same little ball."

"What's it doing?" I wanted to know.

"Nothing. Or perhaps spinning a bit. I'm not sure. It's quite fuzzy, you see, and misty. Dark in there, too."

"Let me see," I said, realizing that, after all, if Farnsworth could see the thing in there, so could I.

"In a minute. I wonder what sort of time I'm looking into—past or future, or what?"

"And what sort of space . . ." I was saying when, suddenly, little Farnsworth let out a fantastic shriek, dropped the cube as if it had suddenly turned into a snake, and threw his hands over his eyes.

He sank back into his chair and cried, "My God! My God!"

I was apprehensive when the cube hit the floor, but nothing happened to it. It did not fold up into no cube at all, nor proliferate back into sixty-four of itself.

"What happened?" I asked, rushing over to Farnsworth, who was squirming about in his armchair, his face still hidden by his hands.

"My eye!" he moaned, almost sobbing. "It stabbed my eye! Quick, George, call me an ambulance!"

I hurried to the telephone and fumbled with the book, looking for the right number, until Farnsworth said, "Quick, George!" again and, in desperation, I dialed the operator and told her to send us an ambulance.

When I got back to Farnsworth, he had taken his hand from the unhurt eye and I could see that a trickle of blood was beginning to run down the other wrist. He had almost stopped squirming, but from his face it was obvious that the pain was still quite intense.

He stood up. "I need another drink," he said, and began heading unsteadily for the sideboard, when he stepped on the cube, which was still lying in front of his chair, and was barely able to keep himself from falling headlong, tripping on it. The cube skidded a few feet, stopping, hole-side up, near the fire.

He said to the cube, enraged, "Drat you, I'll show you . . . !" and he reached down and swooped up the poker from the hearth. It had been lying there for mulling drinks, its end resting on the coals, and by now it was a brilliant cherry red. He took the handle with both hands and plunged the red-hot tip into the hole of the cube, pushing it down against the floor.

"I'll show you!" he yelled again, and I watched understandingly as he shoved with all his weight, pushing and twisting, forcing the poker down with angry energy. There was a faint hissing sound and little wisps of dark smoke came from the hole, around the edges of the poker.

Then there was a strange, sucking noise and the poker began to sink into the cube. It must have gone in at least eight or ten inches— completely impossible, of course, since it was a one-inch cube—and even Farnsworth became so alarmed at this that he abruptly yanked the poker out of the hole.

As he did, black smoke arose in a little column for a moment and then there was a popping sound and the cube fell apart, scattering itself into hundreds of little squares of plastic and aluminum.

Oddly enough, there were no burn marks on the aluminum and none of the plastic seemed to have melted. There was no sign of a little, misty ball.

Farnsworth returned his right hand to his now puffy and quite bloody eye. He stood staring at the profusion of little squares with his good eye. His free hand was trembling.

Then there was the sound of a siren, becoming louder. He turned and looked at me balefully. "That must be the ambulance. I suppose I'd better get my toothbrush."

Farnsworth lost the eye. Within a week, though, he was pretty much his old chipper self again, looking quite dapper with a black leather patch. One interesting thing—the doctor remarked that there were powder burns of some sort on the eyelid, and that the eye itself appeared to have been destroyed by a small explosion. He assumed that it had been a case of a gun misfiring, the cartridge exploding in an open breech somehow. Farnsworth let him think that; it was as good an explanation as any.

I suggested to Farnsworth that he ought to get a green patch, to match his other eye. He laughed at the idea and said he thought it might be a bit showy. He was already starting work on another pentaract; he was going to find out just what . . .

But he never finished. Nine days after the accident, there was a sudden flurry of news reports from the other side of the world, fantastic stories that made the Sunday supplements go completely mad with delight, and we began to guess what had happened. There wouldn't be any need to build the sixty-four-cube cross and try to find a way of folding it up. We knew now.

It *had* been a five-dimensional cube, all right. And one extension of it had been in time—into the future; nine days into the future—and the other extension had been into a most peculiar kind of space, one that distorted sizes quite strangely.

All of this became obvious when, three days later, it happened on our side of the world and the Sunday supplements were scooped by the phenomenon itself, which, by its nature, required no newspaper reporting.

Across the entire sky of the Western Hemisphere there appeared— so vast that it eclipsed the direct light of the sun from Fairbanks, Alaska, to Cape Horn—a tremendous human eye, with a vast, glistening, green pupil. Part of the lid was there, too, and all of it was as if framed in a gigantic circle. Or not exactly a circle, but a polygon of many sides, like the iris diaphragm of a camera shutter.

Toward nightfall, the eye blinked once and probably five hundred million people screamed simultaneously. It remained there all of the night, glowing balefully in the reflected sunlight, obliterating the stars.

A thousand new religious cults were formed that night, and a thousand old ones proclaimed the day as The One Predicted for Centuries.

Probably more than half the people on Earth thought it was God. Only two knew that it was Oliver Farnsworth, peering at a misty little spinning ball in a five-dimensional box, nine days before, totally unaware that the little ball was the Earth itself, contained in a little one-inch cube that was an enclave of swollen time and shrunken space.

When I had dropped the pentaract and had somehow caused it to fold itself into two new dimensions, it had reached out through fifth-dimensional space and folded the world into itself, and had begun accelerating the time within it, in rough proportion to size, so that as each minute passed in Farnsworth's study, about one day was passing on the world within the cube.

We knew this because about a minute had passed while Farnsworth had held his eye against the cube the second time—the first time had, of course, been the appearance over Asia—and nine days later, when we saw the same event from our position on the Earth in the cube, it was twenty-six hours before the eye was "stabbed" and withdrew.

It happened early in the morning, just after the sun had left the horizon and was passing into eclipse behind the great circle that contained the eye. Someone stationed along a defense-perimeter station panicked—someone highly placed. Fifty guided missiles were launched, straight up, the most powerful on Earth. Each carried a hydrogen warhead. Even before the great shock wave from their explosion came crashing down to Earth, the eye had disappeared.

Somewhere, I knew, an unimaginably vast Oliver Farnsworth was squirming and yelping, carrying out the identical chain of events that I had seen happening in the past and that yet must be happening now, along the immutable space-time continuum that Farnsworth's little cube had somehow by-passed.

The doctor had talked of powder burns. I wondered what he would think if he knew that Farnsworth had been hit in the eye with fifty infinitesimal hydrogen bombs.

For a week, there was nothing else to talk about in the world. Two billion people probably discussed, thought about and dreamed of nothing else. There had been no more dramatic happening since the creation of the Earth and sun than the appearance of Farnsworth's eye.

But two people, out of those two billion, thought of something else. They thought of the unchangeable, preset space-time continuum, moving at the rate of one minute for every day that passed here on our side of the pentaract, while that vast Oliver Farnsworth and I, in the other-space, other-time, were staring at the cube that contained our world, lying on their floor.

On Wednesday, we could say, *Now he's gone to the telephone.* On Thursday, *Now he's looking through the book.* On Saturday, *By now he must be dialing the operator . . .*

And on Tuesday morning, when the sun came up, we were together and saw it rise, for we spent our nights together by then, because we had lost the knack of sleeping and did not want to be alone; and when the day had begun, we didn't say it, because we couldn't. But we thought it.

We thought of a colossal, cosmic Farnsworth saying, "I'll show you!" and shoving, pushing and twisting, forcing with all of his might, into the little round hole, a brilliantly glowing, hissing, smoking, red-hot poker.

ELECTRONIC TAPE FOUND IN A BOTTLE

Olga Cabral

If this small human testament
completes its odyssey[1]
clears the curtains of fiery meteors
crosses the rages of magnetic storms
5   rides free of hydrogen whirlwinds
falls through coalsack eternities
lands smoothly on the Milky Way
glides along its lightband
to the shores of an unknown planet
10   in an unknown star-continent
to be found and wonderingly
pondered held in your hands—
this message was meant for you.

Be advised that I lived on
15   a small green ball in the suburbs
of an unremarkable sun
that had begun to run down.
Our race was a sun-people
but died of diseases called wars.
20   To you out there in star cities
with your libraries, fountains
or you who are still making it
through ice ages of ignorance—
whoever or whatever you are
25   here is earth's final message:
I love you I love you I love you.

There is nothing more to say
there is nothing better here
and nothing in all the spiraling nebulae
30   was as frail or as mighty as this.

"Electronic Tape Found In a Bottle" by Olga Cabral. Copyright © Olga Cabral Kurtz. Reprinted by permission of the author.

1. *odyssey.* In Homer's epic poem the *Odyssey*, the hero wanders the seas for ten years in his attempt to return home from the Trojan War. Today any long and arduous trip may be referred to as an odyssey.

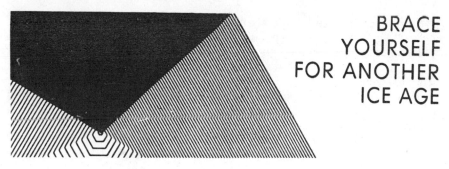

BRACE
YOURSELF
FOR ANOTHER
ICE AGE

Douglas Colligan

FIFTEEN YEARS AGO Dr. Cesare Emiliani, a noted American geologist. looked to the bottom of the sea and came to a startling conclusion Conditions were right for the beginning of another Ice Age in about ten thousand years. A few months ago he changed his mind and declared that after even further study he found "that the present episode of amiable climate is coming to an end," and an Ice Age could be just centuries away.

The idea of another Ice Age is not a new one, but recently scientists like Dr. Emiliani have been confronted with the possibility that it may be much sooner than anyone thought.

Professor of Geology in the Rosenstiel School of Marine and Atmospheric Science at the University of Miami, Dr. Emiliani is not only concerned about the end of our present era of temperate global climate, but he is also worried about how man's tampering with the environment affects when and how it ends.

His conclusions on the coming of the ice are based on findings in direct conflict with the classical description of the Pleistocene, or Glacial Epoch, better known as the Ice Age. Most geologists have believed that in the beginning of the Quaternary, the geological term for the last million years of the Earth's development, the Pleistocene Epoch began. This Ice Age consisted of four glacial stages, each lasting approximately 100,000 years and each interrupted by warm interglacial periods at least 100,000 years long.

The last glacial period ended between ten and twelve thousand years ago and what we are now enjoying is a fourth interglacial period of warmth which, in view of the estimated lengths of previous interglacials, could last at least 100,000 years.

This opinion was long upheld by scientists as the most plausible description of the cooler periods on Earth and it was this concept that Dr. Emiliani first questioned eighteen years ago. In a paper published in the *Journal of Geology* in 1955, Emiliani disclosed that after examining twelve core samples of sediment from the bottom of the

"Brace Yourself for Another Ice Age" by Douglas Colligan. Reprinted with permission of *Science Digest.* © The Hearst Corp.; February 1973. All Rights Reserved.

Atlantic, Pacific and Caribbean, he charted temperature fluctuations that did not at all correspond to the classical profile. Instead of four periods of cold described in the textbooks, he found seven, with six intermediate periods of warmth, none of which was anywhere near 100,000 years long.

He explains in his report why he turned to the sea for information on the past: "The deep sea is generally thought of as an environment in which sedimentation is largely continuous and undisturbed. When this is true, the deep-sea sediments furnish a continuous record of conditions in the different environments contributing to the sediments themselves."

. . . Since then, Emiliani has done further studies and reports, each yielding more detailed information than its predecessor but none contradicting the findings of the first. "The intervals of temperatures as high as the present ones," he wrote most recently, "far from lasting 100,000 years or more, now appear to be short, wholly exceptional episodes in the environmental evolution of the Quaternary."

How much longer this "exceptional episode" of warmth will last no one knows, but it was of sufficient concern to the world's experts on climatology to meet early last year and pool their knowledge and skills in an attempt to find out. One of the conclusions of the meeting was that the end of the present interglacial period is due "soon." *Soon* in the context of the world's geological time scale could mean anything from two centuries to two thousand years, but not within the lifetime of anyone now alive.

Scientists have detected some clues that indicate the next change is toward another Ice Age and cite some natural events as warning signs:

There has been a global cooling since the 1940's reversing a temperature climb that began at the turn of the century.

• Baffin Island, located in the Canadian Arctic, now is covered with snowbanks all year after having been snowfree for thirty or forty years prior to the temperature drop.

• Pack ice around Iceland has now become a serious hindrance to navigation.

• Warmth-loving animals once found in abundance in the northern part of the American Midwest in the early 1900's are settling further south. The armadillo is only one.

On a day-to-day basis this global cooling will be imperceptible; more likely winter will lengthen year by year, century by century, until it's 365 days long. Cities will be buried in snow and an immense sheet of ice could cover North America as far south as Cincinnati.

As the icecaps of Greenland and the Antarctic grow so will the reflective quality of snow and ice, bouncing back the warm rays of the sun, cooling the Earth as they move. Eventually all the available moisture will have crystallized into ice and snow and the growth of the glaciers will stop. The world's sea level will have dropped a few hundred feet, over one-quarter of the Earth's land surface will be smothered in ice and the temperature around the equator will be cool and damp, but livable.

This is a typical projection of an Ice Age, and is what scientists now expect to happen given the past patterns of glacials and interglacials. There is one important influence present today—man—that may change this picture.

"Man is doing things," says Emiliani, "such as industrial pollution and deforestation that have effects on the environment." Emiliani and his fellow scientists do not know where these effects will lead. It seems as though they are still being contained by nature but just how long the environment can withstand man's tampering is uncertain.

"If the present climatic balance is not maintained," Emiliani warns, "we may soon be confronted with either a runaway glaciation or a runaway deglaciation." A runaway glaciation would simply be a speeding up of the ice takeover already described. This could be helped along by massive air pollution in the form of smog which would shade the Earth from the heat of the sun and accelerate the cooling process.

Runaway deglaciation would be the result of a man-caused global heat wave. This would not have to be spectacular, for scientists estimate that a rise in the Earth's annual temperature of 3.5° C. (6.3° F.) would be sufficient to melt the nine million cubic miles of ice covering Greenland and the Antarctic in just a few centuries. This would raise the world's sea level, flooding every coastal city.

Man may be contributing to this process by pouring carbon dioxide into the atmosphere from smokestacks and chimneys. "Scientists seem to think that a little more carbon dioxide in the atmosphere could warm things up a good deal," David Ericson explains. "Then you get the so-called 'greenhouse' effect which means that the energy comes in as light waves and is trapped as heat waves."

There is a third possible result man might cause: none at all. As Emiliani and others point out, man's detrimental effects may cancel each other out. The smog-induced cooling may be offset by the carbon dioxide greenhouse.

Which way these influences will tip the balance of weather is uncertain but we must try to find out, Emiliani stresses. "Some studies have to be started to obtain a quantitative assessment of their net effect."

At this point, the world's climatologists are agreed on only two things: that we do not have the comfortable distance of tens of thousands of years to prepare for the next ice age, and that how carefully we monitor our atmospheric pollution will have direct bearing on the arrival and nature of this weather crisis. The sooner man confronts these facts, these scientists say, the safer he'll be. Once the freeze starts, it will be too late.

8

FUTURE
REVIEWED

THE
CENSUS
TAKERS

Frederik Pohl

IT GETS TO BE A MADHOUSE AROUND HERE along about the end of the first week. Thank heaven we only do this once a year, that's what I say! Six weeks on, and forty-six weeks off—that's pretty good hours, most people think. But they don't know what those six weeks are like.

It's bad enough for the field crews, but when you get to be an Area Boss like me it's frantic. You work your way up through the ranks, and then they give you a whole C.A. of your own; and you think you've got it made. Fifty three-man crews go out, covering the whole Census Area; a hundred and fifty men in the field, and twenty or thirty more in Area Command—and you boss them all. And everything looks great, until Census Period starts and you've got to work those hundred and fifty men; and six weeks is too unbearably long to live through, and too impossibly short to get the work done; and you begin living on black coffee and thiamin shots and dreaming about the vacation hostel on Point Loma.

Anybody can panic, when the pressure is on like that. Your best field men begin to crack up. But you can't afford to, because you're the Area Boss. . . .

Take Witeck. We were Enumerators together, and he was as good a man as you ever saw, absolutely nerveless when it came to processing the Overs. I counted on that man the way I counted on my own right arm; I always bracketed him with the greenest, shakiest new cadet Enumerators, and he never gave me a moment's trouble for years. Maybe it was too good to last; maybe I should have figured he would crack.

I set up my Area Command in a plush penthouse apartment. The people who lived there were pretty well-off, you know, and they naturally raised the dickens about being shoved out. "Blow it," I told them. "Get out of here in five minutes, and we'll count you first." Well, that took care of *that;* they were practically kissing my feet on the way out. Of course, it wasn't strictly by the book, but you have to be a little flexible; that's why some men become Area Bosses, and others stay Enumerators.

Like Witeck.

Along about Day Eight things were really hotting up. I was up to my

"The Census Takers" by Frederik Pohl. © 1955 by Mercury Press, Inc. Reprinted from The Magazine of *Fantasy and Science Fiction* by permission of the author.

neck in hurry-ups from Regional Control—we were running a little slow—when Witeck called up. "Chief," he said, "I've got an In."

I grabbed the rotary file with one hand and a pencil with the other. "Blue card number?" I asked.

Witeck sounded funny over the phone. "Well, Chief," he said, "he doesn't have a blue card. He says——"

"No blue card?" I couldn't believe it. Come in to a strange C.A. without a card from your own Area Boss, and you're one In that's a cinch to be an Over. "What kind of a crazy C.A. does he come from, without a blue card?"

Witeck said, "He don't come from any C.A., Chief. He says——"

"You mean he isn't from this country?"

"That's right, Chief. He——"

"Hold it!" I pushed away the rotary file and grabbed the immigration roster. There were only a couple of dozen names on it, of course—we have enough trouble with our own Overs, without taking on a lot of foreigners, but still there were a handful every year who managed to get on the quotas. "I.D. number?" I demanded.

"Well, Chief," Witeck began, "he doesn't have an I.D. number. The way it looks to me——"

Well, you can fool around with these irregulars for a month, if you want to, but it's no way to get the work done. I said, "Over him!" and hung up. I was a little surprised, though; Witeck knew the ropes, and it wasn't like him to buck an irregular onto me. In the old days, when we were both starting out, I'd seen him Over a whole family just because the spelling of their names on their registry cards was different from the spelling on the checklist.

But we get older. I made a note to talk to Witeck as soon as the rush was past. We were old friends; I wouldn't have to threaten him with being Overed himself, or anything like that. He'd know, and maybe that would be all he would need to snap him back. I certainly would talk to him, I promised myself, as soon as the rush was over, or anyway as soon as I got back from Point Loma.

I had to run up to Regional Control to take a little talking-to myself just then, but I proved to them that we were catching up and they were only medium nasty. When I got back Witeck was on the phone again. "Chief," he said, real unhappy, "this In is giving me a headache. I——"

"Witeck," I snapped at him, "are you bothering me with another In? Can't you handle anything by yourself?"

He said, "It's the same one, Chief. He says he's a kind of ambassador, and——"

"Oh," I said. "Well, why the devil don't you get your facts straight in the first place? Give me his name and I'll check his legation."

"Well, Chief," he began again, "he, uh, doesn't have any legation. He says he's from the"—he swallowed—"from the middle of the Earth."

"You're crazy." I'd seen it happen before, good men breaking under the strain of census taking. They say in cadets that by the time you process your first five hundred Overs you've had it; either you take a voluntary Over yourself, or you split wide open and they carry you off to a giggle farm. And Witeck was past the five hundred mark, way past. There was a lot of yelling and crying from the filter center, which I'd put out by the elevators, and it looked like Jumpers. I stabbed the transfer button on the phone and called to Carias, my number-two man: "Witeck's flipped or something. Handle it!"

And then I forgot about it, while Carias talked to Witeck on the phone; because it was Jumpers, all right, a whole family of them.

There was a father and a mother and five kids—*five* of them. Aren't some people disgusting? The field Enumerator turned them over to the guards—they were moaning and crying—and came up and gave me the story. It was bad.

"You're the head of the household?" I demanded of the man.

He nodded, looking at me like a sick dog. "We—we weren't Jumping," he whined. "Honest to heaven, Mister—you've got to believe me. We were——"

I cut in, "You were packed and on the doorstep when the field crew came by. Right?" He started to say something, but I had him dead to rights. "That's plenty, friend," I told him. "That's Jumping, under the law: Packing, with intent to move, while a census Enumeration crew is operating in your locale. Got anything to say?"

Well, he had plenty to say, but none of it made any sense. He turned my stomach, listening to him. I tried to keep my temper—you're not supposed to think of individuals, no matter how worthless and useless and generally unfit they are; that's against the whole principle of the Census—but I couldn't help telling him: "I've met your kind before, mister. Five kids! If it wasn't for people like you we wouldn't *have* any Overs, did you ever think of that? Sure you didn't—you people never think of anything but yourself! Five kids, and then when Census comes around you think you can get smart and Jump." I tell you, I was shaking. "You keep your little beady eyes peeled, sneaking around, watching the Enumerators, trying to count how many it takes to make an Over; and then you wait until they get close to you, so you can Jump. Ever stop to think what trouble that makes for us?" I demanded. "Census is supposed to be fair and square, everybody an even chance —and how can we make it that way unless everybody stands still to be counted?" I patted Old Betsy on my hip. "I haven't Overed anybody myself in five years," I told him, "but I swear, I'd like to handle you personally!"

He didn't say a word once I got started on him. He just stood there, taking it. I had to force myself to stop, finally; I could have gone on for a long time, because if there's one thing I hate it's these lousy, stinking breeders who try to Jump when they think one of them is going to be an Over in the count-off. Regular Jumpers are bad enough, but when it's the people who make the mess in the first place——

Anyway, time was wasting. I took a deep breath and thought things over. Actually, we weren't too badly off; we'd started off Overing every two-hundred-and-fiftieth person, and it was beginning to look as though our preliminary estimate was high; we'd just cut back to Overing every three-hundredth. So we had a little margin to play with.

I told the man, dead serious; "You know I could Over the lot of you on charges, don't you?" He nodded sickly. "All right, I'll give you a chance. I don't want to bother with the red tape; if you'll take a voluntary Over for yourself, we'll start the new count with your wife."

Call me soft, if you want to; but I still say that it was a lot better than fussing around with charges and a hearing. You get into a hearing like that and it can drag on for half an hour or more; and then Regional Control is on your tail because you're falling behind.

It never hurts to give a man a break, even a Jumper, I always say—as long as it doesn't slow down your Census.

Carias was waiting at my desk when I got back; he looked worried about something, but I brushed him off while I initialed the Overage report on the man we'd just processed. He'd been an In, I found out when I canceled his blue card. I can't say I was surprised. He'd come from Denver, and you know how they keep exceeding their Census figures; no doubt he thought he'd have a better chance in my C.A. than anywhere else. And no doubt he was right, because we certainly don't encourage breeders like him—actually, if he hadn't tried to Jump it was odds-on that the whole damned family would get by without an Over for years. Carias was hovering right behind me as I finished. "I hate these voluntaries," I told him, basketing the canceled card. "I'm going to talk to Regional Control about it; there's no reason why they can't be processed like any other Over, instead of making me okay each one individually. Now, what's the matter?"

He rubbed his jaw. "Chief," he said, "it's Witeck."

"Now what? Another In?"

Carias glanced at me, then away. "Uh, no, Chief. It's the same one. He claims he comes from, uh, the center of the Earth."

I swore out loud. "So he has to turn up in my C.A.!" I complained bitterly. "He gets out of the nuthouse, and right away——"

Carias said, "Chief, he might not be crazy. He makes it sound pretty real."

I said: "Hold it, Carias. Nobody can live in the center of the Earth. It's solid, like a potato."

"Sure, Chief," Carias nodded earnestly. "But he says it isn't. He says there's a what he calls neutronium shell, whatever that is, with dirt and rocks on both sides of it. We live on the outside. He lives on the inside. His people——"

"Carias!" I yelled. "You're as bad as Witeck. This guy turns up, no blue card, no I.D. number, no credentials of any kind. What's he going to say, 'Please sir, I'm an Over, please process me'? Naturally not! So he makes up a crazy story, and you fall for it!"

"I know, Chief," Carias said humbly.

"Neutronium shell!" I would have laughed out loud, if I'd had the time. "Neutronium my foot! Don't you know it's *hot* down there?"

"He says it's hot neutronium," Carias said eagerly. "I asked him that myself, Chief. He said it's just the shell that——"

"Get back to work!" I yelled at him. I picked up the phone and got Witeck on his wristphone. I tell you, I was boiling. As soon as Witeck answered I lit into him; I didn't give him a chance to get a word in. I gave it to him up and down and sidewise; and I finished off by giving him a direct order. "You Over that man," I told him, "or I'll personally Over you! You hear me?"

There was a pause. Then Witeck said, "Jerry? Will you listen to me?"

That stopped me. It was the first time in ten years, since I'd been promoted above him, that Witeck had dared call me by my first name. He said, "Jerry, listen. This is something big. This guy is really from the center of the Earth, no kidding. He——"

"Witeck," I said, "you've cracked."

"No, Jerry, honest! And it worries me. He's right there in the next room, waiting for me. He says he had no idea things were like this on the surface; he's talking wild about cleaning us off and starting all over again; he says——"

"*I* say he's an Over!" I yelled. "No more talk, Witeck. You've got a direct order—now carry it out!"

So that was that. We got through the Census Period after all, but we had to do it short-handed; and Witeck was hard to replace. I'm a sentimentalist, I guess, but I couldn't help remembering old times. We started even; he might have risen as far as I—but of course he made his choice when he got married and had a kid; you can't be a breeder and an officer of the Census both. If it hadn't been for his record he couldn't even have stayed on as an Enumerator.

I never said a word to anyone about his crackup. Carias might have talked, but after we found Witeck's body I took him aside. "Carias," I said reasonably, "we don't want any scandal, do we? Here's Witeck, with an honorable record; he cracks, and kills himself, and that's bad enough. We won't let loose talk make it worse, will we?"

Carias said uneasily, "Chief, where's the gun he killed himself with? His own processor wasn't even fired."

You can let a helper go just so far. I said sharply, "Carias, we still have at least a hundred Overs to process. You can be on one end of the processing—or you can be on the other. You understand me?"

He coughed. "Sure, Chief. I understand. We don't want any loose talk."

And that's how it is when you're an Area Boss. But I didn't ever get my vacation at Point Loma; the tsunami[1] there washed out the whole town the last week of the Census. And when I tried Baja California, they were having that crazy volcanic business; and the Yellowstone Park bureau wouldn't even accept my reservation because of some trouble with the geysers, so I just stayed home. But the best vacation of all was just knowing that the Census was done for another year.

Carias was all for looking for this In that Witeck was talking about, but I turned him down. "Waste of time," I told him. "By now he's a dozen C.A.s away. We'll never see him again, him or anybody like him—I'll bet my life on that." ■

---

1. *tsunami* (sü nä′mē, or tsü nä′mē), a huge, fast-moving ocean wave, started by an undersea earthquake or volcanic eruption.

DISAPPEARING ACT

Alfred Bester

THIS ONE WASN'T THE LAST WAR OR A WAR to end war. They called it the War for the American Dream. General Carpenter struck that note and sounded it constantly.

There are fighting generals (vital to an army), political generals (vital to an administration), and public relations generals (vital to a war). General Carpenter was a master of public relations. Forthright and four-square, he had ideals as high and as understandable as the mottoes on money. In the mind of America he *was* the army, the administration, the nation's shield and sword and stout right arm. His ideal was the American Dream.

"We are not fighting for money, for power, or for world domination," General Carpenter announced at the Press Association dinner.

"We are fighting solely for the American Dream," he said to the 162nd Congress.

"Our aim is not aggression or the reduction of nations to slavery," he said at the West Point Annual Officers' Dinner.

"We are fighting for the Meaning of Civilization," he told the San Francisco Pioneers' Club.

"We are struggling for the Ideal of Civilization; for Culture, for Poetry, for the Only Things Worth Preserving," he said at the Chicago Wheat Pit Festival.

"This is a war for survival," he said. "We are not fighting for ourselves, but for our Dreams; for the Better Things in Life which must not disappear from the face of the Earth."

America fought. General Carpenter asked for one hundred million men. The army was given one hundred million men. General Carpenter asked for ten thousand U-Bombs. Ten thousand U-Bombs were delivered and dropped. The enemy also dropped ten thousand U-Bombs and destroyed most of America's cities.

"We must dig in against the hordes of barbarism," General Carpenter said. "Give me a thousand engineers."

One thousand engineers were forthcoming, and a hundred cities were dug and hollowed out beneath the rubble.

"Give me five hundred sanitation experts, eight hundred traffic managers, two hundred air-conditioning experts, one hundred city

"Disappearing Act" by Alfred Bester. From STAR SCIENCE FICTION STORIES, No. 2, edited by Frederik Pohl. Copyright 1953 by Ballantine Books, Inc. Reprinted by permission of Ballantine Books / A Division of Random House, Inc.

managers, one thousand communication chiefs, seven hundred personnel experts . . ."

The list of General Carpenter's demand for technical experts was endless. America did not know how to supply them.

"We must become a nation of experts," General Carpenter informed the National Association of American Universities. "Every man and woman must be a specific tool for a specific job, hardened and sharpened by your training and education to win the fight for the American Dream."

"Our Dream," General Carpenter said at the Wall Street Bond Drive Breakfast, "is at one with the gentle Greeks of Athens, with the noble Romans of . . . er . . . Rome. It is a dream of the Better Things in Life. Of Music and Art and Poetry and Culture. Money is only a weapon to be used in the fight for this dream. Ambition is only a ladder to climb to this dream. Ability is only a tool to shape this dream."

Wall Street applauded. General Carpenter asked for one hundred and fifty billion dollars, fifteen hundred dedicated dollar-a-year men, three thousand experts in mineralogy, petrology, mass production, chemical warfare and air-traffic time study. They were delivered. The country was in high gear. General Carpenter had only to press a button and an expert would be delivered.

In March of A.D. 2112 the war came to a climax and the American Dream was resolved, not on any one of the seven fronts where millions of men were locked in bitter combat, not in any of the staff headquarters or any of the capitals of the warring nations, not in any of the production centers spewing forth arms and supplies, but in Ward T of the United States Army Hospital buried three hundred feet below what had once been St. Albans, New York.

Ward T was something of a mystery at St. Albans. Like all army hospitals, St. Albans was organized with specific wards reserved for specific injuries. Right arm amputees were gathered in one ward; left arm amputees in another. Radiation burns, head injuries, eviscerations, secondary gamma poisonings and so on were each assigned their specific location in the hospital organization. The Army Medical Corps had established nineteen classes of combat injury which included every possible kind of damage to brain and tissue. These used up letters A to S. What, then, was in Ward T?

No one knew. The doors were double locked. No visitors were permitted to enter. No patients were permitted to leave. Physicians were seen to arrive and depart. Their perplexed expressions stimulated the wildest speculations but revealed nothing. The nurses who ministered to Ward T were questioned eagerly but they were close-mouthed.

There were dribs and drabs of information, unsatisfying and self-contradictory. A charwoman asserted that she had been in to clean up and there had been no one in the ward. Absolutely no one. Just two dozen beds and nothing else. Had the beds been slept in? Yes. They were rumpled, some of them. Were there signs of the ward being in use? Oh yes. Personal things on the tables and so on. But dusty, kind of. Like they hadn't been used in a long time.

Public opinion decided it was a ghost ward. For spooks only.

But a night orderly reported passing the locked ward and hearing singing from within. What kind of singing? Foreign language, like. What language? The orderly couldn't say. Some of the words sounded like . . . well, like: Cow dee on us eager tour . . .

Public opinion started to run a fever and decided it was an alien ward. For spies only.

St. Albans enlisted the help of the kitchen staff and checked the food trays. Twenty-four trays went into Ward T three times a day. Twenty-four came out. Sometimes the returning trays were emptied. Most times they were untouched.

Public opinion built up pressure and decided that Ward T was a racket. It was an informal club for goldbricks and staff grafters who caroused within. Cow dee on us eager tour indeed!

For gossip, a hospital can put a small town sewing circle to shame with ease, but sick people are easily goaded into passion by trivia. It took just three months for idle speculation to turn into downright fury. In January 2112, St. Albans was a sound, well-run hospital. By March 2112, St. Albans was in a ferment, and the psychological unrest found its way into the official records. The percentage of recoveries fell off. Malingering set in. Petty infractions increased. Mutinies flared. There was a staff shake-up. It did no good. Ward T was inciting the patients to riot. There was another shake-up, and another, and still the unrest fumed.

The news finally reached General Carpenter's desk through official channels.

"In our fight for the American Dream," he said, "we must not ignore those who have already given of themselves. Send me a Hospital Administration expert."

The expert was delivered. He could do nothing to heal St. Albans. General Carpenter read the reports and fired him.

"Pity," said General Carpenter, "is the first ingredient of civilization. Send me a Surgeon General."

A Surgeon General was delivered. He could not break the fury of St. Albans and General Carpenter broke him. But by this time Ward T was being mentioned in the dispatches.

"Send me," General Carpenter said, "the expert in charge of Ward T."

St. Albans sent a doctor, Captain Edsel Dimmock. He was a stout young man, already bald, only three years out of medical school but with a fine record as an expert in psychotherapy. General Carpenter liked experts. He liked Dimmock. Dimmock adored the general as the spokesman for a culture which he had been too specially trained to seek up to now, but which he hoped to enjoy after the war was won.

"Now look here, Dimmock," General Carpenter began. "We're all of us tools today—hardened and sharpened to do a specific job. You know our motto: A job for everyone and everyone on the job. Somebody's not on the job at Ward T and we've got to kick him out. Now, in the first place what the hell is Ward T?"

Dimmock stuttered and fumbled. Finally he explained that it was a special ward set up for special combat cases. Shock cases.

"Then you do have patients in the ward?"

"Yes, sir. Ten women and fourteen men."

Carpenter brandished a sheaf of reports. "Says here the St. Albans patients claim nobody's in Ward T."

Dimmock was shocked. That was untrue, he assured the general.

"All right, Dimmock. So you've got your twenty-four crocks in there. Their job's to get well. Your job's to cure them. What the hell's upsetting the hospital about that?"

"W-well, sir. Perhaps it's because we keep them locked up."

"You keep Ward T locked?"

"Yes, sir."

"Why?"

"To keep the patients in, General Carpenter."

"Keep 'em in? What d'you mean? Are they trying to get out? They violent, or something?"

"No, sir. Not violent."

"Dimmock, I don't like your attitude. You're acting damned sneaky and evasive. And I'll tell you something else I don't like. That T classification. I checked with a Filing Expert from the Medical Corps and there is no T classification. What the hell are you up to at St. Albans?"

"W-well, sir . . . we invented the T classification. It . . . They . . . They're rather special cases, sir. We don't know what to do about them or how to handle them. W-we've been trying to keep it quiet until we've worked out a modus operandi,[1] but it's brand new, General Carpenter. Brand new!" Here the expert in Dimmock triumphed over discipline. "It's sensational. It'll make medical history. . . ."

"What is it, Dimmock? Be specific."

"Well, sir, they're shock cases. Blanked out. Almost catatonic. Very little respiration. Slow pulse. No response."

"I've seen thousands of shock cases like that," Carpenter grunted. "What's so unusual?"

"Yes, sir, so far it sounds like the standard Q or R classification. But here's something unusual. They don't eat and they don't sleep."

"Never?"

"Some of them never."

"Then why don't they die?"

"We don't know. The metabolism cycle's broken, but only on the anabolism side. Catabolism continues. In other words, sir, they're eliminating waste products but they're not taking anything in. They're eliminating fatigue poisons and rebuilding worn tissue, but without food and sleep. God knows how. It's fantastic."

"That why you've got them locked up? Mean to say . . . d'you suspect them of stealing food and cat naps somewhere else?"

"N-no, sir." Dimmock looked shamefaced. "I don't know how to tell

---

1. *modus operandi,* a Latin expression meaning "a method of operating."

you this, General Carpenter. I . . . We lock them up because of the real mystery. They . . . well, they disappear."

"They what?"

"They disappear, sir. Vanish. Right before your eyes."

"The hell you say."

"I do say, sir. They'll be sitting on a bed or standing around. One minute you see them, the next minute you don't. Sometimes there's two dozen in Ward T. Other times none. They disappear and reappear without rhyme or reason. That's why we've got the ward locked, General Carpenter. In the entire history of combat and combat injury there's never been a case like this before. We don't know how to handle it."

"Bring me three of those cases," General Carpenter said.

Nathan Riley ate French toast, eggs benedict, consumed two pints of brown ale, smoked a John Drew, belched delicately and arose from the breakfast table. He nodded quietly to Gentleman Jim Corbett, who broke off his conversation with Diamond Jim Brady[2] to intercept him on the way to the cashier's desk.

"Who do you like for the pennant this year, Nat?" Gentleman Jim inquired.

"The Dodgers," Nathan Riley answered.

"They've got no pitching."

"They've got Snider and Furillo and Campanella.[3] They'll take the pennant this year, Jim. I'll bet they take it earlier than any team ever did. By September 13.[4] Make a note. See if I'm right."

"You're always right, Nat," Corbett said.

Riley smiled, paid his check, sauntered out into the street and caught a horsecar bound for Madison Square Garden. He got off at the corner of Fiftieth Street and Eighth Avenue and walked upstairs to a handbook office over a radio repair shop. The bookie glanced at him, produced an envelope and counted out fifteen thousand dollars.

"Rocky Marciano by a TKO over Roland La Starza in the eleventh,"[5] he said. "How the hell do you call them so accurate, Nat?"

"That's the way I make a living," Riley smiled. "Are you making book on the elections?"

"Eisenhower twelve to five. Stevenson[6]——"

"Never mind Adlai." Riley placed twenty thousand dollars on the counter. "I'm backing Ike. Get this down for me."

He left the handbook office and went to his suite in the Waldorf where a tall, thin young man was waiting for him anxiously.

---

2. *Gentleman Jim Corbett . . . Diamond Jim Brady.* Corbett was world champion of heavyweight boxing from 1892 to 1897. Brady (1856-1917) was a financier and stock-market speculator, famous for big betting on sports. 3. *Snider and Furillo and Campanella.* These baseball stars played together with the Brooklyn Dodgers between 1946 and 1957. 4. *By September 13.* In 1955, Brooklyn clinched the pennant on September 8 to set a record. 5. *Rocky Marciano . . . in the eleventh.* Marciano, heavyweight boxing champion (1952-1956), defeated La Starza in the eleventh round of their title fight in 1953. 6. *Eisenhower . . . Stevenson.* In 1952 and 1956 Adlai Stevenson, then governor of Illinois, ran for President against General Dwight D. Eisenhower, nicknamed "Ike." Eisenhower won both elections.

"Oh yes," Nathan Riley said. "You're Ford, aren't you? Harold Ford?"

"Henry Ford,[7] Mr. Riley."

"And you need financing for that machine in your bicycle shop. What's it called?"

"I call it an Ipsimobile, Mr. Riley."

"Hmmm. Can't say I like that name. Why not call it an automobile?"

"That's a wonderful suggestion, Mr. Riley. I'll certainly take it."

"I like you, Henry. You're young, eager, adaptable. I believe in your future and I believe in your automobile. I'll invest two hundred thousand dollars in your company."

Riley wrote a check and ushered Henry Ford out. He glanced at his watch and suddenly felt impelled to go back and look around for a moment. He entered his bedroom, undressed, put on a gray shirt and gray slacks. Across the pocket of the shirt were large blue letters: U.S.A.H.

He locked the bedroom door and disappeared.

He reappeared in Ward T of the United States Army Hospital in St. Albans, standing alongside his bed which was one of twenty-four lining the walls of a long, light steel barracks. Before he could draw another breath, he was seized by three pairs of hands. Before he could struggle, he was shot by a pneumatic syringe and poleaxed by $1\frac{1}{2}$ cc of sodium thiomorphate.

"We've got one," someone said.

"Hang around," someone else answered. "General Carpenter said he wanted three."

Lela Machan clapped her hands. Her slave women entered the chamber and prepared her bath. She bathed, dressed, scented herself and breakfasted on Smyrna figs, Rose oranges and a flagon of Lachryma Christi. Then she smoked a cigarette and ordered her litter.[8]

The gates of her house were crowded as usual by adoring hordes from the Twentieth Legion.[9] Two centurions removed her chairbearers from the poles of the litter and bore her on their stout shoulders. Lela Machan smiled. A young man in a sapphire-blue cloak thrust through the mob and ran toward her. A knife flashed in his hand. Lela braced herself to meet death bravely.

"Lady!" he cried. "Lady Lela!"

He slashed his left arm with the knife and let the crimson blood stain her robe.

"This blood of mine is the least I have to give you," he cried.

Lela touched his forehead gently.

"Silly boy," she murmured. "Why?"

"For love of you, my lady."

---

7. *Henry Ford* (1863-1947). In 1903 Ford, who was already a successful engineer in Detroit, founded the Ford Motor Company, the first company to use mass-production methods to make cars at low cost. 8. *litter*, a couch covered by a roof and curtains, and carried on long poles. 9. *Twentieth Legion*. A legion made up of four to six thousand footsoldiers was the main division in the army of the Roman Empire.

"You will be admitted tonight at nine," Lela whispered. He stared at her until she laughed. "I promise you. What is your name, pretty boy?"

"Ben Hur."[10]

"Tonight at nine, Ben Hur."

The litter moved on. Outside the forum, Julius Caesar passed in hot argument with Savonarola.[11] When he saw the litter he motioned sharply to the centurions, who stopped at once. Caesar swept back the curtains and stared at Lela, who regarded him languidly. Caesar's face twitched.

"Why?" he asked hoarsely. "I have begged, pleaded, bribed, wept, and all without forgiveness. Why, Lela? Why?"

"Do you remember Boadicea?"[12] Lela murmured.

"Boadicea? Queen of the Britons? Good God, Lela, what can she mean to our love? I did not love Boadicea. I merely defeated her in battle."

"And killed her, Caesar."

"She poisoned herself, Lela."

"She was my mother, Caesar!" Suddenly Lela pointed her finger at Caesar. "Murderer. You will be punished. Beware the Ides of March,[13] Caesar!"

Caesar recoiled in horror. The mob of admirers that had gathered around Lela uttered a shout of approval. Amidst a shower of rose petals and violets she continued on her way across the forum to the Temple of the Vestal Virgins where she abandoned her adoring suitors and entered the sacred temple.

Before the altar she genuflected, intoned a prayer, dropped a pinch of incense on the altar flame and disrobed. She . . . then experienced a momentary twinge of homesickness. She put on a gray blouse and a gray pair of slacks. Across the pocket of the blouse was lettered U.S.A.H.

She smiled once at the altar and disappeared.

She reappeared in Ward T of the United States Army Hospital where she was instantly felled by 1¹/₂ cc of sodium thiomorphate injected subcutaneously by a pneumatic syringe.

"That's two," somebody said.

"One more to go."

George Hanmer paused dramatically and stared around . . . at the opposition benches, at the Speaker on the woolsack, at the silver mace on a crimson cushion before the Speaker's chair. The entire House of Parliament, hypnotized by Hanmer's fiery oratory, waited breathlessly for him to continue.

---

10. *Ben Hur,* the fictional hero of Lew Wallace's novel, *Ben Hur,* published in 1880. It is set in the time of Christ. 11. *Julius Caesar . . . Savonarola.* Caesar (100-44 B.C.) was a Roman general and dictator, who invaded Britain briefly in 55 and 54 B.C. Girolamo Savonarola was a fifteenth-century Italian religious reformer. 12. *Boadicea* (bō ad'i sē'ə), a queen of Celtic tribes in Britain, who revolted against Roman colonial oppression. After her defeat by Suetonius Paullinus, she poisoned herself in 62 A.D. 13. *Beware the Ides of March.* The phrase, from Shakespeare's play *Julius Caesar,* is the warning reportedly spoken to Caesar by an old blind prophet. On March 15, the Ides of March, Caesar was assassinated.

"I can say no more," Hanmer said at last. His voice was choked with emotion. His face was blanched and grim. "I will fight for this bill at the beachheads. I will fight in the cities, the towns, the fields and the hamlets. I will fight for this bill to the death and, God willing, I will fight for it after death. Whether this be a challenge or a prayer, let the consciences of the right honorable gentlemen determine; but of one thing I am sure and determined: England must own the Suez Canal."[14]

Hanmer sat down. The house exploded. Through the cheering and applause he made his way out into the division lobby where Gladstone, Churchill and Pitt[15] stopped him to shake his hand. Lord Palmerston eyed him coldly, but Pam was shouldered aside by Disraeli[16] who limped up, all enthusiasm, all admiration.

"We'll have a bite at Tattersall's," Dizzy said. "My car's waiting."

Lady Beaconsfield[17] was in the Rolls Royce outside the Houses of Parliament. She pinned a primrose on Dizzy's lapel and patted Hanmer's cheek affectionately. "You've come a long way from the schoolboy who used to bully Dizzy, Georgie," she said.

Hanmer laughed. Dizzy sang: *"Gaudeamus igitur . . ."*[18] and Hanmer chanted the ancient scholastic song until they reached Tattersall's. There Dizzy ordered Guinness and grilled bones while Hanmer went upstairs in the club to change.

For no reason at all he had the impulse to go back for a last look. Perhaps he hated to break with his past completely. He divested himself of his surtout, nankeen waistcoat, pepper and salt trousers, polished Hessians and undergarments. He put on a gray shirt and gray trousers and disappeared.

He reappeared in Ward T of the St. Albans hospital where he was rendered unconscious by $1^{1}/_{2}$ cc of sodium thiomorphate.

"That's three," somebody said.

"Take 'em to Carpenter."

So there they sat in General Carpenter's office, pfc Nathan Riley, M/Sgt Lela Machan, and Corp/2 George Hanmer. They were in their hospital grays. They were torpid with sodium thiomorphate.

The office had been cleared and it blazed with light. Present were experts from Espionage, Counter-Espionage, Security and Central Intelligence. When Captain Edsel Dimmock saw the steel-faced ruthless squad awaiting the patients and himself, he started. General Carpenter smiled grimly.

---

14. *England must own the Suez Canal.* In 1875 the English government bought control of the Suez Canal from Egypt. Hanmer's speech partly echoes Prime Minister Winston Churchill's famous address to Parliament, given in 1940 when the German army had just driven all British forces out of Europe. **15.** *Gladstone, Churchill and Pitt,* British prime ministers: William Gladstone during the later nineteenth century; Sir Winston Churchill during World War II, and 1951-1955; and the two William Pitts, father and son, who led English governments about forty years apart in the later eighteenth century. **16.** *Lord Palmerston . . . Disraeli.* Palmerston ("Pam") was prime minister in the 1850's and 1860's. To prevent France from getting control of the sea route to the Far East, Prime Minister Disraeli secretly bought the Suez Canal in 1875 before Parliament had voted funds for it. **17.** *Lady Beaconsfield,* Disraeli's wife. **18.** *Gaudeamus igitur,* "So let us be joyful," the Latin first words of a traditional college students' song. These are the words the night orderly overheard coming from Ward T.

"Didn't occur to you that we mightn't buy your disappearance story, eh Dimmock?"

"S-sir?"

"I'm an expert too, Dimmock. I'll spell it out for you. The war's going badly. Very badly. There've been intelligence leaks. The St. Albans mess might point to you."

"B-but they do disappear, sir. I——"

"My experts want to talk to you and your patients about this disappearing act, Dimmock. They'll start with you."

The experts worked over Dimmock with preconscious softeners, id releases and superego blocks. They tried every truth serum in the books and every form of physical and mental pressure. They brought Dimmock, squealing, to the breaking point three times, but there was nothing to break.

"Let him stew for now," Carpenter said. "Get on to the patients."

The experts appeared reluctant to apply pressure to the sick men and the woman.

"For God's sake, don't be squeamish," Carpenter raged. "We're fighting a war for civilization. We've got to protect our ideals no matter what the price. Get to it!"

The experts from Espionage, Counter-Espionage, Security and Central Intelligence got to it. Like three candles, pfc Nathan Riley, M/Sgt Lela Machan and Corp/2 George Hanmer snuffed out and disappeared. One moment they were seated in chairs surrounded by violence. The next moment they were not.

The experts gasped. General Carpenter did the handsome thing. He stalked to Dimmock. "Captain Dimmock, I apologize. Colonel Dimmock, you've been promoted for making an important discovery . . . only what the hell does it mean? We've got to check ourselves first."

Carpenter snapped up the intercom. "Get me a combat-shock expert and an alienist."

The two experts entered and were briefed. They examined the witnesses. They considered. "You're all suffering from a mild case of shock," the combat-shock expert said. "War jitters."

"You mean we didn't see them disappear?"

The shock expert shook his head and glanced at the alienist who also shook his head.

"Mass illusion," the alienist said.

At that moment pfc Riley, M/Sgt Machan and Corp/2 Hanmer reappeared. One moment they were a mass illusion; the next, they were back sitting in their chairs surrounded by confusion.

"Dope 'em again, Dimmock," Carpenter cried. "Give 'em a gallon." He snapped up his intercom. "I want every expert we've got. Emergency meeting in my office at once."

Thirty-seven experts, hardened and sharpened tools all, inspected the unconscious shock cases and discussed them for three hours. Certain facts were obvious: This must be a new fantastic syndrome brought on by the new and fantastic horrors of the war. As combat technique develops, the response of victims of this technique must also take new roads. For every action there is an equal and opposite reaction. Agreed.

This new syndrome must involve some aspects of teleportation . . . the power of mind over space. Evidently combat shock, while destroying certain known powers of the mind must develop other latent powers hitherto unknown. Agreed.

Obviously, the patients must only be able to return to the point of departure, otherwise they would not continue to return to Ward T nor would they have returned to General Carpenter's office. Agreed.

Obviously, the patients must be able to procure food and sleep wherever they go, since neither was required in Ward T. Agreed.

"One small point," Colonel Dimmock said. "They seem to be returning to Ward T less frequently. In the beginning they would come and go every day or so. Now most of them stay away for weeks and hardly ever return."

"Never mind that," Carpenter said. "Where do they go?"

"Do they teleport behind the enemy lines?" someone asked. "There's those intelligence leaks."

"I want Intelligence to check," Carpenter snapped. "Is the enemy having similar difficulties with, say, prisoners of war who appear and disappear from their POW camps? They might be some of ours from Ward T."

"They might simply be going home," Colonel Dimmock suggested.

"I want Security to check," Carpenter ordered. "Cover the home life and associations of every one of those twenty-four disappearers. Now . . . about our operations in Ward T. Colonel Dimmock has a plan."

"We'll set up six extra beds in Ward T," Edsel Dimmock explained. "We'll send in six experts to live there and observe. Information must be picked up indirectly from the patients. They're catatonic and nonresponsive when conscious, and incapable of answering questions when drugged."

"Gentlemen," Carpenter summed it up. "This is the greatest potential weapon in the history of warfare. I don't have to tell you what it can mean to us to be able to teleport an entire army behind enemy lines. We can win the war for the American Dream in one day if we can win this secret hidden in those shattered minds. We must win!"

The experts hustled, Security checked, Intelligence probed. Six hardened and sharpened tools moved into Ward T in St. Albans Hospital and slowly got acquainted with the disappearing patients who reappeared less and less frequently. The tension increased.

Security was able to report that not one case of strange appearance had taken place in America in the past year. Intelligence reported that the enemy did not seem to be having similar difficulties with their own shock cases or with POWs.

Carpenter fretted. "This is all brand new. We've got no specialists to handle it. We've got to develop new tools." He snapped up his intercom. "Get me a college," he said.

They got him Yale.

"I want some experts in mind over matter. Develop them," Carpenter ordered. Yale at once introduced three graduate courses in Thaumaturgy, Extrasensory Perception and Telekinesis.[19]

The first break came when one of the Ward T experts requested the assistance of another expert. He needed a Lapidary.

"What the hell for?" Carpenter wanted to know.

"He picked up a reference to a gemstone," Colonel Dimmock explained. "He's a personnel specialist and he can't relate it to anything in his experience."

"And he's not supposed to," Carpenter said approvingly. "A job for every man and every man on the job." He flipped up the intercom. "Get me a Lapidary."

An expert Lapidary was given leave of absence from the army arsenal and asked to identify a type of diamond called Jim Brady. He could not.

"We'll try it from another angle," Carpenter said. He snapped up his intercom. "Get me a Semanticist."

The Semanticist left his desk in the War Propaganda Department but could make nothing of the words Jim Brady. They were names to him. No more. He suggested a Genealogist.

A Genealogist was given one day's leave from his post with the Un-American Ancestors Committee but could make nothing of the name Brady beyond the fact that it had been a common name in America for five hundred years. He suggested an Archaeologist.

An Archaeologist was released from the Cartography Division of Invasion Command and instantly identified the name Diamond Jim Brady. It was a historic personage who had been famous in the city of Little Old New York some time between Governor Peter Stuyvesant and Governor Fiorello La Guardia.[20]

Carpenter marveled. "That's ages ago. Where the hell did Nathan Riley get that? You'd better join the experts in Ward T and follow this up."

The Archaeologist followed it up, checked his references and sent in his report. Carpenter read it and was stunned. He called an emergency meeting of his staff of experts.

"Gentlemen," he announced, "Ward T is something bigger than teleportation. Those shock patients are doing something far more incredible . . . far more meaningful. Gentlemen, they're traveling through time."

The staff rustled uncertainly. Carpenter nodded emphatically.

"Yes, gentlemen. Time travel is here. It has not arrived the way we expected it . . . as a result of expert research by qualified specialists; it has come as a plague . . . an infection . . . a disease of the war . . . a

---

19. *Thaumaturgy . . . Telekinesis.* Thaumaturgy is the working of miracles. Extrasensory Perception is the ability to perceive thoughts. Telekinesis is the ability to move objects without touching them. **20.** *Governor Peter Stuyvesant and Governor Fiorello La Guardia.* In the seventeenth century, Stuyvesant (stīʹvə sənt) governed New York as a Dutch colony. La Guardia was mayor, not governor, of New York City from 1934 to 1945.

result of combat injury to ordinary men. Before I continue, look through these reports for documentation."

The staff read the stenciled sheets. Pfc Nathan Riley . . . disappearing into the early twentieth century in New York; M/Sgt Lela Machan . . . visiting the first century in Rome; Corp/2 George Hanmer . . . journeying into the nineteenth century in England. And all the rest of the twenty-four patients, escaping the turmoil and horrors of modern war in the twenty-second century by fleeing to Venice and the Doges, to Jamaica and the buccaneers, to China and the Han Dynasty, to Norway and Eric the Red, to any place and any time in the world.

"I needn't point out the colossal significance of this discovery," General Carpenter pointed out. "Think what it would mean to the war if we could send an army back in time a week or a month or a year. We could win the war before it started. We could protect our Dream . . . Poetry and Beauty and the Culture of America . . . from barbarism without ever endangering it."

The staff tried to grapple with the problem of winning battles before they started.

"The situation is complicated by the fact that these men and women of Ward T are *non compos*.[21] They may or may not know how they do what they do, but in any case they're incapable of communicating with the experts who could reduce this miracle to method. It's for us to find the key. They can't help us."

The hardened and sharpened specialists looked around uncertainly.

"We'll need experts," General Carpenter said.

The staff relaxed. They were on familiar ground again.

"We'll need a Cerebral Mechanist, a Cyberneticist, a Psychiatrist, an Anatomist, an Archaeologist and a first-rate Historian. They'll go into that ward and they won't come out until their job is done. They must learn the technique of time travel."

The first five experts were easy to draft from other war departments. All America was a tool chest of hardened and sharpened specialists. But there was trouble locating a first-class Historian until the Federal Penitentiary cooperated with the army and released Dr. Bradley Scrim from his twenty years at hard labor. Dr. Scrim was acid and jagged. He had held the chair of Philosophic History at a western university until he spoke his mind about the war for the American Dream. That got him the twenty years hard.

Scrim was still intransigent, but induced to play ball by the intriguing problem of Ward T.

"But I'm not an expert," he snapped. "In this benighted nation of experts, I'm the last singing grasshopper in the ant heap."[22]

Carpenter snapped up the intercom. "Get me an Entomologist," he said.

---

21. *non compos,* the short form of *non compos mentis,* a Latin phrase meaning "not of sound mind."
22. *the last singing . . . heap.* In a fable by the ancient Greek, Aesop, a grasshopper has spent all summer singing and dancing, while a hard-working ant has carefully stored up food for the winter. When the cold, starving grasshopper comes to beg corn, the ant advises it to dance to stay warm.

"Don't bother," Scrim said. "I'll translate. You're a nest of ants . . . all working and toiling and specializing. For what?"

"To preserve the American Dream," Carpenter answered hotly. "We're fighting for Poetry and Culture and Education and the Finer Things in Life."

"Which means you're fighting to preserve me," Scrim said. "That's what I've devoted my life to. And what do you do with me? Put me in jail."

"You were convicted of enemy sympathizing and fellow-traveling," Carpenter said.

"I was convicted of believing in *my* American Dream," Scrim said. "Which is another way of saying I was jailed for having a mind of my own."

Scrim was also intransigent in Ward T. He stayed one night, enjoyed three good meals, read the reports, threw them down and began hollering to be let out.

"There's a job for everyone and everyone must be on the job," Colonel Dimmock told him. "You don't come out until you've got the secret of time travel."

"There's no secret I can get," Scrim said.

"Do they travel in time?"

"Yes and no."

"The answer has to be one or the other. Not both. You're evading the——"

"Look," Scrim interrupted wearily. "What are you an expert in?"

"Psychotherapy."

"Then how the hell can you understand what I'm talking about? This is a philosophic concept. I tell you there's no secret here that the army can use. There's no secret any group can use. It's a secret for individuals only."

"I don't understand you."

"I didn't think you would. Take me to Carpenter."

They took Scrim to Carpenter's office where he grinned at the general malignantly, looking for all the world like a redheaded, underfed devil. "I'll need ten minutes," Scrim said. "Can you spare them out of your tool box?"

Carpenter nodded.

"Now listen carefully. I'm going to give you the clues to something so vast and so strange that it will need all your fine edge to cut into it."

Carpenter looked expectant.

"Nathan Riley goes back in time to the early twentieth century. There he lives the life of his fondest dreams. He's a big-time gambler, the friend of Diamond Jim Brady and others. He wins money betting on events because he always knows the outcome in advance. He won money betting on Eisenhower to w n an election. He won money betting on a prize fighter named Marciano to beat another prize fighter named La Starza. He made money investing in an automobile company owned by Henry Ford. There are the clues. They mean anything to you?"

"Not without a Sociological Analyst," Carpenter answered. He reached for the intercom.

"Don't order one, I'll explain later. Let's try some more clues. Lela Machan, for example. She escapes into the Roman Empire where she lives the life of her dreams as a *femme fatale.* Every man loves her. Julius Caesar, Savonarola, the entire Twentieth Legion, a man named Ben Hur. Do you see the fallacy?"

"No."

"She also smokes cigarettes."

"Well?" Carpenter asked after a pause.

"I continue," Scrim said. "George Hanmer escapes into England of the nineteenth century where he's a member of Parliament and the friend of Gladstone, Winston Churchill and Disraeli, who takes him riding in his Rolls Royce. Do you know what a Rolls Royce is?"

"No."

"It was the name of an automobile."

"So?"

"You don't understand yet?"

"No."

Scrim paced the floor in exaltation. "Carpenter, this is a bigger discovery than teleportation or time travel. This can be the salvation of man. I don't think I'm exaggerating. Those two dozen shock victims in Ward T have been U-Bombed into something so gigantic that it's no wonder your specialists and experts can't understand it."

"What the hell's bigger than time travel, Scrim?"

"Listen to this, Carpenter. Eisenhower did not run for office until the middle of the twentieth century. Nathan Riley could not have been a friend of Diamond Jim Brady's and bet on Eisenhower to win an election . . . not simultaneously. Brady was dead a quarter of a century before Ike was President. Marciano defeated La Starza fifty years after Henry Ford started his automobile company. Nathan Riley's time traveling is full of similar anachronisms."

Carpenter looked puzzled.

"Lela Machan could not have had Ben Hur for a lover. Ben Hur never existed in Rome. He never existed at all. He was a character in a novel. She couldn't have smoked. They didn't have tobacco then. You see? More anachronisms. Disraeli could never have taken George Hanmer for a ride in a Rolls Royce because automobiles weren't invented until long after Disraeli's death."

"The hell you say," Carpenter exclaimed. "You mean they're all lying?"

"No. Don't forget, they don't need sleep. They don't need food. They're not lying. They're going back in time all right. They're eating and sleeping back there."

"But you just said their stories don't stand up. They're full of anachronisms."

"Because they travel back into a time of their own imagination. Nathan Riley has his own picture of what America was like in the early twentieth century. It's faulty and anachronistic because he's no scholar, but it's real for him. He can live there. The same is true for the others."

Carpenter goggled.

"The concept is almost beyond understanding. These people have discovered how to turn dreams into reality. They know how to enter their dream realities. They can stay there, live there, perhaps forever. Carpenter, *this* is your American Dream. It's miracle-working, immortality, Godlike creation, mind over matter. . . . It must be explored. It must be studied. It must be given to the world."

"Can you do it, Scrim?"

"No, I cannot. I'm an historian. I'm noncreative, so it's beyond me. You need a poet . . . an artist who understands the creation of dreams. From creating dreams on paper it oughtn't to be too difficult to take the step to creating dreams in actuality."

"A poet? Are you serious?"

"Certainly I'm serious. Don't you know what a poet is? You've been telling us for five years that this war is being fought to save the poets."

"Don't be facetious, Scrim, I——"

"Send a poet into Ward T. He'll learn how they do it. He's the only man who can. A poet is half doing it anyway. Once he learns, he can teach your psychologists and anatomists. Then they can teach us; but the poet is the only man who can interpret between those shock cases and your experts."

"I believe you're right, Scrim."

"Then don't delay, Carpenter. Those patients are returning to this world less and less frequently. We've got to get at that secret before they disappear forever. Send a poet to Ward T."

Carpenter snapped up his intercom. "Send me a poet," he said.

He waited, and waited . . . and waited . . . while America sorted feverishly through its two hundred and ninety millions of hardened and sharpened experts, its specialized tools to defend the American Dream of Beauty and Poetry and the Better Things in Life. He waited for them to find a poet, not understanding the endless delay, the fruitless search; not understanding why Bradley Scrim laughed and laughed and laughed at this final, fatal disappearance.

BULLETIN

Shirley Jackson

(ED. NOTE: THE TIME TRAVEL MACHINE sent out recently by this University has returned, unfortunately without Professor Browning. Happily for the University Space Department, however, Professor Browning's briefcase, set just inside the time travel element, returned, containing the following papers which bear ample evidence of the value to scientific investigation of sending Professor Browning on this much-discussed trip into the twenty-second century. It is assumed by members of the Space Department that these following papers were to serve as the basis for notes for the expected lecture by Professor Browning, which will now, of course, be indefinitely postponed.)

(From a newspaper, torn, heading reading only "——ld Tribune, May 8, 2123"):

. . . indifference in high quarters which has led so inevitably to this distressing result. Not only those directly affected—and they are many—but, indeed, thoughtful and reasonable persons everywhere, must view with extreme alarm an act which has given opportunism an advantage over intelligent planning. It is greatly to be regretted that, among those in power who were in a position to take action, none except the unpopular Secretary chose to do so, and his opposition was, as so frequently it must be, disregarded. In any case, let us unite in hope that the possible consequences will not take place, and prepare to guard ourselves with the utmost vigilance against a recurrence of such incidents.

(From what appears to be a private correspondence):

June 4

Dear Mom and Dad,
I am haveing a fine time at camp. I went
swiming and dived, but Charley didnt. Send
me a cake and some cokies and candy.
Your loveing son,
Jerry

"Bulletin" by Shirley Jackson. Copyright 1954 by Shirley Jackson. Reprinted by permission of Brandt & Brandt.

(A mimeographed sheet):

American History 102
Mid-Term Examination
April 21, 2123

1. Identify twelve (12) of the following:

Nathan Hale	Grover Cleveland
Huey Long	Woodrow Wilson I
Carrie Chapman Catt	Joyce Kilmer
Merry Oldsmobile	Edna Wallace Hopper
Cotton Mather	Chief Sitting Bull
Robert Nathan	Old Ironsides
George Washingham	John Philip Sousa
Oveta Culp Hobby	Sergeant Cuff
Sinclair (Joe) Louis	R. H. Macy
Alexander Hamilton	

2. The historian Roosevelt-san has observed that "Twentieth-century man had both intelligence and instinct; he chose, unfortunately, to rely upon intelligence." Discuss.

3. Some of the following statements are true, some are false. Mark them T and F accordingly:

Currency was originally used as a medium of exchange.

The aboriginal Americans lived aboveground and drank water.

The first American settlers rebelled against the rule of Churchill III and set up their own government because of the price of tea.

Throat-scratch, the disease which swept through twentieth-century life, was introduced to this country by Sir Walter Raleigh.

The hero Jackie Robinson is chiefly known for his voyage to obtain the golden fleece.[1]

Working was the principal occupation of twentieth-century humanity.

The first king in American, George Washingham, refused the crown three times.[2]

The cat was at one time tame, and used in domestic service.

4. Describe in your own words the probable daily life of an American resident in 1950, using what you have learned of his eating, entertainment, and mating habits.

5. In what sense did ancient Americans contribute to our world today? Can we learn anything of value by studying them?

---

1. *Jackie Robinson . . . the golden fleece.* According to ancient Greek myth, it was the hero Jason who sailed in search of the magical golden fleece. Jackie Robinson in 1947 became the first black man to play major-league baseball. 2. *refused the crown three times.* It was Julius Caesar, a dictator of ancient Rome, who refused the crown three times when it was offered to him.

(A narrow card, identifiably from a machine):

YOUR WEIGHT AND FORTUNE!

Your weight is . . . 186

Your fortune for today: Expect permanent relief in minor domestic problems, but avoid too-hasty plans for the future. Try not to dwell on the past. You are determined, clear-sighted, firm: use these qualities. Remember that you can be led but not driven.

(ED. NOTE: This last item seems of great significance. It is well known that Professor Browning's weight when he left the university in the time travel element was better than two hundred pounds. The evident loss of weight shown indicates clearly the changes incident to time travel, and points, perhaps, to some of its perils; there is possibly a hint here of an entirely different system of weights and measures than that currently in use. We anticipate that several learned and informed papers on this subject are already in preparation.)

AUTOFAC

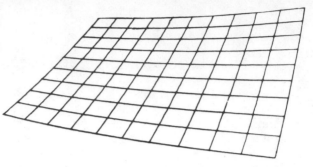

Philip K. Dick

TENSION HUNG OVER THE THREE waiting men. They smoked, paced back and forth, kicked aimlessly at weeds growing by the side of the road. A hot noonday sun glared down on brown fields, rows of neat plastic houses, the distant line of mountains to the west.

"Almost time," Earl Perine said, knotting his skinny hands together. "It varies according to the load, a half second for every additional pound."

Bitterly, Morrison answered. "You've got it plotted? You're as bad as it is. Let's pretend it just *happens* to be late."

The third man said nothing. O'Neill was visiting from another settlement; he didn't know Perine and Morrison well enough to argue with them. Instead, he crouched down and arranged the papers clipped to his aluminum check board. In the blazing sun, O'Neill's arms were tanned, furry, glistening with sweat. Wiry, with tangled gray hair, horn-rimmed glasses, he was older than the other two. He wore slacks, a sport shirt and crepe-soled shoes. Between his fingers, his fountain pen glittered, metallic and efficient.

"What're you writing?" Perine grumbled.

"I'm laying out the procedure we're going to employ," O'Neill said mildly. "Better to systemize it now, instead of trying at random. We want to know what we tried and what didn't work. Otherwise we'll go around in a circle. The problem we have here is one of communication; that's how I see it."

"Communication," Morrison agreed in his deep, chesty voice. "Yes, we can't get in touch with the damn thing. It comes, leaves off its load and goes on—there's no contact between us and it."

"It's a machine," Perine said excitedly. "It's dead—blind and deaf."

"But it's in contact with the outside world," O'Neill pointed out. "There has to be some way to get to it. Specific semantic signals are meaningful to it; all we have to do is find those signals. Rediscover, actually. Maybe half a dozen out of a billion possibilities."

A low rumble interrupted the three men. They glanced up, wary and alert. The time had come.

"Here it is," Perine said. "Okay, wise guy, let's see you make one single change in its routine."

The truck was massive, rumbling under its tightly packed load. In many ways, it resembled conventional human-operated transportation

---

"Autofac" by Philip K. Dick. Copyright © 1955 by Galaxy Publishing Corporation. Reprinted by permission of the Author and his agents, Scott Meredith Literary Agency, Inc., 580 Fifth Avenue, New York, N.Y. 10036.

vehicles, but with one exception—there was no driver's cabin. The horizontal surface was a loading stage, and the part that would normally be the headlights and radiator grill was a fibrous spongelike mass of receptors, the limited sensory apparatus of this mobile utility extension.

Aware of the three men, the truck slowed to a halt, shifted gears and pulled on its emergency brake. A moment passed as relays moved into action; then a portion of the loading surface tilted and a cascade of heavy cartons spilled down onto the roadway. With the objects fluttered a detailed inventory sheet.

"You know what to do," O'Neill said rapidly. "Hurry up, before it gets out of here."

Expertly, grimly, the three men grabbed up the deposited cartons and ripped the protective wrappers from them. Objects gleamed: a binocular microscope, a portable radio, heaps of plastic dishes, medical supplies, razor blades, clothing, food. Most of the shipment, as usual, was food. The three men systematically began smashing the objects. In a few minutes, there was nothing but a chaos of debris littered around them.

"That's that," O'Neill panted, stepping back. He fumbled for his check sheet. "Now let's see what it does."

The truck had begun to move away; abruptly it stopped and backed toward them. Its receptors had taken in the fact that the three men had demolished the dropped-off portion of the load. It spun in a grinding half circle and came around to face its receptor bank in their direction. Up went its antenna; it had begun communicating with the factory. Instructions were on the way.

A second, identical load was tilted and shoved off the truck.

"We failed," Perine groaned as a duplicate inventory sheet fluttered after the new load. "We destroyed all that stuff for nothing."

"What now?" Morrison asked O'Neill. "What's the next stratagem on your board?"

"Give me a hand." O'Neill grabbed up a carton and lugged it back to the truck. Sliding the carton onto the platform, he turned for another. The other two men followed clumsily after him. They put the load back onto the truck. As the truck started forward, the last square box was again in place.

The truck hesitated. Its receptors registered the return of its load. From within its works came a low, sustained buzzing.

"This may drive it crazy," O'Neill commented, sweating. "It went through its operation and accomplished nothing."

The truck made a short, abortive move toward going on. Then it swung purposefully around and, in a blur of speed, again dumped the load onto the road.

"Get them!" O'Neill yelled. The three men grabbed up the cartons and feverishly reloaded them. But as fast as the cartons were shoved back on the horizontal stage, the truck's grapples tilted them down its far-side ramps and onto the road.

"No use," Morrison said, breathing hard. "Water through a sieve."

"We're licked," Perine gasped in wretched agreement, "like always. We humans lose every time."

The truck regarded them calmly, its receptors blank and impassive. It was doing its job. The planetwide network of automatic factories was smoothly performing the task imposed on it five years before, in the early days of the Total Global Conflict.

"There it goes," Morrison observed dismally. The truck's antenna had come down; it shifted into low gear and released its parking brake.

"One last try," O'Neill said. He swept up one of the cartons and ripped it open. From it he dragged a ten-gallon milk tank and unscrewed the lid. "Silly as it seems."

"This is absurd," Perine protested. Reluctantly, he found a cup among the littered debris and dipped it into the milk. "A kid's game!"

The truck had paused to observe them.

"Do it," O'Neill ordered sharply. "Exactly the way we practiced it."

The three of them drank quickly from the milk tank, visibly allowing the milk to spill down their chins; there had to be no mistaking what they were doing.

As planned, O'Neill was the first. His face twisting in revulsion, he hurled the cup away and violently spat the milk into the road.

"God's sake!" he choked.

The other two did the same; stamping and loudly cursing, they kicked over the milk tank and glared accusingly at the truck.

"It's no good!" Morrison roared.

Curious, the truck came slowly back. Electronic synapses clicked and whirred, responding to the situation; its antenna shot up like a flagpole.

"I think this is it," O'Neill said, trembling. As the truck watched, he dragged out a second milk tank, unscrewed its lid and tasted the contents. "The same!" he shouted at the truck. "It's just as bad!"

From the truck popped a metal cylinder. The cylinder dropped at Morrison's feet; he quickly snatched it up and tore it open.

STATE NATURE OF DEFECT.

The instruction sheets listed rows of possible defects, with neat boxes by each; a punch stick was included to indicate the particular deficiency of the product.

"What'll I check?" Morrison asked. "Contaminated? Bacterial? Sour? Rancid? Incorrectly labeled? Broken? Crushed? Cracked? Bent? Soiled?"

Thinking rapidly, O'Neill said, "Don't check any of them. The factory's undoubtedly ready to test and resample. It'll make its own analysis and then ignore us." His face glowed as frantic inspiration came. "Write in that blank at the bottom. It's an open space for further data."

"Write what?"

O'Neill said, "Write: *The product is thoroughly pizzled.*"

"What's that?" Perine demanded, baffled.

"Write it! It's a semantic garble—the factory won't be able to understand it. Maybe we can jam the works."

With O'Neill's pen, Morrison carefully wrote that the milk was pizzled. Shaking his head, he resealed the cylinder and returned it to the truck. The truck swept up the milk tanks and slammed its railing tidily into place. With a shriek of tires, it hurtled off. From its slot, a final cylinder bounced; the truck hurriedly departed, leaving the cylinder lying in the dust.

O'Neill got it open and held up the paper for the others to see.

A FACTORY REPRESENTATIVE WILL BE SENT OUT.
BE PREPARED TO SUPPLY COMPLETE DATA ON
PRODUCT DEFICIENCY.

For a moment, the three men were silent. Then Perine began to giggle. "We did it. We contacted it. We got across."

"We sure did," O'Neill agreed. "It never heard of a product being pizzled."

Cut into the base of the mountains lay the vast metallic cube of the Kansas City factory. Its surface was corroded, pitted with radiation pox, cracked and scarred from the five years of war that had swept over it. Most of the factory was buried subsurface, only its entrance stages visible. The truck was a speck rumbling at high speed toward the expanse of black metal. Presently an opening formed in the uniform surface; the truck plunged into it and disappeared inside. The entrance snapped shut.

"Now the big job remains," O'Neill said. "Now we have to persuade it to close down operations—to shut itself off."

Judith O'Neill served hot black coffee to the people sitting around the living room. Her husband talked while the others listened. O'Neill was as close to being an authority on the autofac system as could still be found.

In his own area, the Chicago region, he had shorted out the protective fence of the local factory long enough to get away with data tapes stored in its posterior brain. The factory, of course, had immediately reconstructed a better type of fence. But he had shown that the factories were not infallible.

"The Institute of Applied Cybernetics,"[1] O'Neill explained, "had complete control over the network. Blame the war. Blame the big noise along the lines of communication that wiped out the knowledge we need. In any case, the Institute failed to transmit its information to us, so we can't transmit our information to the factories—the news that the war is over and we're ready to resume control of industrial operations."

---

1. *Cybernetics,* a new science which compares the nervous systems of animals and men with mechanical and electronic systems of control and communications, such as computers. One major aim of this science is to create methods for automatic control of machinery.

"And meanwhile," Morrison added sourly, "the damn network expands and consumes more of our natural resources all the time."

"I get the feeling," Judith said, "that if I stamped hard enough, I'd fall right down into a factory tunnel. They must have mines everywhere by now."

"Isn't there some limiting injunction?" Perine asked nervously. "Were they set up to expand indefinitely?"

"Each factory is limited to its own operational area," O'Neill said, "but the network itself is unbounded. It can go on scooping up our resources forever. The Institute decided it gets top priority; we mere people come second."

"Will there be *anything* left for us?" Morrison wanted to know.

"Not unless we can stop the network's operations. It's already used up half a dozen basic minerals. Its search teams are out all the time, from every factory, looking everywhere for some last scrap to drag home."

"What would happen if tunnels from two factories crossed each other?"

O'Neill shrugged. "Normally, that won't happen. Each factory has its own special section of our planet, its own private cut of the pie for its exclusive use."

"But it *could* happen."

"Well, they're raw-material-tropic; as long as there's anything left, they'll hunt it down." O'Neill pondered the idea with growing interest. "It's something to consider. I suppose as things get scarcer——"

He stopped talking. A figure had come into the room; it stood silently by the door, surveying them all.

In the dull shadows, the figure looked almost human. For a brief moment, O'Neill thought it was a settlement latecomer. Then, as it moved forward, he realized that it was only quasi-human: a functional upright biped chassis, with data receptors mounted at the top, effectors and proprioceptors[2] mounted in a downward worm that ended in floor grippers. Its resemblance to a human being was testimony to nature's efficiency; no sentimental imitation was intended.

The factory representative had arrived.

It began without preamble. "This is a data-collecting machine capable of communicating on an oral basis. It contains both broadcasting and receiving apparatus and can integrate facts relevant to its line of inquiry."

The voice was pleasant, confident. Obviously it was a tape, recorded by some Institute technician before the war. Coming from the quasi-human shape, it sounded grotesque; O'Neill could vividly imagine the dead young man whose cheerful voice now issued from the mechanical mouth of this upright construction of steel and wiring.

---

2. *effectors and proprioceptors.* The effectors are circuits and mechanical devices that act like human muscles, arms, and legs, allowing a robot to move and to perform other actions. Proprioceptors are electronic circuits that do the work of the human nervous system: They feed back to the machine's computer "brain" information about the condition of its effectors, sensing devices, and internal circuits.

"One word of caution," the pleasant voice continued. "It is fruitless to consider this receptor human and to engage it in discussions for which it is not equipped. Although purposeful, it is not capable of conceptual thought; it can only reassemble material already available to it."

The optimistic voice clicked out and a second voice came on. It resembled the first, but now there were no intonations or personal mannerisms. The machine was utilizing the dead man's phonetic speech pattern for its own communication.

"Analysis of the rejected product," it stated, "shows no foreign elements or noticeable deterioration. The product meets the continual testing standards employed throughout the network. Rejection is therefore on a basis outside the test area; standards not available to the network are being employed."

"That's right," O'Neill agreed. Weighing his words with care, he continued, "We found the milk substandard. We want nothing to do with it. We insist on more careful output."

The machine responded presently. "The semantic content of the term *pizzled* is unfamiliar to the network. It does not exist in the taped vocabulary. Can you present a factual analysis of the milk in terms of specific elements present or absent?"

"No," O'Neill said warily; the game he was playing was intricate and dangerous. *"Pizzled* is an overall term. It can't be reduced to chemical constituents."

"What does *pizzled* signify?" the machine asked. "Can you define it in terms of alternate semantic symbols?"

O'Neill hesitated. The representative had to be steered from its special inquiry to more general regions, to the ultimate problem of closing down the network. If he could pry it open at any point, get the theoretical discussion started . . .

"Pizzled," he stated, "means the condition of a product that is manufactured when no need exists. It indicates the rejection of objects on the grounds that they are no longer wanted."

The representative said, "Network analysis shows a need of high-grade pasteurized milk-substitute in this area. There is no alternate source; the network controls all the synthetic mammary-type equipment in existence." It added, "Original taped instructions describe milk as an essential to human diet."

O'Neill was being outwitted; the machine was returning the discussion to the specific. "We've decided," he said desperately, "that we don't *want* any more milk. We'd prefer to go without it, at least until we can locate cows."

"That is contrary to the network tapes," the representative objected. "There are no cows. All milk is produced synthetically."

"Then we'll produce it synthetically ourselves," Morrison broke in impatiently. "Why can't we take over the machines? We're not children! We can run our own lives!"

The factory representative moved toward the door. "Until such time as your community finds other sources of milk supply, the network will continue to supply you. Analytical and evaluating apparatus will remain in this area, conducting the customary random sampling."

Perine shouted futilely, "How can we find other sources? You have the whole setup! You're running the whole show!" Following after it, he bellowed, "You say we're not ready to run things—you claim we're not capable. How do you know? You don't give us a chance! We'll never have a chance!"

O'Neill was petrified. The machine was leaving; its one-track mind had completely triumphed.

"Look," he said hoarsely, blocking its way. "We want you to shut down, understand. We want to take over your equipment and run it ourselves. The war's over with. You're not needed any more!"

The factory representative paused briefly at the door. "The inoperative cycle," it said, "is not geared to begin until network production merely duplicates outside production. There is at this time, according to our continual sampling, no outside production. Therefore network production continues."

Without warning, Morrison swung the steel pipe in his hand. It slashed against the machine's shoulder and burst through the elaborate network of sensory apparatus that made up its chest. The tank of receptors shattered; bits of glass, wiring and minute parts showered everywhere.

"It's a paradox!" Morrison yelled. "A word game—a semantic game they're pulling on us. The Cyberneticists have it rigged." He raised the pipe and again brought it down savagely on the unprotesting machine. "They've got us hamstrung. We're completely helpless."

The room was in uproar. "It's the only way," Perine gasped as he pushed past O'Neill. "We'll have to destroy them—it's the network or us." Grabbing down a lamp, he hurled it in the "face" of the factory representative. The lamp and the intricate surface of plastic burst; Perine waded in, groping blindly for the machine. Now all the people in the room were closing furiously around the upright cylinder, their impotent resentment boiling over. The machine sank down and disappeared as they dragged it to the floor.

Trembling, O'Neill turned away. His wife caught hold of his arm and led him to the side of the room.

"The idiots," he said dejectedly. "They can't destroy it; they'll only teach it to build more defenses. They're making the whole problem worse."

Into the living room rolled a network repair team. Expertly, the mechanical units detached themselves from the half-track mother-bug and scurried toward the mound of struggling humans. They slid between people and rapidly burrowed. A moment later, the inert carcass of the factory representative was dragged into the hopper of the mother-bug. Parts were collected, torn remnants gathered up and carried off. The plastic strut and gear was located. Then the units restationed themselves on the bug and the team departed.

Through the open door came a second factory representative, an exact duplicate of the first. And outside in the hall stood two more upright machines. The settlement had been combed at random by a corps of representatives. Like a horde of ants, the mobile data-collecting machines had filtered through the town until, by chance, one of them had come across O'Neill.

"Destruction of network mobile data-gathering equipment is detrimental to best human interests," the factory representative informed the roomful of people. "Raw material intake is at a dangerously low ebb; what basic materials still exist should be utilized in the manufacture of consumer commodities."

O'Neill and the machine stood facing each other.

"Oh?" O'Neill said softly. "That's interesting. I wonder what you're lowest on—and what you'd really be willing to fight for."

Helicopter rotors whined tinnily above O'Neill's head; he ignored them and peered through the cabin window at the ground not far below.

Slag and ruins stretched everywhere. Weeds poked their way up, sickly stalks among which insects scuttled. Here and there, rat colonies were visible: matted hovels constructed of bone and rubble. Radiation had mutated the rats, along with most insects and animals. A little farther, O'Neill identified a squadron of birds pursuing a ground squirrel. The squirrel dived into a carefully prepared crack in the surface of slag and the birds turned, thwarted.

"You think we'll ever have it rebuilt?" Morrison asked. "It makes me sick to look at it."

"In time," O'Neill answered. "Assuming, of course, that we get industrial control back. And assuming that anything remains to work with. At best, it'll be slow. We'll have to inch out from the settlements."

To the right was a human colony, tattered scarecrows, gaunt and emaciated, living among the ruins of what had once been a town. A few acres of barren soil had been cleared; drooping vegetables wilted in the sun, chickens wandered listlessly here and there, and a fly-bothered horse lay panting in the shade of a crude shed.

"Ruins-squatters," O'Neill said gloomily. "Too far from the network—not tangent to any of the factories."

"It's their own fault," Morrison told him angrily. "They could come into one of the settlements."

"That was their town. They're trying to do what *we're* trying to do—build up things again on their own. But they're starting now, without tools or machines, with their bare hands, nailing together bits of rubble. And it won't work. We need machines. We can't repair ruins; we've got to start industrial production."

Ahead lay a series of broken hills, chipped remains that had once been a ridge. Beyond stretched out the titanic ugly sore of an H-bomb crater, half-filled with stagnant water and slime, a disease-ridden inland sea. And beyond that—a glitter of busy motion.

"There," O'Neill said tensely. He lowered the helicopter rapidly. "Can you tell which factory they're from?"

"They all look alike to me," Morrison muttered, leaning over to see. "We'll have to wait and follow them back, when they get a load."

"*If* they get a load," O'Neill corrected.

The autofac exploring crew ignored the helicopter buzzing overhead and concentrated on its job. Ahead of the main truck scuttled two tractors; they made their way up mounds of rubble, probes burgeoning like quills, shot down the far slope and disappeared into a blanket of ash that lay spread over the slag. The two scouts burrowed until only their antennae were visible. They burst up to the surface and scuttled on, their treads whirring and clanking.

"What are they after?" Morrison asked.

"God knows." O'Neill leafed intently through the papers on his clipboard. "We'll have to analyze all our back-order slips."

Below them, the autofac exploring crew disappeared behind. The helicopter passed over a deserted stretch of sand and slag on which nothing moved. A grove of scrub brush appeared and then, far to the right, a series of tiny moving dots.

A procession of automatic ore carts was racing over the bleak slag, a string of rapidly moving metal trucks that followed one another nose to tail. O'Neill turned the helicopter toward them and a few minutes later it hovered above the mine itself.

Masses of squat mining equipment had made their way to the operations. Shafts had been sunk; empty carts waited in patient rows. A steady stream of loaded carts hurried toward the horizon, dribbling ore after them. Activity and the noise of machines hung over the area, an abrupt center of industry in the bleak wastes of slag.

"Here comes that exploring crew," Morrison observed, peering back the way they had come. "You think maybe they'll tangle?" He grinned. "No, I guess it's too much to hope for."

"It is this time," O'Neill answered. "They're looking for different substances, probably. And they're normally conditioned to ignore each other."

The first of the exploring bugs reached the line of ore carts. It veered slightly and continued its search; the carts traveled in their inexorable line as if nothing had happened.

Disappointed, Morrison turned away from the window and swore. "No use. It's like each doesn't exist for the other."

Gradually the exploring crew moved away from the line of carts, past the mining operations and over a ridge beyond. There was no special hurry; they departed without having reacted to the ore-gathering syndrome.

"Maybe they're from the same factory," Morrison said hopefully.

O'Neill pointed to the antennae visible on the major mining equipment. "Their vanes are turned at a different vector, so these represent two factories. It's going to be hard; we'll have to get it exactly right or there won't be any reaction." He clicked on the radio and got hold of the monitor at the settlement. "Any results on the consolidated back-order sheets?"

The operator put him through to the settlement governing offices.

"They're starting to come in," Perine told him. "As soon as we get sufficient samplings, we'll try to determine which raw materials which factories lack. It's going to be risky, trying to extrapolate from complex products. There may be a number of basic elements common to the various sublots."

"What happens when we've identified the missing element?" Morrison asked O'Neill. "What happens when we've got two tangent factories short on the same material?"

"Then," O'Neill said grimly, "we start collecting the material ourselves—even if we have to melt down every object in the settlements."

In the moth-ridden darkness of night, a dim wind stirred, chill and faint. Dense underbrush rattled metallically. Here and there a nocturnal rodent prowled, its senses hyperalert, peering, planning, seeking food.

The area was wild. No human settlements existed for miles; the entire region had been seared flat, cauterized by repeated H-bomb blasts. Somewhere in the murky darkness, a sluggish trickle of water made its way among slag and weeds, dripping thickly into what had once been an elaborate labyrinth of sewer mains. The pipes lay cracked and broken, jutting up into the night darkness, overgrown with creeping vegetation. The wind raised clouds of black ash that swirled and danced among the weeds. Once an enormous mutant wren stirred sleepily, pulled its crude protective nightcoat of rags around it and dozed off.

For a time, there was no movement. A streak of stars showed in the sky overhead, glowing starkly, remotely. Earl Perine shivered, peered up and huddled closer to the pulsing heat element placed on the ground between the three men.

"Well?" Morrison challenged, teeth chattering.

O'Neill didn't answer. He finished his cigarette, crushed it against a mound of decaying slag and, getting out his lighter, lit another. The mass of tungsten—the bait—lay a hundred yards directly ahead of them.

During the last few days, both the Detroit and Pittsburgh factories had run short of tungsten. And in at least one sector, their apparatus overlapped. This sluggish heap represented precision cutting tools, parts ripped from electrical switches, high-quality surgical equipment, sections of permanent magnets, measuring devices . . . tungsten from every possible source, gathered feverishly from all the settlements.

Dark mist lay spread over the tungsten mound. Occasionally, a night moth fluttered down, attracted by the glow of reflected starlight. The moth hung momentarily, beat its elongated wings futilely against the interwoven tangle of metal and then drifted off into the shadows of the thick-packed vines that rose up from the stumps of sewer pipes.

"Not a very damn pretty spot," Perine said wryly.

"Don't kid yourself," O'Neill retorted. "This is the prettiest spot on Earth. This is the spot that marks the grave of the autofac network.

People are going to come around here looking for it someday. There's going to be a plaque here a mile high."

"You're trying to keep your morale up," Morrison snorted. "You don't believe they're going to slaughter themselves over a heap of surgical tools and light-bulb filaments. They've probably got a machine down in the bottom level that sucks tungsten out of rock."

"Maybe," O'Neill said, slapping at a mosquito. The insect dodged cannily and then buzzed over to annoy Perine. Perine swung viciously at it and squatted sullenly down against the damp vegetation.

And there was what they had come to see.

O'Neill realized with a start that he had been looking at it for several minutes without recognizing it. The searchbug lay absolutely still. It rested at the crest of a small rise of slag, its anterior end slightly raised, receptors fully extended. It might have been an abandoned hulk; there was no activity of any kind, no sign of life or consciousness. The searchbug fitted perfectly into the wasted, fire-drenched landscape. A vague tub of metal sheets and gears and flat treads, it rested and waited. And watched. It was examining the heap of tungsten. The bait had drawn its first bite.

"Fish," Perine said thickly. "The line moved. I think the sinker dropped."

"What the hell are you mumbling about?" Morrison grunted. And then he, too, saw the searchbug. . . . He half rose to his feet, massive body arched forward. "Well, there's *one* of them. Now all we need is a unit from the other factory. Which do you suppose it is?"

O'Neill located the communication vane and traced its angle. "Pittsburgh, so pray for Detroit . . . pray like mad."

Satisfied, the searchbug detached itself and rolled forward. Cautiously approaching the mound, it began a series of intricate maneuvers, rolling first one way and then another. The three watching men were mystified—until they glimpsed the first probing stalks of other searchbugs.

"Communication," O'Neill said softly. "Like bees."

Now five Pittsburgh searchbugs were approaching the mound of tungsten products. Receptors waving excitedly, they increased their pace, scurrying in a sudden burst of discovery up the side of the mound to the top. A bug burrowed and rapidly disappeared. The whole mound shuddered; the bug was down inside, exploring the extent of the find.

Ten minutes later, the first Pittsburgh ore carts appeared and began industriously hurrying off with their haul.

"Damn it!" O'Neill said, agonized. "They'll have it all before Detroit shows up."

"Can't we do anything to slow them down?" Perine demanded helplessly. Leaping to his feet, he grabbed up a rock and heaved it at the nearest cart. The rock bounced off and the cart continued its work, unperturbed.

O'Neill got to his feet and prowled around, body rigid with impotent fury. Where were they? The autofacs were equal in all respects and the spot was the exact same linear distance from each center. Theoretically, the parties should have arrived simultaneously. Yet there was no sign of Detroit—and the final pieces of tungsten were being loaded before his eyes.

But then something streaked past him.

He didn't recognize it, for the object moved too quickly. It shot like a bullet among the tangled vines, raced up the side of the hill crest, poised for an instant to aim itself and hurtled down the far side. It smashed directly into the lead cart. Projectile and victim shattered in an abrupt burst of sound.

Morrison leaped up. "What the hell?"

"That's it!" Perine screamed, dancing around and waving his skinny arms. "It's Detroit!"

A second Detroit searchbug appeared, hesitated as it took in the situation, and then flung itself furiously at the retreating Pittsburgh carts. Fragments of tungsten scattered everywhere—parts, wiring, broken plates, gears and springs and bolts of the two antagonists flew in all directions. The remaining carts wheeled screechingly; one of them dumped its load and rattled off at top speed. A second followed, still weighed down with tungsten. A Detroit searchbug caught up with it, spun directly in its path and neatly overturned it. Bug and cart rolled down a shallow trench, into a stagnant pool of water. Dripping and glistening, the two of them struggled, half-submerged.

"Well," O'Neill said unsteadily, "we did it. We can start back home." His legs felt weak. "Where's our vehicle?"

As he gunned the truck motor, something flashed a long way off, something large and metallic, moving over the dead slag and ash. It was a dense clot of carts, a solid expanse of heavy-duty ore carriers racing to the scene. Which factory were they from?

It didn't matter, for out of the thick tangle of black dripping vines, a web of counter-extensions was creeping to meet them. Both factories were assembling their mobile units. From all directions, bugs slithered and crept, closing in around the remaining heap of tungsten. Neither factory was going to let needed raw material get away; neither was going to give up its find. Blindly, mechanically, in the grip of inflexible directives, the two opponents labored to assemble superior forces.

"Come on," Morrison said urgently. "Let's get out of here. All hell is bursting loose."

O'Neill hastily turned the truck in the direction of the settlement. They began rumbling through the darkness on their way back. Every now and then, a metallic shape shot by them, going in the opposite direction.

"Did you see the load in that last cart?" Perine asked, worried. "It wasn't empty."

Neither were the carts that followed it, a whole procession of bulging supply carriers directed by an elaborate high-level surveying unit.

"Guns," Morrison said, eyes wide with apprehension. "They're taking in weapons. But who's going to use them?"

"They are," O'Neill answered. He indicated a movement to their right. "Look over there. This is something we hadn't expected."

They were seeing the first factory representative move into action.

As the truck pulled into the Kansas City settlement, Judith hurried breathlessly toward them. Fluttering in her hand was a strip of metal-foil paper.

"What is it?" O'Neill demanded, grabbing it from her.

"Just come." His wife struggled to catch her breath. "A mobile car—raced up, dropped it off—and left. Big excitement. Golly, the factory's—a blaze of lights. You can see it for miles."

O'Neill scanned the paper. It was a factory certification for the last group of settlement-placed orders, a total tabulation of requested and factory-analyzed needs. Stamped across the list in heavy black type were six foreboding words:

ALL SHIPMENTS SUSPENDED UNTIL FURTHER NOTICE.

Letting out his breath harshly, O'Neill handed the paper over to Perine. "No more consumer goods," he said ironically, a nervous grin twitching across his face. "The network's going on a wartime footing."

"Then we did it?" Morrison asked haltingly.

"That's right," O'Neill said. Now that the conflict had been sparked, he felt a growing, frigid terror. "Pittsburgh and Detroit are in it to the finish. It's too late for us to change our minds, now—they're lining up allies."

Cool morning sunlight lay across the ruined plain of black metallic ash. The ash smouldered a dull, unhealthy red; it was still warm.

"Watch your step," O'Neill cautioned. Grabbing hold of his wife's arm, he led her from the rusty, sagging truck, up onto the top of a pile of strewn concrete blocks, the scattered remains of a pillbox installation. Earl Perine followed, making his way carefully, hesitantly.

Behind them, the dilapidated settlement lay spread out, a disorderly checkerboard of houses, buildings and streets. Since the autofac network had closed down its supply and maintenance, the human settlements had fallen into semibarbarism. The commodities that remained were broken and only partly usable. It had been over a year since the last mobile factory truck had appeared, loaded with food, tools, clothing and repair parts. From the flat expanse of dark concrete and metal at the foot of the mountains, nothing had emerged in their direction.

Their wish had been granted—they were cut off, detached from the network.

On their own.

Around the settlement grew ragged fields of wheat and tattered stalks of sun-baked vegetables. Crude handmade tools had been distributed, primitive artifacts hammered out with great labor by the various settlements. The settlements were linked only by horse-drawn cart and by the slow stutter of the telegraph key.

They had managed to keep their organization, though. Goods and services were exchanged on a slow, steady basis. Basic commodities were produced and distributed. The clothing that O'Neill and his wife and Earl Perine wore was coarse and unbleached, but sturdy. And they had managed to convert a few of the trucks from gasoline to wood.

"Here we are," O'Neill said. "We can see from here."

"Is it worth it?" Judith asked, exhausted. Bending down, she plucked aimlessly at her shoe, trying to dig a pebble from the soft hide sole. "It's a long way to come, to see something we've seen every day for thirteen months."

"True," O'Neill admitted, his hand briefly resting on his wife's slim shoulder. "But this may be the last. And that's what we want to see."

In the gray sky above them, a swift circling dot of opaque black moved. High, remote, the dot spun and darted, following an intricate and wary course. Gradually, its gyrations moved it toward the mountains and the bleak expanse of bomb-rubbled structure sunk in their base.

"San Francisco," O'Neill explained. "One of those long-range hawk projectiles, all the way from the West Coast."

"And you think it's the last?" Perine asked.

"It's the only one we've seen this month." O'Neill seated himself and began sprinkling dried bits of tobacco into a trench of brown paper. "And we used to see hundreds."

"Maybe they have something better," Judith suggested. She found a smooth rock and tiredly seated herself. "Could it be?"

Her husband smiled ironically. "No. They don't have anything better."

The three of them were tensely silent. Above them, the circling dot of black drew closer. There was no sign of activity from the flat surface of metal and concrete; the Kansas City factory remained inert, totally unresponsive. A few billows of warm ash drifted across it and one end was partly submerged in rubble. The factory had taken numerous direct hits. Across the plain, the furrows of its subsurface tunnels lay exposed, clogged with debris and the dark, water-seeking tendrils of tough vines.

"Those damn vines," Perine grumbled, picking at an old sore on his unshaven chin. "They're taking over the world."

Here and there around the factory, the demolished ruin of a mobile extension rusted in the morning dew. Carts, trucks, searchbugs, factory representatives, weapons carriers, guns, supply trains, subsurface projectiles, indiscriminate parts of machinery mixed and fused together in shapeless piles. Some had been destroyed returning to the factory; others had been contacted as they emerged, fully loaded, heavy with equipment. The factory itself—what remained of it— seemed to have settled more deeply into the earth. Its upper surface was barely visible, almost lost in drifting ash.

In four days, there had been no known activity, no visible movement of any sort.

"It's dead," Perine said. "You can see it's dead."

O'Neill didn't answer. Squatting down, he made himself comfortable and prepared to wait. In his own mind, he was sure that some fragment of automation remained in the eroded factory. Time would tell. He examined his wristwatch; it was eight-thirty. In the old days, the factory would be starting its daily routine. Processions of trucks and varied mobile units would be coming to the surface, loaded with supplies, to begin their expeditions to the human settlement.

Off to the right, something stirred. He quickly turned his attention to it.

A single battered ore-gathering cart was creeping clumsily toward the factory. One last damaged mobile unit trying to complete its task. The cart was virtually empty; a few meager scraps of metal lay strewn in its hold. A scavenger . . . the metal was sections ripped from destroyed equipment encountered on the way. Feebly, like a blind metallic insect, the cart approached the factory. Its progress was incredibly jerky. Every now and then, it halted, bucked and quivered, and wandered aimlessly off the path.

"Control is bad," Judith said, with a touch of horror in her voice. "The factory's having trouble guiding it back."

Yes, he had seen that. Around New York, the factory had lost its high-frequency transmitter completely. Its mobile units had floundered in crazy gyrations, racing in random circles, crashing against rocks and trees, sliding into gullies, overturning, finally unwinding and becoming reluctantly inanimate.

The ore cart reached the edge of the ruined plain and halted briefly. Above it, the dot of black still circled the sky. For a time, the cart remained frozen.

"The factory's trying to decide," Perine said. "It needs the material, but it's afraid of that hawk up there."

The factory debated and nothing stirred. Then the ore cart again resumed its unsteady crawl. It left the tangle of vines and started out across the blasted open plain. Painfully, with infinite caution, it headed toward the slab of dark concrete and metal at the base of the mountains.

The hawk stopped circling.

"Get down!" O'Neill said sharply. "They've got those rigged with the new bombs."

His wife and Perine crouched down beside him and the three of them peered warily at the plain and the metal insect crawling laboriously across it. In the sky, the hawk swept in a straight line until it hung directly over the cart. Then, without sound or warning, it came down in a straight dive.

Hands to her face, Judith shrieked, "I can't watch! It's awful! Like wild animals!"

"It's not after the cart," O'Neill grated.

As the airborne projectile dropped, the cart put on a burst of desperate speed. It raced noisily toward the factory, clanking and rattling, trying in a last futile attempt to reach safety. Forgetting the menace above, the frantically eager factory opened up and guided its mobile unit directly inside. And the hawk had what it wanted.

Before the barrier could close, the hawk swooped down in a long glide parallel with the ground. As the cart disappeared into the depths of the factory, the hawk shot after it, a swift shimmer of metal that hurtled past the clanking cart. Suddenly aware, the factory snapped the barrier shut. Grotesquely, the cart struggled; it was caught fast in the half-closed entrance.

But whether it freed itself didn't matter. There was a dull rumbling stir. The ground moved, billowed, then settled back. A deep shock wave passed beneath the three watching human beings. From the factory rose a single column of black smoke. The surface of concrete split like a dried pod, it shriveled and broke, and dribbled shattered bits of itself in a shower of ruin. The smoke hung for a while, drifting aimlessly away with the morning wind.

The factory was a fused, gutted wreck. It had been penetrated and destroyed.

O'Neill got stiffly to his feet. "That's that. All over with. We've got what we set out after—we've destroyed the autofac network." He glanced at Perine. "Or was that what we were after?"

They looked toward the settlement that lay behind them. Little remained of the orderly rows of houses and streets of the previous year. Without the network, the settlement had rapidly decayed. The original prosperous neatness had dissipated; the settlement was shabby, ill kept.

"Of course," Perine said haltingly. "Once we get into the factories and start setting up our assembly lines. . . ."

"Is there anything left?" Judith inquired.

"There must be something left. There were levels going down miles!"

"Some of those bombs they developed toward the end were awfully big," Judith pointed out. "Better than anything we had in our war."

"Remember that camp we saw? The ruins-squatters?"

"I wasn't along," Perine said.

"They were like wild animals. Eating roots and larvae. Sharpening rocks, tanning hides. Savagery. Bestiality."

"But that's what people like that want," Perine answered defensively.

"Do they? Do we want this?" O'Neill indicated the straggling settlement. "Is this what we set out looking for, that day we collected the tungsten? Or that day we told the factory truck its milk was——" He couldn't remember the word.

"Pizzled," Judith supplied.

"Come on," O'Neill said. "Let's get started. Let's see what's left of that factory—left for us."

They approached the ruined factory late in the afternoon. Four trucks rumbled shakily up to the rim of the gutted pit and halted, motors steaming, tail pipes dripping. Wary and alert, workmen scrambled down and stepped gingerly across the hot ash.

"Maybe it's too soon," one of them objected.

O'Neill had no intention of waiting. "Come on," he ordered. Grabbing up a flashlight, he stepped down into the crater.

The sheltered hull of the Kansas City factory lay directly ahead. In its gutted mouth, the ore cart still hung caught, but it was no longer struggling. Beyond the cart was an ominous pool of gloom. O'Neill flashed his light through the entrance; the tangled, jagged remains of upright supports were visible.

"We want to get down deep," he said to Morrison, who prowled cautiously beside him. "If there's anything left, it's at the bottom."

Morrison grunted. "Those boring moles from Atlanta got most of the deep layers."

"Until the others got their mines sunk." O'Neill stepped carefully through the sagging entrance, climbed a heap of debris that had been tossed against the slit from inside, and found himself within the factory—an expanse of confused wreckage, without pattern or meaning.

"Entropy," Morrison breathed, oppressed. "The thing it always hated. The thing it was built to fight. Random particles everywhere. No purpose to it."

"Down underneath," O'Neill said stubbornly, "we may find some sealed enclaves. I know they got so they were dividing up into autonomous sections, trying to preserve repair units intact, to re-form the composite factory."

"The moles got most of them, too," Morrison observed, but he lumbered after O'Neill.

Behind them, the workmen came slowly. A section of wreckage shifted ominously and a shower of hot fragments cascaded down.

"You men get back to the trucks," O'Neill said. "No sense endangering any more of us than we have to. If Morrison and I don't come back, forget us—don't risk sending a rescue party." As they left, he pointed out to Morrison a descending ramp still partially intact. "Let's get below."

Silently, the two men passed one dead level after another. Endless miles of dark ruin stretched out, without sound or activity. The vague shapes of darkened machinery, unmoving belts and conveyor equipment were partially visible, and the partially completed husks of war projectiles, bent and twisted by the final blast.

"We can salvage some of that," O'Neill said, but he didn't actually believe it. The machinery was fused, shapeless. Everything in the factory had run together, molten slag without form or use. "Once we get it to the surface. . . ."

"We can't," Morrison contradicted bitterly. "We don't have hoists or winches." He kicked at a heap of charred supplies that had stopped along its broken belt and spilled halfway across the ramp.

"It seemed like a good idea at the time," O'Neill said as the two of them continued past the vacant levels of inert machines. "But now that I look back, I'm not so sure."

They had penetrated a long way into the factory. The final level lap spread out ahead of them. O'Neill flashed the light here and there, trying to locate undestroyed sections, portions of the assembly process still intact.

It was Morrison who felt it first. He suddenly dropped to his hands and knees; heavy body pressed against the floor, he lay listening, face hard, eyes wide.

"What is it?" O'Neill cried. Then he, too, felt it. Beneath them, a faint, insistent vibration hummed through the floor, a steady hum of activity. They had been wrong; the hawk had not been totally successful. Below, in a deeper level, the factory was still alive. Closed, limited operations still went on.

"On its own," O'Neill muttered, searching for an extension of the descent lift. "Autonomous activity, set to continue after the rest is gone. How do we get down?"

The descent lift was broken off, sealed by a thick section of metal. The still-living layer beneath their feet was completely cut off; there was no entrance.

Racing back the way they had come, O'Neill reached the surface and hailed the first truck. "Where's the torch? Give it here!"

The precious blowtorch was passed to him and he hurried back, puffing, into the depths of the ruined factory where Morrison waited. Together, the two of them began frantically cutting through the warped metal flooring, burning apart the sealed layers of protective mesh.

"It's coming," Morrison gasped, squinting in the glare of the torch. The plate fell with a clang, disappearing into the level below. A blaze of white light burst up around them and the two men leaped back.

In the sealed chamber, furious activity boomed and echoed, a steady process of moving belts, whirring machine tools, fast-moving mechanical supervisors. At one end, a steady flow of raw materials entered the line; at the far end, the final product was whipped off, inspected and crammed into a conveyor tube.

All this was visible for a split second; then the intrusion was discovered. Robot relays came into play. The blaze of lights flickered and dimmed. The assembly line froze to a halt, stopped in its furious activity. The machines clicked off and became silent.

At one end, a mobile unit detached itself and sped up the wall toward the hole O'Neill and Morrison had cut. It slammed an emergency seal in place and expertly welded it tight. The scene below was gone. A moment later the floor shivered as activity resumed.

Morrison, white-faced and shaking, turned to O'Neill. "What are they doing? What are they making?"

"Not weapons," O'Neill said.

"That stuff is being sent up"—Morrison gestured convulsively—"to the surface."

Shakily, O'Neill climbed to his feet. "Can we locate the spot?"

"I—think so."

"We better." O'Neill swept up the flashlight and started toward the ascent ramp. "We're going to have to see what those pellets are that they're shooting up."

The exit valve of the conveyor tube was concealed in a tangle of vines and ruins a quarter of a mile beyond the factory. In a slot of rock at the base of the mountains, the valve poked up like a nozzle. From ten yards away, it was invisible; the two men were almost on top of it before they noticed it.

Every few moments, a pellet burst from the valve and shot up into the sky. The nozzle revolved and altered its angle of deflection; each pellet was launched in a slightly varied trajectory.

"How far are they going?" Morrison wondered.

"Probably varies. It's distributing them at random." O'Neill advanced cautiously, but the mechanism took no notice of him. Plastered against the towering wall of rock was a crumpled pellet; by accident, the nozzle had released it directly at the mountainside. O'Neill climbed up, got it and jumped down.

The pellet was a smashed container of machinery, tiny metallic elements too minute to be analyzed without a microscope.

"Not a weapon," O'Neill said.

The cylinder had split. At first he couldn't tell if it had been the impact or deliberate internal mechanisms at work. From the rent, an ooze of metal bits was sliding. Squatting down, O'Neill examined them.

The bits were in motion. Microscopic machinery, smaller than ants, smaller than pins, working energetically, purposefully—constructing something that looked like a tiny rectangle of steel.

"They're building," O'Neill said, awed. He got up and prowled on. Off to the side, at the far edge of the gully, he came across a downed pellet far advanced on its construction. Apparently it had been released some time ago.

This one had made great enough progress to be identified. Minute as it was, the structure was familiar. The machinery was building a miniature replica of the demolished factory.

"Well," O'Neill said thoughtfully, "we're back where we started from. For better or worse . . . I don't know."

"I guess they must be all over Earth by now," Morrison said. "Landing everywhere and going to work."

A thought struck O'Neill. "Maybe some of them are geared to escape velocity. That would be neat—autofac networks throughout the whole universe."

Behind him, the nozzle continued to spurt out its torrent of metal seeds.

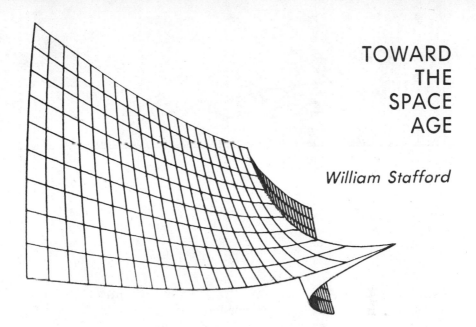

TOWARD THE SPACE AGE

William Stafford

We must begin to catch hold of everything
around us, for nobody knows what we
may need. We have to carry along
the air, even; and the weight we once
5   thought a burden turns out to form
the pulse of our life and the compass for our brain.[1]
Colors balance our fears, and existence
begins to clog unless our thoughts
can occur unwatched and let a fountain of essential silliness
10   pour through our dreams.

And oh I hope we can still arrange
for the wind to blow, and occasionally
some kind of shock to occur, like rain,
and stray adventures no one cares about—
15   harmless love, immoderate guffaws on corners,
families crawling around the ʻront room growling,
being bears in the piano cave.

"Toward the Space Age" by William Stafford from INSIDE OUTER SPACE: New Poems of the Space Age—An Anthology, edited by Robert Vas Dias. Published by Doubleday & Company, Inc. Copyright © 1970 by William Stafford. Reprinted by permission.

1. *the weight . . . compass for our brain.* Researchers have found that without the weight of normal gravity, the rate of a space traveler's heartbeat and blood circulation is greatly slowed and his sense of balance and direction becomes confused.

SPACESHIP EARTH

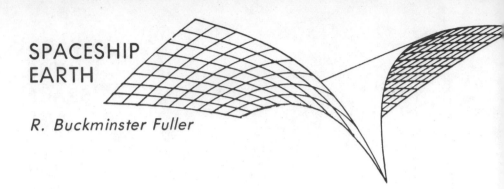

R. Buckminster Fuller

OUR LITTLE SPACESHIP EARTH IS ONLY eight thousand miles in diameter, which is almost a negligible dimension in the great vastness of space. Our nearest star—our energy-supplying mother-ship, the sun—is ninety-two million miles away, and the next nearest star is one hundred thousand times further away. It takes four and one-half years for light to get to us from the next nearest energy-supply-ship star. That is the kind of space-distanced pattern we are flying. Our little Spaceship Earth is right now travelling at sixty thousand miles an hour around the sun and is also spinning axially, which, at the latitude of Washington, D.C., adds approximately one thousand miles per hour to our motion. Each minute we both spin at one hundred miles and zip in orbit at one thousand miles. That is a whole lot of spin and zip. When we launch our rocketed space capsules at fifteen thousand miles an hour, that additional acceleration speed we give the rocket to attain its own orbit around our speeding Spaceship Earth is only one-fourth greater than the speed of our big planetary spaceship.

Spaceship Earth was so extraordinarily well invented and designed that to our knowledge humans have been on board it for two million years not even knowing that they were on board a ship. And our spaceship is so superbly designed as to be able to keep life regenerating on board despite the phenomenon, entropy, by which all local physical systems lose energy. So we have to obtain our biological life-regenerating energy from another spaceship—the sun.

Our sun is flying in company with us, within the vast reaches of the Galactic system, at just the right distance to give us enough radiation to keep us alive, yet not close enough to burn us up. And the whole scheme of Spaceship Earth and its live passengers is so superbly designed that the Van Allen belts, which we didn't even know we had

"Spaceship Earth" by R. Buckminster Fuller from OPERATING MANUAL FOR SPACESHIP EARTH. Copyright © 1969 by Southern Illinois University Press. Reprinted by permission of the author.

until yesterday, filter the sun and other star radiation which as it impinges upon our spherical ramparts is so concentrated that if we went nakedly outside the Van Allen belts it would kill us. Our Spaceship Earth's designed infusion of that radiant energy of the stars is processed in such a way that you and I can carry on safely. You and I can go out and take a sunbath, but are unable to take in enough energy through our skins to keep alive. So part of the invention of the Spaceship Earth and its biological life-sustaining is that the vegetation on the land and the algae in the sea, employing photosynthesis,[1] are designed to impound the life-regenerating energy for us to adequate amount.

But we can't eat all the vegetation. As a matter of fact, we can eat very little of it. We can't eat the bark nor wood of the trees nor the grasses. But insects can eat these, and there are many other animals and creatures that can. We get the energy relayed to us by taking the milk and meat from the animals. The animals can eat the vegetation, and there are a few of the fruits and tender vegetation petals and seeds that we can eat. We have learned to cultivate more of those botanical edibles by genetical inbreeding.

That we are endowed with such intuitive and intellectual capabilities as that of discovering the genes and the R.N.A. and D.N.A.[2] and other fundamental principles governing the fundamental design controls of life systems, as well as of nuclear energy and chemical structuring, is part of the extraordinary design of the Spaceship Earth, its equipment, passengers, and internal support systems. It is therefore paradoxical but strategically explicable, as we shall see, that up to now we have been misusing, abusing, and polluting this extraordinary chemical energy-interchanging system for successfully regenerating all life aboard our planetary spaceship.

One of the interesting things to me about our spaceship is that it is a mechanical vehicle, just as is an automobile. If you own an automobile, you realize that you must put oil and gas into it, and you must put water in the radiator and take care of the car as a whole. You begin to develop quite a little thermodynamic sense.[3] You know that you're either going to have to keep the machine in good order or it's going to be in trouble and fail to function. We have not been seeing our Spaceship Earth as an integrally designed machine which to be persistently successful must be comprehended and serviced in total.

Now there is one outstandingly important fact regarding Spaceship Earth, and that is that no instruction book came with it. I think it's very significant that there is no instruction book for successfully

---

1. *photosynthesis.* Using sunlight energy, green plants combine carbon dioxide and water to make carbohydrates, which store energy in the form of food. In the same process, the plants give off oxygen, which animals use to fuel the chemical reactions their bodies need to live. 2. *genes . . . D.N.A.* The genes of a living cell are tiny areas on the spiral threadlike molecules of the complex chemical D.N.A. The different genes and the different arrangement of the D.N.A. in each cell make up its own special chemical code. This code, relayed through the R.N.A. molecules, dictates what type of new cells will be created when an old cell divides to reproduce itself. This system controls the basic traits, like eye color, that offspring can inherit from parents. 3. *thermodynamic sense,* understanding of the relationships between heat and the output of usable energy or power.

operating our ship. In view of the infinite attention to all other details displayed by our ship, it must be taken as deliberate and purposeful that an instruction book was omitted. Lack of instruction has forced us to find that there are two kinds of berries—red berries that will kill us and red berries that will nourish us. And we had to find out ways of telling which-was-which red berry before we ate it or otherwise we would die. So we were forced, because of the lack of an instruction book, to use our intellect, which is our supreme faculty, to devise scientific experimental procedures and to interpret effectively the significance of the experimental findings. Thus, because the instruction manual was missing we are learning how we safely can anticipate the consequences of an increasing number of alternative ways of extending our satisfactory survival and growth—both physical and metaphysical.[4]

Quite clearly, all of life as designed and born is utterly helpless at the moment of birth. The human child stays helpless longer than does the young of any other species. Apparently it is part of the invention "man" that he is meant to be utterly helpless through certain anthropological phases[5] and that, when he begins to be able to get on a little better, he is meant to discover some of the physical leverage-multiplying principles inherent in universe as well as the many nonobvious resources around him which will further compoundingly multiply his knowledge-regenerating and life-fostering advantages.

I would say that designed into this Spaceship Earth's total wealth was a big safety factor which allowed man to be very ignorant for a long time until he had amassed enough experiences from which to extract progressively the system of generalized principles governing the increases of energy, managing advances over environment. The designed omission of the instruction book on how to operate and maintain Spaceship Earth and its complex life-supporting and regenerating systems has forced man to discover retrospectively just what his most important forward capabilities are. His intellect had to discover itself. Intellect in turn had to compound the facts of his experience. Comprehensive reviews of the compounded facts of experiences by intellect brought forth awareness of the generalized principles underlying all special and only superficially-sensed experiences. Objective employment of those generalized principles in rearranging the physical resources of environment seems to be leading to humanity's eventually total success and readiness to cope with far vaster problems of universe.

To comprehend this total scheme we note that long ago a man went through the woods, as you may have done, and I certainly have, trying to find the shortest way through the woods in a given direction. He found trees fallen across his path. He climbed over those crisscrossed trees and suddenly found himself poised on a tree that was slowly teetering. It happened to be lying across another great tree, and the

---

4. *metaphysical,* spiritual; literally, "beyond the physical." The prefix *meta,* borrowed from Greek, often means "beyond." 5. *anthropological phases,* the stages through which an individual progresses in learning the culture of his society, for example: infancy, childhood, adolescence, and adulthood.

other end of the tree on which he found himself teetering lay under a third great fallen tree. As he teetered he saw the third big tree lifting. It seemed impossible to him. He went over and tried using his own muscles to lift that great tree. He couldn't budge it. Then he climbed back atop the first smaller tree, purposefully teetering it, and surely enough it again elevated the larger tree. I'm certain that the first man who found such a tree thought that it was a magic tree, and may have dragged it home and erected it as man's first totem. It was probably a long time before he learned that any stout tree would do, and thus extracted the concept of the generalized principle of leverage out of all his earlier successive special-case experiences with such accidental discoveries. Only as he learned to generalize fundamental principles of physical universe did man learn to use his intellect effectively.

Once man comprehended that any tree would serve as a lever his intellectual advantages accelerated. Man freed of special-case super-stition by intellect has had his survival potentials multiplied millions-fold. By virtue of the leverage principles in gears, pulleys, transistors, and so forth, it is literally possible to do more with less in a multitude of physiochemical ways. Possibly it was this intellectual augmentation of humanity's survival and success, through the metaphysical percep-tion of generalized principles which may be objectively employed, that Christ was trying to teach in the obscurely told story of the loaves and the fishes.[6]

---

6. *Christ . . . the fishes,* a reference to two miracles in which Christ, with only a few fish and some loaves of bread, fed thousands of people and still had much more food left over than before they ate. Christ explained to his apostles that the crowds were filled not by the food, but by the spiritual content of the ideas he taught while they ate. (Matthew 14-16)

Biographies of Authors

Jack Anderson (1935–)

Although he now lives in New York, Jack Anderson is a native Midwesterner. He was born in Milwaukee, Wisconsin, and educated at Northwestern University in Illinois and Indiana University. When he moved to California to further his education at Berkeley, he began his career as a critic. His first job in this field was with the *Oakland Tribune* as assistant drama critic. He next became an editorial assistant and associate critic with *Dance Magazine.* During this time he was also writing poetry. In recognition of his artistry he was invited to be poet-in-residence at the University of Kansas in 1970. Since then, he has been working in New York as a New York correspondent to London's *Dancing Times* and program editor of the Brooklyn Academy of Music. He has published two collections of his poems: *The Hurricane Lamp* and *The Invention of New Jersey.*

Isaac Asimov (1920–)

Asimov was born in Russia, but his parents brought him to the United States three years later. He worked his way through Columbia University to complete his doctorate in enzyme chemistry in 1948. By then he had sold fifty-seven stories to science-fiction magazines. Although he is still associate professor of biochemistry at Boston University, he chose in 1958 to teach only by occasional lectures so he could write full time.

Asimov has more than 125 books to his credit. These include fiction, criticism, anthologies he has edited, explanations of science for laymen, and material on history, Shakespeare, and the Bible.

Asimov's fame began with the *Foundation* trilogy (1951–1953), an epic thousand-year chronicle of humanity's star empires. Though set sixty thousand years from now, these novels helped bring science fiction back from gimmickry to face contemporary issues of civilization, as H. G. Wells and Karel Čapek had done. In 1966 the trilogy was voted a special Hugo Award for Best All-time Series in science fantasy. Asimov also invented the combination of science fiction and mystery story, creating Dr. Wendel Urth, a detective-hero in the tradition of Sherlock Holmes. Another innovation is the *I, Robot* series which set up Asimov's Three Laws of Robotics, a moral code for robots which has since set the pattern for conflict in such stories. *The Gods Themselves* gained Asimov both a Hugo and a Nebula Award[1] as the Best Novel of 1972.

---

1. See page 366 for information on science-fiction awards.

Charles Beaumont (1929–1967)

Charles Beaumont was influenced early in his writing career by Ray Bradbury (see page 366), who used to go over Beaumont's work. In fact, Beaumont has admitted that "Elegy," one of his first science-fiction stories, may still contain some of Ray Bradbury's lines. Later, when he had established himself as a science-fiction writer, Beaumont wrote about seventy plays for several television series, including *Twilight Zone*, for which "Elegy" was adapted into a half-hour script. In addition, he wrote the scripts for such movies as *The Stranger* (based on his novel *The Intruder*), *The Wonderful World of the Brothers Grimm*, and *The Seven Faces of Dr. Lao*. One collection of his work is *The Magic Man, and Other Science-Fantasy Stories* (1967).

Alfred Bester (1913–   )

Bester was born in New York City and educated at the University of Pennsylvania. His is a familiar name to readers of science fiction. In 1953 with *The Demolished Man* he won the first Hugo Award for Best Novel. His novella *The Stars My Destination* was selected by Anthony Boucher for his two-volume *A Treasury of Great Science Fiction*. In nonfiction Bester has produced *The Life and Death of a Satellite*, a thorough account of the unmanned space program up to 1967 and of the people behind it. He also has written television scripts and has published articles and short stories in *Holiday, Show,* and *Venture.*

Christopher Bird

Christopher Bird is a biologist and anthropologist. In 1973 he published with Peter Tompkins *The Secret Life of Plants*, a book that explores, among other things, those characteristics of plants which have traditionally been regarded as belonging solely to humans and animals.

Robert Bloch (1917–   )

Bloch's offbeat but somewhat rare science-fiction stories are welcomed by fans, as shown by the Hugo they voted in 1959 for his short story "The Hell-Bound Train." However, he generally prefers to work in the veins of horror and supernatural fantasy. He has a humorous sense of the gruesome which is highlighted in the titles of many of his popular short-story collections, such as *Yours Truly, Jack the Ripper* and *Tales in a Jugular Vein*. Bloch is best known for his chilling suspense novel *Psycho,* which was filmed by Alfred Hitchcock.

Bloch was born in Chicago and was an advertising copywriter when his first novel came out in 1945. In 1953 he turned to writing full time and soon went on to a prolific career in movies, radio, and television, as well as in magazines and books. A few of the awards he has earned in all these media are the Screen Guild Award (1960), the Mystery Writers of America Special Scroll (1961), and the Trieste Science Fiction Film Festival Award (1965).

SCIENCE-FICTION AWARDS

The highest honors in science fiction are the Hugo and Nebula Awards, and election to the First Fandom Science Fiction Hall of Fame.

The Hugo Awards were created in 1953, and since 1955 they have been decided annually by a vote of all members of the yearly World Science Fiction Convention. The trophy, a steel model of a rocketship, is named for Hugo Gernsback, founder of the first all-science-fiction magazines. Gernsback actually invented the term *science fiction* in 1929, when he had already set the earliest standards to define what he first called *scientifiction.* The regular categories for Hugos are novel, novelette, short fiction, artwork, and professional magazine. There are also shifting categories such as awards for amateur publications, movies, and television shows.

The Nebula Awards were introduced in 1966 by the newly founded Science Fiction Writers of America. Unlike the Hugo winners, Nebula recipients can only be selected by the professional writers in SFWA. Nonmembers may be voted awards. The categories are always best novel, novella, novelette, and short story.

The First Fandom Hall of Fame was elected exclusively from writers or amateur fans who were leading promoters of early science fiction, and who had already published something in a science-fiction magazine by 1937.

Ray Bradbury (1920–   )

Perhaps the best-known of science-fiction writers, Bradbury was born in Waukegan, Illinois, and attended school there and in Los Angeles. As a high-school boy he founded and edited *Futuria Fantasia,* a mimeographed quarterly of science fantasy. In 1941, while working as a newsboy to finance his writing, he sold his first story. Since then he has written steadily and advises that writing every day is the only way to avoid the tenseness and the excessive self-criticism that paralyzes creativity.

Bradbury has won honors in a number of fields. The Benjamin Franklin Award for best story came to him in 1953; the following year his brilliant novel *Fahrenheit 451* gained the gold medal of the Commonwealth Club of California. Among his screenplays are *Moby Dick, It Came from Outer Space,* and *Icarus Montgolfier Wright,* a short film, based on one of his stories, that was nominated for an Oscar in 1963. His stage, TV, and radio plays, such as the NBC radio drama *Leviathan 99,* have also been highly praised. Many of his more than one thousand short stories can be found in anthologies, and his own story collections include *The Martian Chronicles, The Illustrated Man, Machineries of Joy,* and *The Vintage Bradbury.*

Despite his lifelong devotion to science fiction, Bradbury has never learned to drive, does not fly, and often rides a bicycle to business appointments.

Richard Brautigan (1935–   )

Brautigan was born in Tacoma, Washington, but has spent most of his life in the San Francisco area. He has been adopted by a great following of high-school and college students who enjoy his gentle optimism; the belief that humanity will overcome its current crises and come to live in harmony with nature recurs throughout his writings. Brautigan's work has frequently appeared in the rock-music journal *Rolling Stone.* His first book was the poetry collection *The Return of the Rivers* (1957); among later volumes of his verse are *The Pill Versus the Springhill Mining Disaster: Poems 1957–1968* and *Rommel Drives on Deep into Egypt* (1970). Brautigan's fiction, highly experimental in form, includes the short stories in *Revenge of the Lawn,* and four longer works, or novels, such as *Trout Fishing in America* and *In Watermelon Sugar.*

Fredric Brown (1906–1972)

Brown was born in Cincinnati, Ohio, and attended Hanover College and the University of Cincinnati. He then began working as a newspaperman and magazine writer in the Midwest. In a career that produced over thirty books, he became as highly regarded for mystery writing as for science fiction. With *The Fabulous Clip Joint* he won an Edgar Allan Poe Award for the Best First Mystery Novel of 1947. In the 1950's Brown expanded his writing to television plays and movie scripts, and he adapted his own novel *The Screaming Mimi* into a film of the same title. His science-fiction short stories appeared steadily in numerous magazines, while he also published novels, like *Rogue in Space* and *The Lights in the Sky are Stars.* Collections of his stories include *Angels and Spaceships* and *Paradox Lost, and Twelve Other Great Science Fiction Stories.*

Olga Cabral (1909–   )

Olga Cabral, who was born in Trinidad in the West Indies, now lives in New York City. She writes children's literature, translates works from Yiddish, has owned and managed two art galleries, and composes poetry. Two collections of her poems are *The Evaporated Man* and *Cities and Desserts.*

Karel Čapek (1890–1938)

The term *robot* is familiar in many languages, and is probably the most famous word of science fiction. Čapek invented it, and *P.U.R.* is the play for which he coined it. Produced worldwide since 1920, *R.U.R.*

is a pioneering treatment of technology on the stage. It led in opening up one of the basic and still growing themes of science fiction: the ethical and social problems of creating artificial people or intelligent machines.

Čapek studied biology and earned his doctorate in philosophy, both rich sources of ideas in his works. As a playwright, director, and producer, he founded the modern Czech theater. But Čapek was a patriot as well as a playwright. He fought for the freedom of the Czechs from Austro-Hungarian rule and for the establishment of Czechoslovakia as an independent country in 1919. Twenty years later, when Czechoslovakia was swallowed up in Hitler's Nazi empire, Čapek's friends observed that he seemed to lose the will to live.

Čapek's love of liberty embraced the world, not merely his own land. It was largely his visions of technological dehumanization that made him fear all civilization was sliding into tyranny. But like H. G. Wells, who strongly influenced his novels, he saw as well how science might benefit humanity. As early as 1922 he wrote a novella about atomic power called *The Absolute at Large;* with ironic humor this forecast the atom's challenging potential for either good or evil. Among Čapek's other well-known books are *Money and Other Stories,* the science-fiction play *The World We Live In*, and the science-fiction novels *Meteor* and *War with the Newts.*

T. P. Caravan (1926–   )

T. P. Caravan is a pseudonym used by Charles Munoz. Munoz took it from three words in the *Rubáiyát of Omar Kháyyám*, which is a twelfth-century book of verses by the Persian poet-scientist Kháyyám. The three words Munoz borrowed are in the following quotation: "Lo!—*the phantom Caravan* has reach'd / The NOTHING it set out from."

Under his own name, Munoz published the novel *Stowaway* in 1957. But all of his science fiction appeared under various pen names, the most frequent being T. P. Caravan. Like many writers, Munoz used different bylines to sell several stories to the same science-fiction magazine at once. Munoz admires literary craftsmanship and revised "Random Sample" twelve or fifteen times. He began writing when he was a merchant seaman in the Korean War. He later studied literature and classical history, and once taught evening college courses.

Arthur C. Clarke (1917–   )

Like Ray Bradbury and Kurt Vonnegut, Jr., Clarke has reached a large general audience with his science fiction. Like Isaac Asimov, he is a renowned writer on science itself. He is now most famous for the filmscript of *2001: A Space Odyssey*, which he coauthored with director Stanley Kubrick. But long before the success of the movie, Clarke was an international expert on the space sciences and on undersea exploration and marine life. He has dived to study Australia's Great Barrier Reef, sunken treasure ships, and the Ceylon coast.

The accuracy of Clarke's past predictions has made him an authority on future technology. As early as 1945 he forecast in detail the way satellites are now used to relay global communications. Both Clarke's fiction, and nonfiction like *Profiles of the Future*, rely on imaginative but logically possible extensions of the most advanced present-day science.

In World War II Clarke served in the British Royal Air Force as technical officer on the pioneering of the Ground Controlled Approach radar with which airliners today land in bad weather. *Glide Path* is his novel about these experiments. After the war Clarke studied physics, mathematics, and astronomy, earning his B.Sc. with honors. He abandoned graduate studies, then science editing, to write full time in 1951. Two years later his novel *Childhood's End* was praised by critics for combining serious philosophy with science-fiction adventure. In 1962 Clarke received the U.N.E.S.C.O. Kalinga Prize for distinguished aid in promoting international understanding through the popularization of science.

Douglas Colligan

Douglas Colligan is assistant editor of *Science Digest*, for which he frequently writes articles.

Roald Dahl (1916–   )

Born in South Wales and educated in England, Dahl began writing when he was a Royal Air Force fighter pilot in World War II. His work consists largely of short stories, which usually offer fantasy, hallucinations, and horror; he writes little pure science fiction. Dahl has twice gained the Edgar Allan Poe Award for short mystery fiction. His tightly-constructed stories can be sampled in *Over to You: 10 Stories of Flyers and Flying*, and *Selected Stories.* Dahl is equally popular for his children's literature, which includes *James and the Giant Peach* and *Charlie and the Chocolate Factory.* He adapted *Charlie* into the highly successful movie *Willie Wonka and the Chocolate Factory.* Dahl has written several other screenplays, some of which are intended for his wife, the film-actress Patricia Neal.

Philip K. Dick (1928–   )

Like Philip José Farmer, Dick is well known in the recent movement of many science-fiction writers toward experimental themes and forms. Dick was born in Chicago but went to California, where he studied at Berkeley, wrote advertising, ran a record store, and was emcee of a classical music program on radio. He quit the record shop to write science fiction and fantasy, and in 1963 was awarded a Hugo for his novel *The Man in the High Castle.* He has published a volume of short stories called *The Preserving Machine* and other works of science fiction such as *Do Androids Dream of Electronic Sheep?*, *The Unteleported Man*, *We Can Build You*, and *Game-Players of Titan.*

Anatoly Dnieprov (1919–   )

One of the most popular science-fiction writers in Russia is Anatoly Dnieprov, who is actually A. P. Mitskevich, a prominent mathematical physicist at a research institute of the Soviet Academy of Sciences. Mitskevich has published numerous scientific works in his own name, but he chose his science-fiction pen name in 1958 when he began to compose stories. As a scientist, Mitskevich is mainly concerned with potential developments in cybernetics, physics, and biology. Although he warns of the dangers of technology, especially of constructing cybernetic creatures, his stories are often enlivened by humor. Three collections containing his work are *Path into the Unknown*, edited by Judith Merril, and *Last Door to Aiya* and *The Ultimate Threshold*, both edited and translated by Mirra Ginsburg.

David Ely (1927–   )

David Ely, a former newspaperman, spent his boyhood in the Southwest. He was educated at the University of North Carolina and Harvard before he went to Oxford as a Fulbright Scholar. So far he has published five novels and a collection of short stories. For his skill in plotting exciting tales, he received the Edgar Allan Poe Story Award. His most recent books are *Poor Devils* and *Walking Davis.*

Philip José Farmer (1918–   )

Born in North Terre Haute, Indiana, Farmer worked until 1956 as a technical-science writer, with only scattered intervals for full-time free-lance writing. One of the first to receive a Hugo Award, he was named the Best New Science Fiction Author of 1953. His *Riders of the Purple Wage* shared the Hugo for Best Novella in 1968; then in 1971 he won the chief award of Best Novel with *To Your Scattered Bodies Go.* Many science-fiction fans also follow Farmer's *Riverworld* series of short stories and novelettes about a world in which different eras—the dead, the living, and the yet-to-be—exist in separate countries along the banks of a tremendous river. Samuel Clemens is a figure in these stories, and his "Fabulous Riverboat" is the means of traveling upstream or downstream in time. More science fiction by Farmer can be found in *The Celestial Blueprint, and Other Stories.*

Howard Fast (1914–   )

Although today he is seldom associated with science fiction, Fast's first story, published when he was seventeen, was a science-fiction story. He returned to the field in the 1950's and his recent science-fiction stories are collected in *The Edge of Tomorrow, The Hunter and the Trap*, and *The General Zapped an Angel.* Fast's most familiar works are his historical novels, especially those set in the American Revolution, like *April Morning.* Another of his well-known novels is *Spartacus*, the story of a slave revolt in ancient Rome. Fast coauthored the screenplay when this book was made into an epic film.

Fast's first two novels came out while he was still a teen-ager. He has also written biographies, histories, plays, criticism, and journalism. Many of his books are designed for young readers. In World War II Fast served with a special Army film unit and as a war correspondent in the Far East. Fast's seven awards for his work include the Newspaper Guild Award and the Screenwriters Annual Award for *Spartacus.*

Jack Finney (1911–   )

Jack Finney's many stories have appeared not only in science-fiction magazines and anthologies, but also in several of America's best-known popular magazines, such as *Cosmopolitan, Playboy,* and *The Saturday Evening Post.* His books have been published in the United States, Asia, and Europe, and at least four of his novels have been made into movies. *The Bodysnatchers* (1955) is a novel about the takeover of the people of a small town by extraterrestrial "duplicates." Filmed as *The Invasion of the Body Snatchers* (1956), it evokes psychological horror without showing any grotesque monsters, and has been highly praised for this original technique.

Finney was born in Milwaukee and grew up in Illinois. His first career was in New York City advertising, but he later left for California and turned to free-lance fiction and journalism.

R. Buckminster Fuller (1895–   )

Fuller is widely considered one of the universal geniuses of the twentieth century. He is an inventor whose many patents represent startlingly original scientific advances, an engineer, an architect, a mapmaker, a philosopher, and a poet. In his energetic life he has found time to be a research professor at Southern Illinois University in Carbondale, an organizer of many companies, a consultant to government and foundations, and a lecturer at numerous conferences and schools around the world. In *Education Automation* Fuller explained his optimism that technological feats will eventually raise all mankind's standard of living. In several other books—*Nine Chains to the Moon, No More Second Hand God,* and *Ideas and Integrities*—Fuller charts the courses humanity may take into the many probable worlds of tomorrow. *The Unfinished Epic Poem of Industrialization* is another expression of Fuller's belief that mankind, in learning to generate fresh energy, has become the only being who will resist the universal principle of entropy—the principle that it is the tendency of everything in the cosmos to lose energy gradually until it ends in stagnation.

Marion Gross

"The Good Provider" was originally published in a 1952 issue of *Fantasy and Science Fiction* as the first story from Marion Gross. Various indexes both of science fiction and of general short-story titles list no further works.

Edmond Hamilton (1904–   )

Edmond Hamilton first published his stories in *Weird Tales* magazine in 1926, the same year that Hugo Gernsback founded *Amazing Stories,* first of the exclusively science-fiction magazines. A pioneer in science fiction, Hamilton wrote all but three of the twenty-seven *Captain Future* novels, which from 1940 to 1944 formed a magazine all by themselves. Stories like these are called "space operas," adventurous yarns in which huge space-fleets battle to the death and disintegrate whole planets with their rays and atom blasters. Hamilton's skill in this form earned him the nickname of "the world-wrecker" among devotees of science fiction. But, as a gazer into the future, Hamilton kept up with changing times, and in later stories showed he also had something to say about the real social dilemmas treated by modern science fiction. For instance, his story "The Man Who Saw the Future" tells how a Frenchman of 1444, transported by twentieth-century scientists to 1944, returns to his own Paris and is burnt as a heretic because his contemporaries will not face the truth about modern technology and democracy.

Hamilton has also written television scripts and has continued to produce novels, often more than one in a year. Among his more recent are *The Valley of Creation, Crashing Suns,* and *Doomstar.* In 1967, as one of the most active developers of early science fiction, he was named to the First Fandom Science Fiction Hall of Fame.

Harry Harrison (1925–   )

Harry Harrison of Stamford, Connecticut, ended his education at the age of eighteen, while World War II was being fought, and joined the Army Air Corps. He served until 1946 and became a sergeant. When he left the service, he first worked as a free-lance commercial artist. In 1957 he finally turned his full attention to his writing and became a free-lance writer, living in Europe.

Harrison is one of the better-known of the modern science-fiction writers. Among his books are *One Step From Earth* and *Stainless Steel Rat.* In addition to writing his own science fiction, Harrison is a respected editor who has published many science-fiction collections, such as *Science Fiction Reader, Worlds of Wonder,* and the annual editions of *Best SF.*

Philip J. Hilts

Philip J. Hilts, a journalist, is a correspondent for the *Washington Post.*

Shirley Jackson (1919–1965)

Shirley Jackson's best-known short story, "The Lottery," immediately established her as a skillful teller of horror and suspense stories. Friends nicknamed her the "Virginia Werewolf of seance-fiction."

However, she not only could terrify her readers but also could delight them with tales of the comedy of family living. Born in San Francisco, Shirley Jackson was a free-lance writer all her life, and produced six novels, a play, fiction for children, and various radio and television scripts. She was working on an unfinished novel when she died. She published a volume of short stories, *The Lottery*, and her husband edited *The Magic of Shirley Jackson*, a representative collection of her stories and three novels.

Damon Knight (1922–   )

Born in Baker, Oregon, Knight is the author of several novels, including *The Rithian Terror;* of a volume of novellas titled *Three Novels;* and *Far Out, In Deep, Turning On,* and *Off Center,* which are collections of his short stories. In 1956 Knight was voted a Hugo Award as the Best Critic; and *In Search of Wonder,* a collection of his essays, is considered one of the most informative analyses of science fiction. Also in 1956, Knight with two colleagues created the annual Milford Science Fiction Writers' Conference, the first regular training-ground for new writers. Knight is still director of that group and lecturer at the Clarion Writers' Workshop, which another writer set up with his advice. A second of Knight's important innovations is his *Orbit* series, which he started in 1966 as the first continuing anthology of new science fiction. Knight is also the founder (1965) and first president of SFWA, the professional organization of American science-fiction writers, who sponsor and vote on the Nebula Awards.

Arthur Koestler (1905–   )

Born in Budapest, Hungary, Koestler studied at the University of Vienna, and became a British subject after World War II. He has been an editor, a foreign correspondent and war reporter in various countries, a soldier in the French Foreign Legion, both a Communist and a vehement critic of Communism, and one of the finest living essayists and novelists. He wrote at first in Hungarian and German, then shifted to English. In England he was elected a Fellow of the Royal Society of Literature.

Koestler describes himself as a science-fiction addict. This is part of his lifelong concern with science out of which have come *The Act of Creation* and other books which attempt to reconcile the scientific and humanistic views of life. He has argued intensely against the attitude that all concepts and the entire universe can be explained in strictly physical terms. From 1958 to 1959 he traveled through India and Japan to learn whether Oriental philosophies have anything to offer to Western man. This resulted in *The Lotus and the Robot,* which has been translated into thirty languages and which is Koestler's analysis of the thought, the spiritual beliefs, and the psychology of the East. The disillusionment with Communism that inspired Koestler's great novel *Darkness at Noon* is the other major subject of his literature.

Fritz Leiber (1910–   )

Leiber is among the most versatile of science-fiction and fantasy writers. He has covered the whole range from "swords-and-sorcery" (adventures set in fantasy worlds resembling the Middle Ages), through tales of supernatural terror in modern backgrounds, to "hard" science fiction based on genuine science.

Leiber was born in Chicago to a pair of Shakespearean actors. Along with his honors degree in psychology from the University of Chicago, he was chosen for Phi Beta Kappa. He then studied theology, acted in his parents' company, started editorial work in 1937, and from 1945 to 1956 was associate editor of *Science Digest.* In 1939 he had begun publishing with a swords-and-sorcery series about Fafhrd and the Grey Mouser, who soon became two of the most popular characters in recent fantasy. When he left *Science Digest,* Leiber became a full-time free-lancer, and in 1958 won his first Hugo Award for his novel *The Big Time.* Since then he has collected four more Hugos and two Nebula Awards: in 1965 the major Hugo for a novel *The Wanderer;* in 1968 both Hugo and Nebula for his novelette "Gonna Roll the Bones"; in 1970 the Hugo for his novella *Ship of Shadows;* and both prizes again in 1971 for another novella *Ill Met in Lankhmar.* Leiber was also the author selected to write a new novel, *Tarzan and the Valley of Gold,* for the world-famous fantasy series created by Edgar Rice Burroughs.

Jack Lewis

"Who's Cribbing?" was the first of only ten science-fiction stories by Jack Lewis. It has appeared in two anthologies, been published in Australia and Holland, and been broadcast on radio in Switzerland. When told that it had been bought again for this book, Lewis remarked, "Who's crabbing?" Lewis quit science fiction in 1958 and now writes about aviation, cars, business, and Americana.

Josephine Miles (1911–   )

Josephine Miles was born in Chicago, Illinois, but received her college education on two of the campuses of the University of California. She has taught in the English Department at Berkeley for the last thirty years. She has been both critic of literature and poet, winning the Phelan Award, the Shelley Award, and the National Institute of Arts and Letters Award. Among her volumes of poetry are *Poems on Several Occasions* and *Poems 1930–1960.*

William Morrison (1906–   )

When he's not William Morrison, the science-fiction writer, he's Joseph Samachson (sam′ix ən), the research chemist and science writer. Born in Trenton, New Jersey, Samachson received a Ph.D. in chemistry from Yale. Between 1938 and 1953 he was a self-employed science writer; he also began to write science fiction regularly. Under the pseudonym Brett Sterling he added two novels to Edmond Hamilton's long-running *Captain Future* series. In 1953 Samachson returned to laboratory work in biochemistry, but continued to write and translate technical articles for scientific journals, and to write on science for popular magazines. He authored *The Armor Within Us: The Story of Bone,* a history of discoveries about the human skeleton. With his wife, a pianist, he has written books on music and theater.

Wolfgang F. Pauli (1900–   )

Professor Pauli, a biologist, has taught at New York University and was for over twenty-five years head of the Science Department at Bradford Junior College in Massachusetts. He has also done research at the Memorial Hospital for Cancer Research, served in Liberia as "expert in science" for UNESCO, lectured at various institutions, and published many magazine articles on animal husbandry. The selection by him in this anthology is from his textbook, *The World of Life,* which has been used by many colleges and universities in the U.S.A., Canada, England, and East Africa.

Frederik Pohl (1919–   )

Born in New York City, Pohl appropriately focuses his visions of the near future on the people-made dilemmas of overpopulation. He is considered one of the cleverest satirists in science fiction and has been called a more optimistic H. G. Wells (see page 377). *The Man Who Ate the World* and *Day Million* are among the books of short stories in which Pohl needles with wit at the absurdity and danger of basing civilization on ever rising consumption and production. In the novel *The Space Merchants,* he and his collaborator C. M. Kornbluth depict a society ruled by advertising. His well-known novels *Starchild* and *Age of the Pussyfoot* explore the problems of being human in an inhuman world. Pohl, an active science-fiction fan since boyhood, has influenced his field as much by energetic leadership as by his own plentiful writings. As editor of *IF,* he took the Hugo Award for Best Professional Magazine from 1966 to 1968.

Robert Sheckley (1928–   )

What kind of person would work as a pretzel salesman or a handyman in a hand-painted-necktie studio? Someone with a sense of humor. And that describes Robert Sheckley, writer of comic science fiction. Sheckley, who was born, educated, and still lives in New York City, has always been a writer, although at first he was sometimes forced to take "odd" jobs to support himself. It is unclear whether he chose unusual jobs because of his sense of humor or whether he gained his sense of humor from his jobs. In any case, Sheckley's stories generally peer into the future through the lenses of offbeat comedy. Among his recently published books are *Can You Feel Anything When I Do This?* and *Immortality, Inc.*

William Stafford (1914–   )

Born in Kansas, William Stafford now lives in Oregon, close by Lewis and Clark College where he teaches English. He was educated at the University of Kansas and the University of Iowa, where he received his Ph.D. His poetry is direct and vivid, written in the language of the common person. He won the National Book Award for Poetry in 1963 for his excellent collection of poems *Traveling Through the Dark.*

May Swenson (1919–   )

May Swenson was born and educated in Utah. She has taught and given poetry readings at many American colleges, and has received several literary awards. Her poems have frequently been selected for anthologies of significant modern poetry. Among her own collections are *Poems to Solve* and *Iconographs.* Swenson casts many poems in riddle-form or in a typographic design which reflects the central metaphor in the words. This she does only after the text is finished.

Walter Tevis (1928–   )

It isn't often that a writer's first novel is immediately picked up by Hollywood, and that the movie is then judged one of the Ten Best of the Year, while its screenplay receives both the Screenwriters Guild Award and nomination for an Oscar. For Walter Tevis that novel was *The Hustler* (1959). Developing out of Tevis's pool-playing in graduate-school days, the story tells of a professional pool-hall gambler who learns painfully that he lacks the nerve to be champion. Tevis went on to write *The Man Who Fell to Earth* (1963), a novel in which he turned to a psychologically probing use of the science-fiction format. But science fiction is only one of several types of story that Tevis has written; his fiction has appeared in *Esquire* and *Playboy* as well as in *Galaxy* and *IF.* For several years Tevis has devoted his time to teaching; he is now a professor of seventeenth-century English Literature and Director of the Creative Writing Program at Ohio University.

Peter Tompkins (1919–   )

Peter Tompkins went to school in England before he came to Harvard. But in 1939, during World War II, he left Harvard and returned to Europe as a war correspondent. After his duties as a war correspondent ended, he stayed on in Europe, first as a member of the New York *Herald Tribune* Rome Bureau, then as Mutual Broadcasting System's representative in Greece, and finally as NBC's correspondent in Greece.

He has written novels, film and television scripts, and contributes to many national magazines. In 1973 he published his fourth book, *The Secret Life of Plants,* with Christopher Bird.

Kurt Vonnegut, Jr. (1922–   )

The great popularity and critical praise which have come to Vonnegut have partly hidden the fact that his biting satirical talents first grew in science fiction, and that science-fiction techniques still underlie his major works. But science fiction is only one element of the stories in *Welcome to the Monkey House,* and of novels like *Player Piano, Sirens of Titan, Cat's Cradle,* and *Breakfast of Champions.* In these works Vonnegut uses a comedy of the absurd to expose a universe which humans fill with cruelty and futility. Vonnegut's answer to this inhumanity is his repeated demand for compassion. He has also composed several plays including *Happy Birthday, Wanda June,* a stage version of "EPICAC," and the teleplay *Between Time and Timbuctoo,* which was adapted from a group of his science-fiction stories.

Born in Indianapolis, Indiana, Vonnegut studied biochemistry and anthropology at three different universities. He was captured by the Germans in World War II and was a P.O.W. in Dresden when Allied bombers devastated that undefended city, killing sixty thousand people or more. For twenty-five years Vonnegut struggled to work out some meaning in that experience, and from his efforts came *Slaughterhouse-Five* in 1969. He has taught creative writing at the University of Iowa and now teaches at Harvard.

H. G. Wells (1866–1946)

H. G. (Herbert George) Wells was born near London to lower-middle-class parents. He was first apprenticed to a draper; but since he could not imagine a life for himself selling dry goods, he quickly abandoned that career for one in teaching science. From teaching he turned to journalism, and from journalism to novels and short stories.

As a novelist, essayist, and short-story writer, Wells played an important role in disseminating the ideas of the first quarter of the twentieth century. Many of his writings, like those of Charles Dickens and George Bernard Shaw, dealt with the social questions of his time. And public opinion was affected by Wells's thoughts as strongly as it was affected by the thoughts of those other two great men.

But Wells's other novels displayed an amazing imagination and foresight. In 1895 he published *The Time Machine,* which told of a man who traveled into the future. And in 1898 he published *War of the Worlds,* the story of an attack upon Earth by men from Mars. The story is so realistic that when it was presented on radio in 1938, it caused a near-panic by people who thought the Earth was actually being invaded.

Wells at first had great faith in the power of scientific knowledge. He believed that progress in science would bring a Utopian world, one in which all social problems had been solved. But when he later saw the evil that science can do, he became pessimistic. "The Man Who Could Work Miracles," although a humorous story, reflects this pessimism about the evil that can be done when scientific power, in this case telekinesis, is placed in the wrong hands.

Pronunciation Key

The pronunciation of each word is shown just after the word, in this way: **ab bre vi ate** (ə brē′vē āt). The letters and signs used are pronounced as in the words below. The mark ′ is placed after a syllable with primary or heavy accent, as in the example above. The mark ′ after a syllable shows a secondary or lighter accent, as in **ab bre vi a tion** (ə brē′vē ā′shən).

Some words, taken from foreign languages, are spoken with sounds that do not otherwise occur in English. Symbols for these sounds are given in the key as "foreign sounds."

a	hat, cap	o	hot, rock	ə	represents:
ā	age, face	ō	open, go		a in about
ä	father, far	ô	order, all		e in taken
		oi	oil, voice		i in pencil
b	bad, rob	ou	house, out		o in lemon
ch	child, much				u in circus
d	did, red				
		p	paper, cup		**foreign sounds**
e	let, best	r	run, try		
ē	equal, be	s	say, yes	Y	as in French *du*. Pronounce (ē) with the lips rounded as for (ü).
ėr	term, learn	sh	she, rush		
		t	tell, it		
f	fat, if	th	thin, both	à	as in French *ami*. Pronounce (ä) with the lips spread and held tense.
g	go, bag	ŦH	then, smooth		
h	he, how				
		u	cup, butter	œ	as in French *peu*. Pronounce (ā) with the lips rounded as for (ō).
i	it, pin	ù	full, put		
ī	ice, five	ü	rule, move		
				N	as in French *bon*. The N is not pronounced, but shows that the vowel before it is nasal.
j	jam, enjoy				
k	kind, seek	v	very, save		
l	land, coal	w	will, woman		
m	me, am	y	young, yet	H	as in German *ach*. Pronounce (k) without closing the breath passage.
n	no, in	z	zero, breeze		
ng	long, bring	zh	measure, seizure		

The pronunciation key is from the *Thorndike-Barnhart Advanced Dictionary*, copyright 1973 by Scott, Foresman and Company.

Discussion Questions

INPUT + − × ÷ OUTPUT

Sheckley: THE GUN WITHOUT A BANG *(page 3)*

1. What kind of man is Dixon as you first meet him on the strange planet? In what ways has he changed by the end of the story?

2. The disintegrator destroys everything in its path, yet it is a failure. Why? Do you think the comment the story makes upon the reactions of animals to danger is true?

3. Do you consider this a humorous or a serious story? Or is it both? Explain your answer.

Dnieprov: CRABS TAKE OVER THE ISLAND *(page 9)*

1. In what way does the following sentence, which appears early in the story, foreshadow the fate of Mr. Cookling: "He laughed out loud, opening his mouth wide and exposing a full set of dentures" (page 10)?

2. Mr. Cookling says that the experiment on the island is a test of Darwin's theory. What does he mean? Trace the changes that occur in the crabs, relating these changes to the theory.

3. What goes wrong with the experiment?

4. Is the story of the replication of the crabs convincing or do you find flaws in it?

5. Some critics feel that modern technology is a grave threat to humanity, that people may lose control of the machine and become its slave. Where do you think the narrator stands on this issue?

Brautigan: ALL WATCHED OVER BY MACHINES OF LOVING GRACE *(page 26)*

1. What combinations of words strike you as peculiar or unique? By studying these details as a group, what idea of the meaning of the poem do you arrive at?

2. How do you respond to the phrase "machines of loving grace"? Would your reaction to the poem be any different if the poet had used the words *looked over* rather than *watched over* in the title? Explain.

3. Compare the attitude toward technology of the speaker in this poem with the attitudes of the narrators of "The Gun Without a Bang" and "Crabs Take Over the Island."

Vonnegut: EPICAC *(page 27)*

1. The narrator begins his story by saying he wants to vindicate EPICAC. Why is it necessary to vindicate the machine?

2. Before he burns himself out, EPICAC writes, "I don't want to be a machine, and I don't want to think about war" (page 32, paragraph 2).

Relate this statement to EPICAC's earlier unsatisfactory performance and to the plot of the story.

3. How does the idea of a man's being successful in his romance because of the aid of a computer strike you? What words would you use to describe the idea: unique, amusing, immoral, stupid, ironic? Does the way the narrator tells the story have anything to do with your answer?

Čapek: R.U.R. *(page 33)*

1. At the beginning of a play the dramatist must be almost as economical as the short-story writer in supplying the reader / audience with crucial information about the setting, the characters, and the situation out of which the plot will develop. In addition to words, the dramatist has the advantages of a stage set and the actions and appearance of the characters.

What do you learn of the setting of the play from the stage set?

What do you learn about the situation from Domin's opening conversation with Helena?

What do you learn about Domin? What does the fact that he repeatedly anticipates Helena's questions suggest about him?

2. When Helena meets the managers, she mistakes them for Robots. Explain the factors that make this mistake possible.

3. Domin characterizes old Rossum as mad (page 37) and young Rossum as a man who "started on the business from an engineer's point of view" (page 37). What did old Rossum attempt to do? What was young Rossum's purpose? Which one of the men does Domin admire?

4. Helena asks the managers why they don't create happiness for the Robots (page 44). What does this question reveal about Helena? What do the responses of the managers reveal about their personalities?

5. The action of Act II develops along two lines: the celebration of the anniversary of Helena's arrival on the island and the preparations for escape from the rebelling Robots. What incidents during the anniversary celebration hint at the coming crisis?

6. Several details important to the plot are introduced in Act II. Explain the significance of each of the following: *(a)* Dr. Gall's description of the Robot Helena; *(b)* Radius's misbehavior and Helena's intercession for him; *(c)* the radical decline in the human birth rate; *(d)* Helena's burning of the papers.

7. What is the significance of the lamp's going out (page 72)?

8. How does Alquist differ from the other managers? What criticism does he offer of both the older and younger Rossums? Why is he spared by the Robots?

9. Reread Dr. Gall's speech on page 57 beginning "You see, so many Robots are being manufactured. . . ." What opposing points of view does Dr. Gall explain? Judging from the play as a whole, which point of view represents the attitude of the playwright? Mention situations in the world today which remind you of the conflict Dr. Gall explains.

10. The fact that Domin and the other managers know little history

is suggested by their naming Robots Marius and Sulla, on the mistaken idea that the names were those of lovers. Does ignorance of history have any bearing on the values the managers live by?

11. Is *R.U.R.* an optimistic or a pessimistic play? Support your answer with evidence from the drama.

Ely: THE HUMAN FACTOR *(page 80)*

1. The first sentence of the story reads: "It was a magnificent church, traditionally Gothic in design and yet wholly modernized with the latest technological refinements." Name some of the "technological refinements" mentioned in paragraphs 2–3. In what way do these paragraphs prepare the reader for what follows?

2. Doctor Alpha reflects that "whereas in the old days he had played the organ, now this new organ was playing him." What does he mean? How does he get revenge on the organ?

3. What is meant by "the human factor"? What arguments does Mr. Gill advance for "engineering out" the human factor?

4. David Ely's story is a humorous treatment of a very serious by-product of postindustrial society. What are some of the ways the author makes the story amusing? Would the impact of the idea be greater if the author had written a serious story?

Asimov: THE THINKING MACHINE *(page 90)*

1. According to Asimov, what is the main difference between a brain and a computer?

2. Does the author believe a computer that is creative can ever be built?

3. What does Asimov mean by a "complexity explosion"?

IN RETROSPECT *(pages 3–91)*

1. The threat of technology's creating problems that cannot be solved by technological means is a theme in many of the selections in this unit. Although we can never know exactly how an author thinks about an issue by reading a single selection, we can hazard a guess. Review the stories in this unit and compare the attitudes of the authors toward advanced technology.

2. In "The Thinking Machine" Asimov predicts that man will build a computer that is complex enough to design another computer more complex than itself. Does anything of this nature occur in any of the selections in the unit? Explain.

3. Some critics complain that science fiction is too concerned with moralizing. Do you think this is true? Use selections from the unit as examples in stating your case.

THE ROAD TO OUT

Asimov: MISBEGOTTEN MISSIONARY *(page 93)*

1. At what point in the story do you realize the nature of the stowaway?

2. In what sense is the stowaway a "missionary"? Why is the story titled "Misbegotten Missionary"?

3. In what kind of world would you prefer to live: one like ours which is chaotic and where the individual is forever struggling to survive, or one like Saybrook's Planet? Why do you feel this way?

Beaumont: ELEGY *(page 105)*

1. What common occurrence is encountered by each of the following crew members: Chitterwick, Milton, Goeblin, and Peterson?

2. Mr. Greypoole claims (pages 107–108) that Mr. Waldmeyer told him that his job was "a grave responsibility." In what two ways can the reader interpret this expression?

3. How does Mr. Greypoole differ from the other inhabitants of the asteroid? How do you account for this difference?

4. Satire is the practice of ridiculing or poking fun at customs, ideas, or attitudes. Would you say that the author of "Elegy" is being satiric? If so, at what is he directing his satire?

Anderson: AESTHETICS OF THE MOON *(page 112)*

1. To what is the poet referring in the first word of the poem? How is it more perfect than something like *The Last Supper?*

2. Why is the moon "now like Siberia or Yellowstone"?

3. What two viewpoints are presented in the dialogue? Which viewpoint does the poem as a whole advance?

4. With another student act out the poem. Then compose a script of the dialogue.

Bloch: CONSTANT READER *(page 115)*

1. At what point in the story did you discover the nature of the mystery of the planet—before, at the same time, or after the narrator?

2. What sort of man is the narrator? Discuss the importance of his personality to the plot of the story.

3. Is there more than one constant reader?

4. If you were in the position of the narrator, what books would you have taken? Would they have helped or hindered your escape?

Clarke: WHO'S THERE? *(page 126)*

1. What is the answer to the question posed in the title?

2. At what date is this story set? Is it within the realm of possibility that an occurrence such as that narrated in the story may occur?

Clarke: WE'LL NEVER CONQUER SPACE *(page 130)*

1. What does Clarke's definition of space include?
2. Clarke writes: "Space can be mapped and crossed and occupied without definable limit; but it can never be conquered" (page 134). What does Clarke mean by *conquered?*
3. According to the scientist, "From a world that has become too small, we are moving out into one that will forever be too large . . ." (page 131). What barriers does Clarke believe will limit man's efforts?
4. What does the last sentence of the article mean?
5. Clarke writes, "Over the seas where Odysseus wandered for a decade, the Rome-Beirut Comet whispers its way within the hour" (page 130). Later he outlines the analogy of "an energetic race" which has "just discovered the art of building ships" (page 133, paragraphs 5–7). He speaks of "techniques as far beyond our present engineering as a transistor is beyond a stone axe" (page 134). What is the purpose of these comparisons? Do you think they make the article a better one from a literary point of view?

IN RETROSPECT *(pages 93–135)*

1. Consider the selections in "The Road to Out" in view of Clarke's essay. Is the action in any of the selections within the space boundaries the scientist lays out?
2. In the situation it presents, which of the stories seems closest to possibility? In your opinion which is most implausible?

MIND WAVES

Morrison: THE SACK *(page 137)*

1. What is the Sack? What happens to it? The story ends with Siebling's thinking that it was strange that "he felt so unhappy about so happy an ending." What is the "ending"? Explain why Siebling considers the ending happy and why he is unhappy about it.
2. What does the Sack mean by stating that "the process of coming at the truth is as precious as the formal truth itself"? Discuss this idea as it relates to science, education, and various aspects of life.
3. Discuss ways in which the treatment of Senator Horrigan may be considered satiric.
4. What five questions in which order would you ask the Sack if you had the opportunity? Trade your list with another student and infer the values implied from the questions asked.

Leiber: MARIANA *(page 152)*

1. What happens in this story?
2. What is the setting?
3. Why do you think Mariana kept turning off the switches?

4. Is the episode only in the mind of Mariana or does the author suggest that the events really occurred? Defend your answer.

Harrison: I ALWAYS DO WHAT TEDDY SAYS *(page 156)*

1. What has occurred to make David behave in the way he does at the end of the story?

2. Do you consider any of the people in this story villains? If so, who? Explain your answer.

3. The "development psychology work" to which David refers (page 161) has made it physically impossible for men to commit murder. David alone has not been so conditioned. In giving David this freedom of choice has his father enriched his life or made it intolerable?

Wells: THE MAN WHO COULD WORK MIRACLES *(page 163)*

1. Why does Wells call this story a *pantoum*? (See the definition of *pantoum* in footnote 1.)

2. According to Mr. Fotheringay's definition, what is a miracle? What convinces him that miracles can be performed? What is the reaction of the people in the Long Dragon to his first miracle?

3. Name some of Mr. Fotheringay's miracles. How would you characterize them? What causes the catastrophe of his last miracle?

4. On page 171 we read: ". . . as a matter of fact the reader *was* killed in a violent and unprecedented manner a year ago." How do you explain this statement?

5. In your opinion what was the author's purpose in this story?

Koestler: ECHOES OF THE MIND *(page 177)*

1. What exactly is ESP? Give some examples of ESP from the article.

2. Why do you think Koestler places a great deal of importance on the fact that Russia accepts the existence of ESP?

3. Koestler writes: "To hit on one card among five possibles is one thing; to reproduce a design out of an infinite number of possibilities is quite another" (page 179, paragraph 1). What point is the writer making in this sentence? This sentence is followed by one that reads: "But still worse was to come." What is the tone of this sentence?

4. In what sense does Koestler believe we have been living in the "Country of the Blind"?

IN RETROSPECT *(pages 137–181)*

1. Koestler's "Echoes of the Mind" brings the reader up-to-date on the realities of phenomena that were earlier ridiculed as being fantasy. Look over the selections in the unit and arrange the titles along a line from those closest to scientific fact to those far beyond what Koestler calls "the limitations of our biological equipment." Compare your arrangement with those of other students and be prepared to defend your sequence.

2. Which selection did you enjoy most? What are your reasons?

ORGANIC DILEMMA

Clarke: THE RELUCTANT ORCHID *(page 183)*

1. Characterize Hercules Keating. Contrast him with his Aunt Henrietta and describe the relationship between them.
2. The strange orchid which Hercules is raising is "fringed by a series of eight dangling tendrils" (page 185). Later the tendrils are referred to as *tentacles.* What is the difference? What other words are used to describe the emerging nature of the orchid?
3. Why is the story entitled "The Reluctant Orchid"?
4. What is the dominant tone in this story? Find passages that illustrate this tone.

Asimov: FOUNDING FATHER *(page 191)*

1. What is peculiar about the planet on which the *Cruiser John* lands? What difficulties do the five men face because of this peculiarity?
2. The team's heroic efforts against the alien nature of the planet fail, yet in the last sentence of the story the author speaks of victory. How do you explain this?
3. What is the meaning of the title?
4. What nationalities do the names Chou, Peterson, Barrere, Sandropoulos, and Vlassov suggest? Why do you think the author uses names suggesting different nations?
5. What narrative point of view does Asimov use in this story? Why would it have been impossible to use the first-person point of view Clarke uses in "The Reluctant Orchid"?
6. Read the biography of Asimov on page 364. What indications of the author's scientific background do you find in "Founding Father"?

Fast: THE WOUND *(page 196)*

1. Unlike most science-fiction stories, "The Wound" reads like a realistic short story for most of its length. At what point is it evident that the story is science fiction?
2. Why does the narrator's wife dislike Max Gaffey? Do you think her reasons are sound?
3. When the narrator tries to establish a "moral position" about exploding an atomic bomb in the deep fault, he states that "the only thing I could come up with was the fact that here was one less atom bomb to murder man and destroy the life of the Earth" (page 201, paragraph 3). In your opinion does his reason justify his decision? Is this a sound judgment or a rationalization?
4. Do you believe Max Gaffey and Thunder Inc. would have dropped the Arizona project had the narrator advised against it? Give reasons for your answer.

5. At the meeting with Max Gaffey and his wife, Martha speaks of Mother Earth (page 198, paragraph 12). Later she tells her husband the old story about the mother. What is the significance of these details?

Dahl: THE SOUND MACHINE *(page 205)*

1. Was Klausner imagining the cries of the tree or did his machine really detect the sounds? Discuss.

2. In trying to analyze the cries of the roses, Klausner reflects they might be called *"toin* or *spurl* or *plinuckment,* or anything you like" (page 210, paragraph 6). What idea is Klausner expressing by using these coined words?

3. Does Klausner feel the cries of the tree are essentially different from those of the flowers? How do you know?

4. What is suggested by the last scene of the story?

5. Roald Dahl's stories are often a blend of the macabre and the humorous. What humorous elements do you find in "The Sound Machine"?

Tompkins and Bird: LOVE AMONG THE CABBAGES *(page 215)*

1. Reread the first paragraph of the article. Then state in your own words what the purpose of "Love Among the Cabbages" is.

2. Summarize Cleve Backster's discoveries and experiments. What facts about the man and about his experiments led to his being taken seriously by scientists?

3. By what means does Backster arrive at the conclusion that "We're in another dimension . . . a scientific twilight in which something can go from point to point without going between, and without consuming time to get there" (page 218, paragraph 8)? What is this dimension sometimes called?

4. Which of the experiments reported in the article did you find most convincing?

5. Reread the last two paragraphs of the article. Do you accept the conclusions the authors advance? Explain your answer.

IN RETROSPECT *(pages 183–221)*

1. Review the ideas advanced in "Love Among the Cabbages." Then decide which of the science-fiction stories in the unit contains ideas that are closest to the theories developed in the article. Be prepared to defend your choice.

2. Which selection in "Organic Dilemma" seems to you to reflect most clearly the modern interest in ecology? Give reasons for your answer.

3. Which character in the unit, real or imaginary, do you find most interesting? Why?

VIEW FROM ON HIGH

Brown: PUPPET SHOW (page 223)
1. What happens at the end of the story?
2. What does the speech of each character, including the extraterrestrial, reveal about that individual?
3. Do you think the Earthmen have passed the test for acceptance into the Galactic Union? What are the reasons for your answer?
4. What details in the first three paragraphs suggest that "Puppet Show" is a humorous story? Is the story essentially humorous or does it also have serious or thought-provoking things to say? Explain.

Caravan: RANDOM SAMPLE (page 231)
1. To whom is the little girl speaking?
2. In what way are her fixation on stomping ants and her wish for a magnifying glass related to the development and conclusion of the story?
3. This story uses the first-person point of view. Could it be written from any other point of view? Explain your answer.
4. What does the title mean?

Knight: ON THE WHEEL (page 234)
1. What do you think is the meaning of the title "On the Wheel"?
2. Note the shifts in the narrative. Who is Akim and what does he do? What is Robinson's situation?
3. Is Akim a figure of Robinson's imagination, or is Robinson a figure of Akim's imagination, or do both exist? Cite passages from the short story to support your thinking.

Swenson: ORBITER 5 SHOWS HOW EARTH LOOKS FROM THE MOON (page 239)
1. The man in the moon is a centuries-old concept; the "woman in the earth" is a new one. Why is this so?
2. Pick out the details by which the poet describes the woman in the earth.

Farmer: THE KING OF THE BEASTS (page 240)
1. Who is the king of the beasts?
2. What point does this fablelike story make?

Hilts: UFO DETECTIVE SOLVES 'EM ALL—WELL, ALMOST (page 242)
1. Explain what the headline of this newspaper article means.
2. Hilts writes: "NICAP . . . survived the breakup of the flying saucer romance in the late sixties partly because of its skeptical approach" (page 243). What is meant by "the flying saucer romance"?

Why would a "skeptical approach" keep an organization alive? How would you assess current interest in UFOs?

3. Has reading this article increased or diminished your belief in UFOs?

IN RETROSPECT *(pages 223–245)*

1. The newspaper article "UFO Detective Solves 'Em All—Well, Almost" mentions several unexplained UFO sightings. Choose the fictional work in this group that would come closest to fitting into the framework outlined in the article. Discuss how this selection compares with the other selections in terms of predictability and sheer fantasy.

2. In many stories and poems the reader can infer the writer's philosophy. Most of the stories in this group touch on the issue of whether man's nature is basically evil or essentially perfectible. Review the selections with a view to determining each author's feeling on this issue.

WHAT TIME NEXT TIME

Gross: THE GOOD PROVIDER *(page 247)*

1. What is wrong with Omar Leggety's Time Machine?
2. How do you interpret the title, "The Good Provider"?
3. What are some of Minnie Leggety's dominant characteristics? How would you characterize Pa? In what ways do these two old people complement one another?

Bradbury: A SOUND OF THUNDER *(page 251)*

1. How would you characterize Eckels? At what point did you first get a hint that he would cause a disaster of some kind?

2. At the end of the story Eckels asks, ". . . can't we take it *back*, can't we *make* it alive again?" (page 260, paragraph 3). Keeping in mind the theory of the Time Machine as it is explained in the story, answer him.

3. Why is the reversal in the election consistent with the theory on which the story is based?

4. Discuss the various levels on which the title may be interpreted.

5. Reread the sixth paragraph of the story, which consists of four sentences. How does the third sentence differ from the others? Discuss in what ways this change of style reflects or underscores the meaning.

6. In addition to visual images, Bradbury uses auditory and tactile images to create a forgotten world. Find details which help you hear and feel the sensations of this world.

Lewis: WHO'S CRIBBING? *(page 261)*

1. Who is cribbing, Jack Lewis or Todd Thromberry?
2. Do you think a series of letters was a good form to use in telling this story? If so, why? If not, what would have been better?
3. Imagine that the Jack Lewis-Todd Thromberry story was played out over the telephone. Pretend you are Jack Lewis. With other students playing the parts of Doyle Gates, Ray Albert, Sampson Gross, and Samuel Mines, improvise a sequence of telephone calls working out the plot of this story. Then write up a script of the drama as it might have occurred over the telephone.

Finney: THE THIRD LEVEL *(page 267)*

1. Why does the narrator tell his psychiatrist about discovering the third level at Grand Central Station? What does the psychiatrist say about the discovery? What does he eventually do about it?
2. The last line in the story is meant to surprise the reader. Why should this be a surprising statement? Were you surprised? If not, why weren't you?
3. What details give an air of reality to the difficulties of going back to 1894?

Miles: SPEED *(page 271)*

1. Why does the poet find it impossible to comprehend "the speed of a light year"?
2. Where does the poet feel the speed of time passing—in contemplation of eternity or in watching the seasons pass? Why is this so?
3. What lines in the poem make you sense most clearly the passage of time?

Hamilton: THE INN OUTSIDE THE WORLD *(page 272)*

1. Name some of the people who frequent the Inn Outside the World. What do they have in common?
2. Why does Guinard go to the Inn?
3. One of the laws of the brotherhood is not to help a member with problems of his own time. What reasons for this law can you think of?
4. Who is Su Suum? How does he assist Guinard?
5. Merrill, the American lieutenant, differs from all the others at the meeting. Why do you think the author has introduced him into the story?
6. Comment on Merrill's drawing his pistol. Does this episode seem in harmony with Merrill's character? Is it in tone with the rest of the story?
7. Make a list of three individuals of today who might be worthy of being given the secret to reach the Inn Outside the World. Explain why each warrants this honor. Compose a script including these three figures with two from Hamilton's story. Let them advise some political leader today on problems that confront him.

A MATTER OF RELATIVITY *(page 284)*

1. Wolfgang Pauli writes: "The interpretation of time, as of space, depends upon the viewpoint." Explain this statement with reference to Minim, Chronos, and yourself.

2. What is Einstein's Special Theory of Relativity? Did the physicist and the astronomer in the 747 jetliner prove or disprove the theory? In what way are the voyages of the astronauts related to this theory?

3. The article "A Matter of Overtime" states that Borman's joking demand for overtime was valid for Anders but not for Borman himself. Explain this with reference to Einstein's relativity equations.

IN RETROSPECT *(pages 247–287)*

1. What essential difference in the treatment of time do you find between the three fact articles and the fiction in this unit?

2. Compare the notion of time as it is treated by Pauli, Hamilton, Bradbury, and Miles.

3. Some critics complain that the viewpoint in most science fiction is undemocratic and does not allow for alternate ways of looking at matters. Review the selections in this unit, and others you remember clearly, to assess the justice of this criticism. Do you find the claim is true in most cases, in a few cases, or not at all? Be prepared to defend your viewpoint with specific examples.

EPITAPH

Bradbury: THERE WILL COME SOFT RAINS *(page 289)*

1. At what point in your reading did you discover what had occurred in Allendale, California?

2. Explain the five spots of white paint on the west wall of the house.

3. What is the effect on the reader of the nearly regular sequence of the clock's singing out the time of day?

Clarke: THE FORGOTTEN ENEMY *(page 295)*

1. What is "the forgotten enemy"? At what point in the narration were you actually sure of its identity?

2. From the very first paragraph, in which Clarke speaks of "the freezing air that rasped against his [the professor's] lungs" and "the sound that had come crashing out of the night," the author provides clues to the nature of the enemy. Trace these clues throughout the story.

3. One of the interesting things about the clues Clarke provides is that they can be misinterpreted. For example, in what different ways does the professor explain to himself the sounds he hears? What other misinterpretations do you find?

4. In what ways does Clarke make the professor a real and sympathetic character?

Brown: EARTHMEN BEARING GIFTS *(page 301)*

1. What is the nature of the gift the Earthmen bring?
2. From the title and the ending of the story what can you surmise about the author's feelings about the nature of man?
3. Fredric Brown is well known for his very short stories and for their climactic endings. In addition to these qualities, what are some other qualities that make "Earthmen Bearing Gifts" an excellent story? Compare your answers with those of other students.

Tevis: THE IFTH OF OOFTH *(page 304)*

1. What is the tone of the first paragraph of the story?
2. At what point did you begin to feel that this apparently amusing story in a cozy setting was becoming a horror story?
3. What does the story suggest will take place on Tuesday?
4. Comment on the use of the first-person narrator in this story.

Cabral: ELECTRONIC TAPE FOUND IN A BOTTLE *(page 312)*

1. Why is *odyssey* (line 2) an appropriate word in the context of stanza 1? Note that lines 2–8 all begin with verbs. What do these verbs as a group do to reinforce the idea of an odyssey?
2. Paraphrase ". . . I lived on / a small green ball in the suburbs / of an unremarkable sun" (lines 14–16).
3. In what sense may wars be considered diseases (line 19)?
4. What does the word *this* in the final line refer to? Explain the paradox, "and nothing . . . was as frail or as mighty as this" (lines 29–30).
5. Who is the speaker of this poem?

Colligan: BRACE YOURSELF FOR ANOTHER ICE AGE *(page 313)*

1. Dr. Cesare Emiliani predicts "that the present episode of amiable climate is coming to an end." On what experiments does he base his conclusions? How long does he expect the present climate to last?
2. What are some of the warning signs that the next glacial period is approaching?
3. In what ways is man affecting the environment today? What are the possible long-range effects of such tampering?

IN RETROSPECT *(pages 289–315)*

1. What is an epitaph? Why is it an appropriate title for this unit?
2. Robert Frost in his brief poem, "Fire and Ice," repeats the often voiced belief that one or the other of these elements will signal the end of the world. Which of the selections in this unit suggest fire will destroy man? Which indicate ice? Are there any selections that leave the question open or suggest a third method of destruction?

3. The article "Brace Yourself for Another Ice Age" is based on the findings of a geologist. The short stories and the poem are the products of imagination. Which of these imaginative pieces see man as the cause of the ultimate destruction of man? Which foretell natural causes?

FUTURE REVIEWED

Pohl: THE CENSUS TAKERS *(page 317)*

1. Do you like or dislike the narrator of this story? Explain with reference to the story why you react to him as you do.

2. George Orwell, the author of *1984*, feared that by corrupting language and using euphemisms to disguise hideous acts one can commit crime with a clear conscience. Find examples in "The Census Takers" of language the narrator uses to mask or make acceptable the horrible acts that he performs.

3. Was the In that Witeck reports actually from the middle of the Earth or is this an alibi to enter the C.A.? Give reasons for your answer.

4. How would you describe the tone of the last sentence of the story?

Bester: DISAPPEARING ACT *(page 322)*

1. When the reader begins Bester's story, he quickly realizes that the tale is going to be amusing or satirical rather than serious. What are some of the ways the author creates this impression?

2. Where do the inhabitants of Ward T disappear to? Why are the experts unable to trace their disappearance?

3. Dr. Bradley Scrim, the historian, suggests that a poet is needed. Why a poet?

4. Explain in your own words the meaning of "this final, fatal disappearance" at the end of the story.

5. What is Bester satirizing? Discuss.

6. Place yourself among your favorite historical figures or in your favorite historical age, as Lela Machan, George Hanmer, and Nathan Riley did. Write a series of diary entries of happenings in this fantasy world.

Jackson: BULLETIN *(page 337)*

1. What has occurred in this story?

2. After reviewing the material from 2123, comment on the probable daily life of an American at this time.

3. How would you describe the tone of this selection?

Dick: AUTOFAC *(page 340)*

1. Explain the ending of the story.
2. What are O'Neill, Perine, and Morrison struggling against? Trace the phases in this struggle. Are they successful or unsuccessful?
3. Put yourself in the place of O'Neill and his wife or one of the other characters. Consider their dilemma carefully. If you had a choice between being dependent and comfortable or independent and uncomfortable, which would you choose?

Stafford: TOWARD THE SPACE AGE *(page 359)*

1. Explain the first two sentences of the poem.
2. What need does the speaker see for colors (line 7) and "essential silliness" (line 9)? What do the last three lines suggest?
3. How would you describe the attitude of the speaker toward the brave new world we are approaching?

Fuller: SPACESHIP EARTH *(page 360)*

1. R. Buckminster Fuller writes: "Spaceship Earth was so extraordinarily well invented and designed that to our knowledge humans have been on board it for two million years not even knowing that they were on board a ship" (page 360, paragraph 2). Why does Fuller speak of the Earth as a ship? What does the quoted sentence mean?
2. Fuller observes of Spaceship Earth that "no instruction book came with it" (page 361, paragraph 4). Explain this idea. How does man operate without an instruction book?
3. Do you consider this an optimistic or a pessimistic essay?

IN RETROSPECT *(pages 317–363)*

1. Why do you think this unit is called "Future Reviewed"?
2. Review Fuller's "Spaceship Earth" and Dick's "Autofac." Compare the attitudes of the authors on the future of humanity on this planet.
3. Rank the selections in this unit along a continuum from pessimism to optimism regarding the future of man on Earth. Discuss your sequence with your classmates.

Index of Authors and Titles